SCIENCE

LEVEL ONE

SECOND EDITION

purposeful design®
p u b l i c a t i o n s

Colorado Springs, Colorado

Development Team

Second Edition

Vice President for Purposeful Design Publications
Steven Babbitt

Editorial Team
Jennifer Bollinger, Gary Brohmer, Barbara Carpenter, Cheryl Chiapperino, Janice Giles, Ellen Johnson, Macki Jones, Kim Pettit, Nancy Sutton, Lorraine Wadman, Lisa Wood

Assistant Director for Textbook Development
Don Hulin

Design Team
Ana Brodie, Claire Coleman, Susanna Garmany

First Edition

Vice President of Academic Affairs
Derek Keenan, EdD

Director of Publishing Services
Steven Babbitt

Assistant Director for Textbook Development
Don Hulin

Authors
Chard Berndt, Pat Blackburn, Sandra Burner, Sue Drake, Dr. Diane Foley, Amy Gruetzmacher, Jacqueline Lauriat, Susan Lovelace, Vince Palmer, Elda Robinson, Pam Van der Werff

Editorial Team
Cynthia Behr, Cheryl Chiapperino, Suzanne Clark, John Conaway, Mary Corcoran, Kristi Crosson, Anita Gordon, David Hill, Stephen Johnson, Macki Jones, JoAnn Keenan, Christy Krenek, Sheri Leasure, Wayne Lowe, Zach Moore, Frieda Nossaman, Vanessa Rough, Kara Underwood, Lisa Wood

Design Team
Lindsay Driscoll, Susanna Garmany, Scot McDonald, Kris Orr, Dan Schultz, Sarah Schultz, Chris Tschamler, Shelley Webb

Consultants
Cheryl Blackmon, PhD
Briarwood Christian School

Bob Burtch, EdD
Wheaton College

Don DeYoung, PhD
Grace College

Ruth Ebeling, MS
Biola University

Ray Gates, MS
Cornerstone University

Jerry Johnson, MS
Corban College

Virginia Johnson, PhD
Biola University

James Van Eaton, PhD
Liberty University

Purposeful Design Publications is grateful to Briarwood Christian School in Birmingham, Alabama, for the contributions they made to the original content of the Purposeful Design Science series.

Purposeful Design

SCIENCE

LEVEL ONE

SECOND EDITION

Purposeful Design Publications is the publishing division of the Association of Christian Schools International (ACSI) and is committed to the ministry of Christian school education, to enable Christian educators and schools worldwide to effectively prepare students for life. As the publisher of textbooks, trade books, and other educational resources within ACSI, Purposeful Design Publications strives to produce biblically sound materials that reflect Christian scholarship and stewardship and that address the identified needs of Christian schools around the world.

References to books, computer software, and other ancillary resources in this series are not endorsements by ACSI. These materials were selected to provide teachers with additional resources appropriate to the concepts being taught and to promote student understanding and enjoyment.

All Scripture quotations in this publication, unless otherwise noted, are taken from the HOLY BIBLE, NEW INTERNATIONAL VERSION ® (NIV) ® Copyright © 1973, 1978, and 1984 by Biblica, Inc.®. All rights reserved worldwide.

The following page numbers refer to those in the Student Edition:
Photograph of the X-48B plane on page 47 courtesy of NASA/nasaimages.org, photographer Carla Thomas.
Photograph of the fossilized wasp on page 61 by Mary Corcoran and used by permission of the Florissant Fossil Beds National Monument.
Photographs of *Sputnik 1*, Neil Armstrong, *Mariner 9*, *Space Shuttle*, and *ISS* on page 123 courtesy of NASA.
Image of Mars rover on page 123 courtesy of NASA/JPL.
Photograph of astronauts on page 124 courtesy of NASA.
Image of *Curiosity* on page 127 courtesy of NASA/JPL-Caltech.
Photographs of lungs on page 181 courtesy of NIDA/NIH.
Image of MyPlate on page 193, on BLM 13.3A, and on TM 13.3A courtesy of USDA.
Photograph of ocellated frogfish on TM-2.7A Amazing Fish courtesy of Nick Hobgood. The photographer does not necessarily endorse, sponsor, or authorize this textbook.
Ivory Bar Soap is a product of Proctor & Gamble Company, which does not necessarily endorse, sponsor, or authorize this textbook.

Purposeful Design Publications
A Division of ACSI
PO Box 65130 • Colorado Springs, CO • 80962-5130
Customer Service Department: 800/367-0798 • Website: www.purposefuldesign.org

Table of Contents

Unit 2: Physical Science

Unit 3: Earth and Space Science

Unit 4: Human Body

Resources

Foreword

The Purposeful Design Science series is an initiative of Christian educators to provide excellence in science instruction for Christian school students worldwide. It seeks to honor the Creator by training a generation of students to understand and embrace God's design of His creation. The truth of God's Word is its foundation.

Purposeful Design Science is the result of a collaborative effort on the part of Christian educators across all educational levels, from elementary teachers to college professors. Their expertise and experience—along with a staff of dedicated and gifted editors and graphic designers—have culminated in the highly interactive, educationally engaging, and colorfully designed Purposeful Design Science series.

We extend our appreciation to the numerous classroom teachers and content consultants across the country who have reviewed each lesson and offered valuable suggestions based on their experience with the natural inquisitiveness of children. Student lessons are structured to offer as many hands-on activities as possible, engaging students in discovery, exploration, and investigation of God's purposefully designed world.

May this purposeful approach in a science instructional program be an instrument in the hands of skilled and gifted teachers to provide a generation of children and future scientists with a God-centered perspective of creation, responsibility, and stewardship. To God be the glory!

Steven Babbitt
Vice President for Purposeful Design Publications

Preface

Teaching science—an intimidating notion to some—is in reality an opportunity to amaze students with God's creative power, complexity, and design. The Purposeful Design Science series uses the following four principles to make science your students' favorite class. First, be explicitly Christian when you teach. Second, be excited about discovery. Third, be a continuous seeker of knowledge. Finally, teach with precision and clarity so the students not only answer their questions about the world but also have the knowledge base to discover more knowledge on their own.

Purposeful Design Science facilitates teaching in an explicitly Christian manner by focusing on the design of creation. Science, more than any other subject in school, allows the learner to see the "mind of God." Science describes the depths and complexity of space, the design of the smallest cell, the complex interrelationships of living things, and the amazing intricacies of light, waves, particles, atoms, molecules, and energy. Our universe is a reflection of our Creator. Paul thought Creation was so incredible that men were without excuse "For since the creation of the world God's invisible qualities—His eternal power and divine nature—have been clearly seen, being understood from what has been made" (Romans 1:20a). Our generation knows so much more and, as teachers, our great privilege is to lead students in the discovery of God's creation.

Allow your students the thrill of discovery. A question asked by many teachers considering discovery learning is why. Why have students learn for themselves what I could tell them in a few seconds? The simple answer is because they will never forget what they prove, observe, or discover for themselves. Remember, the appreciation they gain for God's creation through experience cannot be replaced by a good lecture or inspired worksheet.

Teach inductively. Allow students to seek new knowledge. Teachers are good at organizing and presenting information in understandable ways. Teachers often help students by giving outlines, notes, study guides, and other documents to assist them in processing information. However, the science teacher uses the same skills but applies them differently. Science teachers organize students' questions and thoughts. They focus classroom activities on the issues raised by the students. They point the way to good questions, appropriate experiments, and additional activities that will reveal the concepts the students are investigating.

Equip students for discovery. Doing science means developing and using a set of skills often called *process skills*. Purposeful Design Science assists learners in the skills of observing, classifying, predicting, inferring, and communicating. Teachers need to teach these skills just as they teach writing and reading skills in language arts. Fully equipped with the skills of science, your students will thrive in the discovery climate created by using Purposeful Design Science.

The teacher's challenge—and privilege—is to inspire the students to see the Creator in every science discovery and to encourage them to good stewardship of all He has provided. Purposeful Design Science equips the teacher and students with the tools, content, and activities to accomplish this goal.

Bennett Schepens, PhD, Nyack College, Nyack, NY

Acknowledgments

The Peer Review process is an important step in the development of this textbook series. ACSI and the Purposeful Design staff greatly appreciate the feedback we receive from the schools and teachers who participate. We highly value the efforts and input of these faculty members; their recommendations and suggestions are extremely helpful. The institutions listed below have assisted us in this way.

Peer Review

Ames Christian School, Ames, IA
Bastrop Nazarene Christian School, Bastrop, TX
Belleview Christian School, Westminster, CO
Calvary Academy, South Holland, IL
Camden Forward School, Camden, NJ
Colorado Springs Christian School, Colorado Springs, CO
Community Christian School, San Leandro, CA
Covenant Christian School, Dandridge, TN
Evangelical Christian Academy, Colorado Springs, CO
Front Range Christian School, Littleton, CO
Heartland Christian Academy, Hines, MN
Heritage Christian School, Milwaukee, WI
Hope Christian School, Albuquerque, NM
Inwood Oaks Christian School, Houston, TX
Jewel Christian Academy, Indianapolis, IN
The King's Academy, West Palm Beach, FL
Laconia Christian School, Laconia, NH
Light and Life Christian School, Escondido, CA
Manhattan Christian Academy, New York, NY
Monument Academy, Monument, CO
Northwood Academy, Charleston, SC
Oak Creek Elementary, Colorado Springs, CO
Peace Lutheran School, Greencastle, IN
Pipe Creek Christian School, Pipe Creek, TX
Pleasant Hill Christian School, Sebastopol, CA
Providence Christian School, Dothan, AL
Saint Stephens School, Colorado Springs, CO
Sunshine Academy, Bradenton, FL
Traders Point Christian Academy, Indianapolis, IN
Westminster Christian Academy, Webster, TX
Young Americans Christian School, Conyers, GA

Photography

Monica Starr Brown, Colorado Springs, CO
Jane Reiner Haley, Charlottesville, VA
Shelley Webb Olivier, Colorado Springs, CO

Art Illustrations

Barbara Crowe, Birmingham, AL
Aline Heiser, North Ridgeville, OH
Pam Sisk-Licaretz, Colorado Springs, CO

Understanding Purposeful Design Science

Overview

The name Purposeful Design relates to the creative work of God. Every chapter in this series weaves together the wonders of the created world and a biblical worldview. Young people have a natural, God-given inquisitiveness and curiosity about the universe. Purposeful Design Science capitalizes on that curiosity as it engages students in investigating, observing, and thinking about the world around them.

For most children, each academic year offers more challenging content and an increased expectation for greater student achievement. Purposeful Design Elementary Science was developed to engage students' interest in the field of science and to challenge students in these ways.

The following *Standards and Content* section explains how this textbook meets rigorous standards as it thoroughly integrates a Christian perspective. The *Components* section lists and describes all the student and teacher materials. The *Instructional Approach*, *Preparing to Teach a Chapter*, and *Assessment* sections show how these materials help the teacher lead students in effective learning experiences. The *Additional Features* section highlights some distinctive features of this textbook, and the *Safety* section provides helpful guidelines for student and classroom safety.

Standards and Content

Purposeful Design Science instructional materials are designed to help students master appropriate science content and skills within the framework of a biblical worldview. This series has been developed for the most comprehensive and challenging standards available. Purposeful Design Science has also raised the bar from basic standards by producing a robust and comprehensive series that includes best practices for every grade level.

Science Standards

The scope and sequence of Purposeful Design Science incorporate proven standards and benchmarks for science literacy and learning. In addition to meeting the depth and breadth of the most challenging science standards, Purposeful Design Science is committed to thoroughly integrating a biblical worldview into all instructional materials. Additional worldview content is provided for the teacher, and all instructional materials take a biblical stance toward the natural world and toward the scientific investigation of that world.

Science Content

Content for the series is organized in seven categories.
- The unit titles in this text reflect the first three categories: Life Science, Physical Science, and Earth and Space Science. (Note: In textbooks from some publishers, study of the human body is included in Life Science chapters; Purposeful Design Science has chosen to treat it in a separate unit.)
- The activity-based, hands-on approach found in this textbook meets the fourth category—Science as Inquiry.
- The last three categories—Science Technology, Science in Personal and Social Perspectives, and History and Nature of Science—are addressed in lessons that deal with applications of technology, societal issues, scientific careers, and key events and personalities in the history of science. When appropriate, the faith of famous scientists is emphasized so students can see that studying God's creation is a natural activity for Christians.

Scientific Inquiry

The natural learning process featured in this textbook parallels the best in age-appropriate scientific inquiry. The process begins by asking a question about something in the physical world that is familiar to students. They are encouraged to predict an outcome. They participate in an investigation to try out their prediction that not only checks the accuracy of their prediction, but also leads them to a more complete understanding of the problem and suggests further questions to be investigated. During this inquiry process, students acquire new information, gain proficiency in research, work collaboratively with other students, think critically, use scientific tools, take measurements, and solve problems—all valuable skills for scientific study. Students then analyze the results and make conclusions. Often, they share the results with other classmates and compare data to further evaluate results.

Biblical Worldview

A Christian perspective is woven throughout the text in both the Teacher and Student Editions. The content helps the teacher approach lessons in the chapter from a faith-based foundation. The lessons not only strengthen the teacher's grasp of key issues but also prepare the teacher to communicate a biblical worldview as a natural part of science instruction. We assume that every teacher will have access to a Bible. From time to time, teachers will be given specific Bible verses in support of the worldview presented. The goal is to help students develop in spirit, soul, and body rather than keeping faith and science in separate compartments. God is Lord of all—including science. Therefore, as students center their life in Him, they can eagerly pursue scientific investigation, confident that whatever they discover will only enhance their sense of awe and stimulate them to worship the Creator to an even greater degree.

A Christian perspective is reinforced throughout these Purposeful Design Science materials. For example, in addition to speaking of God as the Creator, every science concept is approached from a biblical worldview. The ideal conditions for life on the earth—conditions that must fall within a narrow range in order for life to exist—point to God's special design and care for this planet and for those He has created in His image. In plants, animals, and human beings there is evidence that living things have been designed for certain functions. Stable natural laws and predictable cycles of nature point to an orderly Creator. As your students study the world around them—whether with unaided eyes, through a microscope, through a telescope, or through mathematical calculations—it is our sincere hope that they will see "the hand of the Lord" that has created everything (Job 12:9).

Teaching Schedule

If your school schedule does not allow for science instruction several times a week throughout the year, this text contains more lessons than you will need. For maximum student benefit, it is recommended that you teach complete chapters, including all of the lessons within a given chapter. You may spend as much or as little time in each lesson as desired. You may choose to extend some lessons over multiple days. Be sure to include at least one chapter from all four units—Life Science, Physical Science, Earth and Space Science, and Human Body.

Components

All the components of Purposeful Design Science combine to create effective instructional experiences for both the teacher and students. Even if science is not their favorite subject, the teacher and students can successfully explore the wonders of science from a Christian perspective.

Student Edition

- Engaging pages stimulate students' interest.
- Colorful and realistic illustrations and photographs capture students' curiosity.
- Age-appropriate text challenges students to expand their vocabulary and reading comprehension skills.
- Science vocabulary words are highlighted in yellow.
- Journal activities provide an opportunity for students to write about what they have learned.
- After a chapter has been completed, the teacher can staple the pages together as a booklet and send them home with students to share with a family member.

Teacher Edition

- A *Chapter Preparation* section explains the major concepts covered in the chapter, summarizes the content of each lesson, and provides materials and resource lists.
- Each lesson contains a lesson objective, content summary, list of materials, step-by-step directions for teaching the lesson, and helpful information found in the sidebars.
- Sidebars include *Preparation* (explains what must be set up or prepared ahead of time as well as gives notice of needs in upcoming lessons), *Alternatives* (offers a replacement for an activity given in the *Introduction* or *Directed Instruction*), *Extension* (provides additional activities for the teacher to use for students to expand their knowledge of the subject given in the *Directed Instruction*), and *Safety* (warns the teacher of possible safety issues involved in the activities).
- Each chapter begins with a motivating activity or lively discussion to engage students and stimulate their interest in the chapter topic. As they follow instructions on student pages and blackline masters, students acquire hands-on experience in the process of scientific inquiry.

Supplemental Materials

- Blackline masters, transparency masters, and computer presentations provide instructional support for the teacher and enhance student learning. Some blackline masters are strictly directions for the teacher and do not need to be printed or distributed to the students. The blackline masters, transparency masters, and the computer presentations are provided on a CD. All supplemental materials can be printed or used in other media presentation formats.
- Answer keys are provided on the CD for blackline masters that require student responses.

Instructional Approach

Purposeful Design Science provides students with multiple opportunities to develop their science skills. The framework of instruction is based on connecting students' prior knowledge to new information, constructing a larger foundation of science knowledge by presenting scientific data and terminology, investigating the topic with hands-on activities, extending the chapter topic by applying the information learned, and assessing knowledge gained with traditional assessments. Level 2 through Level 6 offer alternative assessment tools as well. The balance among these instructional methods creates a series that provides a well-rounded science education.

Students know, think, and explore science in many different ways. Sometimes they work on their own; sometimes they work cooperatively with other students. At times, the teacher directs specific activities; at other times, students design their own activities. Students spend time reading and writing; they also spend time interacting with others. Students learn that there is not just one way to investigate science and that science is not limited to science class. Science affects all aspects of life and is useful in many ways. The skills they learn will help them in whatever career paths they take in the future, science-based or otherwise.

Preparing to Teach a Chapter

Each chapter begins with a *Chapter Preparation* section, which gives the teacher helpful information that can be used to better plan for lessons. In an introductory section, the teacher is given a brief synopsis about the value and purpose of the chapter content.

About This Chapter

This section provides the teacher with a brief informative description of each lesson. A list of the materials needed to teach each lesson is also included.

Supplemental Materials

All supplemental instructional materials necessary for teaching the chapter are listed—blackline masters, transparency masters, and computer presentations. The teacher can see at a glance the teaching resources for each lesson.

Sidebars

Provided in the *Chapter Preparation* are three sidebars. *Looking Ahead* gives teachers an advance notice of special or unusual supply needs to allow for ample time to acquire the materials. It also offers the opportunity for teachers to begin preparing for future activities in subsequent chapters. Carefully chosen books, videos, and CDs are listed in the *Teacher Resources* and *Student Resources* sidebars. Teacher resources include idea books and additional reference materials that may prove useful in lesson preparation. Some of these teacher resources may also be used by students, but the teacher should evaluate each before allowing students to make use of the materials. Student resources are deemed appropriate for the students.

Assessment

Both traditional and alternative assessment measures are embedded within this science series.

Traditional

- The teacher can assess student progress informally as he or she observes students' participation and involvement during activities and experiments.
- Class discussions also provide the teacher with valuable information about what students are learning.
- The teacher text provides review questions that can be asked to monitor student understanding at various points in the lesson. Review questions and activities are also provided at the end of each lesson.
- Chapter Reviews in the Student Edition provide students with the opportunity to practice and reinforce information and concepts from the chapter in a cumulative manner before the summative assessment.
- Blackline masters provide the summative evaluations of student performance.

Alternative

- Projects and alternative assessments show students' ability to use both science knowledge and process skills to complete a practical, analytical task. Projects are excellent entries for portfolio selections. If your school requires students to compile portfolios, students may choose to include work samples from these projects to show their progress in understanding science knowledge and process skills.

- A list of guidelines allows students to monitor their own progress during the project.
- A rubric allows the teacher to assess student performance. Some standards listed in the rubrics may incorporate two or more criteria to be evaluated. For instance, if the guidelines for the activity state "Include five vocabulary words," the teacher would use this standard to evaluate the number as well as the appropriate use of the words. Therefore, an evaluation of *1* or *2* would be given to a student who may have included five words but did not use any of them correctly.

Additional Features
Specialized Activities
Several lessons suggest possible outings, field trips, or alternative options. Teachers should check the *Looking Ahead*, *Preparation*, *Extension*, and *Alternatives* sidebars well in advance in order to allow ample time to schedule events, recruit parental involvement, and acquire materials.

Science Equipment and Materials
Many of the experiments, demonstrations, and activities can be performed by using common household items. However, others will require basic scientific equipment and specific materials. The *Chapter Preparation* section lists equipment and materials in order to allow sufficient preparation time for the teacher. Scientific equipment may include items such as lenses, thermometers, metersticks, spring scales, and different types of magnets. Specific materials are those that are important to the chapter and integral to the directed instruction. There are several places where specialized materials—while not required to teach the lesson—can greatly enhance the learning experience for both teacher and student. Some of these materials can take additional time and effort to acquire. Many are available in the ACSI Science Equipment Kit.

Websites
Many universities and government websites provide activities and research resources for both teachers and students. Some of these websites are referred to for the teacher. Teachers should preview these sites for accuracy and age-appropriateness.

Cross-curricular Links
Science is not just limited to "science-time." Here are a few examples of how these science links are integrated into other subject areas.
- Fine Arts: Some lessons give students the opportunity to draw pictures, play games, role-play, or perform skits and plays.
- Health and Physical Education: Students gain helpful information about healthful diets, sleep patterns, human development, and exercise as they study about the human body.
- Language Arts: Many activities involve written and verbal communication skills. Several of the report options for chapter projects provide opportunities for cross-curricular instruction.
- Reading: Lists of recommended books—fiction and nonfiction—are suggested in each chapter.
- Mathematics: Computational skills, measurement, logic, and mathematical reasoning are used. The students will see that mathematical skills are vital to scientific inquiry.

- Social Studies: Students will study a wide range of geographic locations, expand their awareness of other people groups and cultures, and discuss events and individuals in the history of science and technology.
- Technology: Suggestions are included for using computers, the Internet, and audiovisual technology in the classroom.

Safety

To make experiments and hands-on activities most profitable, the teacher should train students in proper safety procedures. Helping students develop good habits now will assist them in their future studies of science. Directions and precautions are listed in the *Safety* sidebars of individual lessons.

General Safety Guidelines
- Display a list of safety rules in the classroom and review them regularly.
- Direct students to wash their hands before and after any experiment or hands-on activity. Have students wear protective gear appropriate to the activity. Some activities require goggles or gloves. Sanitize safety goggles after each use.
- Instruct students to report any spills or breakage to the teacher immediately.
- Store equipment and materials in a safe location and make sure they are returned to their designated places after use. Always test and check materials prior to use in the classroom.
- Model safety for the students.
- Direct students not to eat or handle supplies unless instructed to do so.
- Be aware of students' health conditions or allergies to science activity materials and take necessary precaution.

Preparing a Lesson

1 The teacher is to note the objective and keep it in mind while preparing to teach the lesson.

2 All of the materials needed to teach the lesson are detailed. Supplemental materials such as blackline masters, transparency masters, or computer presentations are also listed.

3 The *Preparation* sidebar identifies materials that need to be obtained and activities that should be performed in advance. The handprint icon denotes the component of the lesson that requires preparation.

4 *Content* provides background information about the topic being studied.

1.3 Special Animals Called Mammals

Mammals

Objective

1 Students will recognize hair and milk as two characteristics of mammals.

Materials

2
Introduction
• TM-1.3A Red the Fox

Directed Instruction
• BLM 1.3A Mammal Facts

🖐 Preparation

3 Select **TM-1.3A Red the Fox** for display. (*Introduction*)

Write the definition of *mammal* on the board. (*Directed Instruction*)

Print **BLM 1.3A Mammal Facts** for each student. (*Directed Instruction*)

Content **4**

In studying the characteristics of living things, scientists observe that some different organisms have common characteristics. Animals with hair, mammary glands to produce milk for their young, and similar skeletal structures are grouped as mammals. These characteristics allow mammals to function and survive in their habitat. God created people with features of mammals. With this form, they can function in their environment to fulfill God's purposes for them. Humans share characteristics—backbones, lungs, warm-bloodedness—with some animals. However, they are uniquely eternal beings. Made in His image and likeness (Genesis 1:26), people are set apart for Him. People can delight in the fact that God formed Adam from the dust of the ground and breathed the breath of life into him and that Adam became a living being (Genesis 2:7).

Introduction 🖐 **5**

Display **TM-1.3A Red the Fox** and read the story below; cover the photos until the story mentions when to reveal them. Instruct the class to listen for two special ways God designed the fox. (hair, milk for its young)

Red the Fox

(*Uncover the first photo.*) Sophia and Aiden watched from the big window. "Look, there's Red!" said Sophia. Aiden grabbed his pencil and pad so he could draw Red. Sophia loved to watch Red, the red fox. Red came out during the day sometimes but hunted at night. Sophia pointed, "He is so beautiful. I love his pointed nose and white-tipped tail." The children always watched from the window and never got close to the wild animal.

During the winter months, Red was by himself. (*Uncover the second photo.*) The children were amazed at how Red pounced on animals, such as mice, to catch them. (*Uncover the third photo.*) On one very cold morning, Aiden noticed, "Look how Red keeps warm. His big, bushy tail curls around him."

(*Uncover the fourth photo.*) Red and his family live in a den, while their young, called *kits*, are small. Sophia and Aiden knew that since foxes are mammals, the mother fox makes milk. She nurses her young to help them survive and grow. After the young grow up a little, they catch food too!

Sophia said, "Isn't it amazing how God designed the red foxes to be able to live in their habitat? He designed their mother to make milk for her young. He gave them hair to keep them warm!" As Aiden finished his picture of Red, he smiled, "God made red foxes beautiful. He sure cares for them!"

Use the following questions to assess listening skills:
• What kind of animal is Red? (a fox)
• Does Red hunt more during the day or night? (night)
• What does Red's tail help him do? (keep warm)
• What animal does Red catch? (mice)
• What is a baby fox called? (a kit)

Directed Instruction 🖐 ⊕ **6**

1 Explain that a fox is a mammal. Point out the definition of *mammal* from the board. **Mammal** refers to *an animal that has hair and can make milk to feed its young.* Convey that God's special design of mammals helps

10

them survive. Discuss how the mammals' hair, or fur, protects them and keeps them warm and mother mammals make milk to feed their young.

Ask students about another mammal, the cow. Inquire about where a cow's habitat would be. (on a farm) How do you think a cow's hair feels? (not soft, stiff) Where does the milk you drink come from? (cows, goats)

2 Direct students' attention to the student pages. Read and discuss the top half of the first page. List some milk products and have students raise their hand if they like that product. State that these products are made using cow's milk. Discuss how the next mammal on the page gets its hair cut or sheared. Note products that are made of wool. Read the sentences on the second page. Restate that *identify* means *to notice a certain thing*. Reiterate that God designed these mammals to have hair and to make milk to feed their young. Point to and complete the Creation web from Lesson 1.1, and emphasize *Mammals* within God's purposeful design.

Permit students to share with a classmate two things they have learned about mammals. Complete the review questions together. Check student work for spelling accuracy and collect the pages.

3 Distribute **BLM 1.3A Mammal Facts**. Reiterate that mammals are living things designed with lungs to breathe air. The giraffe's whole skeleton helps the giraffe move. In addition, mammals keep the same body temperature, no matter how hot or cold it is outside. The body temperature of a giraffe ranges from 99°F–101.5°F, with an average of 100.5°F. A healthy giraffe keeps this temperature range, no matter how hot the air temperature is.

⊕ **Extension**

Materials **7**
• CP-1.3 Animal Habitats: Mammals and Fish, Part 1

Present **CP-1.3 Animal Habitats: Mammals and Fish, Part 1** and discuss the slides about mammals.

Share with students that people have hair and that human mothers are able to make milk for their babies. God designed people to fellowship with Him. They are made in God's image and likeness (Genesis 1:26).

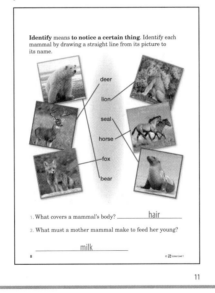

8 *Special Animals Called Mammals* 1.3

Mammals are a special group of animals. They have hair and can make milk to feed their young.

The cow has hair. How do you think the hair feels?

The mother cow makes milk to feed her young. Milk from the cow is used to make ice cream, yogurt, cheese, butter, and milk to drink.

Is the cow a mammal? Write **yes** or **no**.

_____ yes _____

This mammal makes milk for her young. It also gets its hair cut or sheared. Its hair is called **wool**.

What is this mammal? _____ sheep _____

Wool from the sheep makes socks, blankets, sweaters, and hats.

7

Identify means **to notice a certain thing**. Identify each mammal by drawing a straight line from its picture to its name.

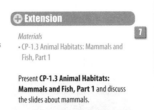

deer
lion
seal
horse
fox
bear

1. What covers a mammal's body? _____ hair _____
2. What must a mother mammal make to feed her young?
_____ milk _____

8

5 *Introduction* contains activities or discussions that will elicit students' interest in the topic.

6 *Directed Instruction* gives step-by-step instructions for the lesson. Vocabulary words are listed in bold print. These words are also highlighted in yellow on the student pages. A glossary containing all of the vocabulary words is located in the back of both the teacher and student editions.

7 *Alternatives*, *Safety*, and *Extension* are other sidebars in which icons will appear. These sidebars provide ways to expedite or simplify activities and offer ideas to enrich certain parts of the lesson. *Extension* activities can also be used for differentiated learning.

8 Readable reductions of each student textbook page allow the teacher to follow along with students as they read. Lesson review questions offer the teacher specific questions to assess students' understanding of lesson content.

Scientific Inquiry

Use these steps to find answers to questions.

1. **Ask a question.** What do you want to know?

   Will both kinds of corn kernels pop when heated?

2. **Make a hypothesis.** What do you think the answer will be?

   I think both kinds of corn kernels will pop when heated.

3. **Plan and do a test.** How will you do your experiment?

   I will heat both kinds of corn kernels.

4. Record and analyze your results.

What did you discover?

	does pop	does not pop
popping corn	✔	
feed corn		✔

Popping corn does pop when heated.
Feed corn does not pop when heated.

5. Make a conclusion. How do the results compare to your hypothesis?

Both kinds of corn kernels do not pop when heated.

6. Share your results. What can others learn from your discovery?

I can share my experiment with a classmate.

Senses

Use your senses to learn about what is around you. Your senses are touch, taste, hear, see, and smell.

Your skin helps you feel the smooth blanket.

Your skin helps you feel the rough sand.

Your tongue helps you taste the sweet apple.

Your tongue helps you taste the salty popcorn.

Your ears help you hear the upbeat music.

Your ears help you hear the quiet whisper.

Your eyes help you see a book up close.

Your eyes help you see the ocean far away.

Your nose helps you smell a fresh flower.

Your nose helps you smell a stinky shoe.

In this book, you will use your five senses to learn about God's creation.

Unit 1
Life Science

Mammals

Chapter 1

Key Ideas

- God created living and nonliving things.
- Living things are further classified into the kingdom of animals and the class of mammals.
- Mammals are animals that have hair and produce milk for their young.

living thing
nonliving thing
animal
habitat
mammal

Looking Ahead

- For **Lesson 1.2**, plan to dig a small hole outside for students to see.
- **Lesson 1.5** requires warm water. Plan for students to feel the warm water and then to conduct an experiment one hour later.
- For **Lesson 1.6**, plan to take students to a large area, such as a gymnasium or the outdoors.

Introduction

One vital connection that first graders must make early in life is between the natural world and God's design of it. Building upon their familiarity with the topic of mammals, students will learn concepts that will help their thinking mature. While learning that all mammals have hair and produce milk, they will also understand God's design and provision for these animals—hair to keep them warm and milk to feed their young. As students practice the new skills of observation and classification, they will wonder, ask questions, and think. Through this process, they will learn to recognize God's purposeful design of all creation.

About This Chapter

Lesson 1.1 – Living and Nonliving Things

Materials
- Crayons

Lesson Content

God created living and nonliving things. Scientists classify these things by their similar characteristics. Living things need water and food to stay alive and a place to live. Living things grow and change. Nonliving things are not alive; they do not grow. God created all things with a purposeful design.

Lesson 1.2 – Animals

Materials
- Trowel
- Globe
- Scissors
- Glue
- Crayons

Lesson Content

Scientists further classify some living things into the kingdom of animals. All animals need water and food and a place to live. The place where an animal lives is its habitat. Many different animals can be found in the same habitat. Some animals walk, crawl, or fly; some eat other animals, plants, or both. Animals have a skeleton and a covering such as fur, feathers, or scales.

Lesson 1.3 – Special Animals Called Mammals

Materials
- No additional materials are needed.

Lesson Content

Mammals are a special class of animals that God purposely designed to have hair and make milk for their young. Mammals have a backbone to help them move. They also maintain a consistent body temperature, no matter the temperature of their environment. People use products such as milk and wool that are produced from mammals.

Lesson 1.4 – Mammals in the Woodlands

Materials
- No additional materials are needed.

Lesson Content

The woodlands are one type of animal habitat. Mammals such as porcupine, rabbit, deer, beaver, and bat make the woodlands their home. Many plant species thrive in the woodlands, providing a home and food for many mammals there. For instance, some mammals find a home in dead trees or near a pond. Some eat other animals within the woodlands, and some feast on the plants.

Lesson 1.5 – A Whale's Warmth

Materials
- Thermos
- Water
- Cups

Lesson Content

A whale's design allows it to survive and function within its habitat. Even though the whale is a mammal, it is able to live underwater by breathing through a blowhole. Blubber helps insulate the whale as well as provide energy for it. Like a thermos, blubber keeps the whale's body at a certain temperature, even in cold water.

Lesson 1.6 – Tech Connect

Materials
- Ball

Lesson Content

Echolocation allows some mammals to find food and survive in their habitat. These mammals send out sounds, which bounce off a nearby object and let that mammal know information about that object. On boats and ships, humans use a form of echolocation called *sonar*. Sonar helps those on the watercraft know if something is in the water nearby.

Lesson 1.7 – Chapter 1 Review

Materials
- Crayons

Supplemental Materials

Blackline Masters
1.1A Koala
1.1B Kite
1.2A Animals in Their Habitats
1.3A Mammal Facts
1.4A "Mammals"
1.6A Mammal Maze
1.7A Chapter 1 Test

Transparency Masters
1.2A More About Animals
1.3A Red the Fox
1.4A The Woodlands
1.4B Animals in the Woodlands
1.7A Meet More Mammals

Computer Presentation
1.3 Animal Habitats: Mammals and Fish, Part 1

1.1 Living and Nonliving Things

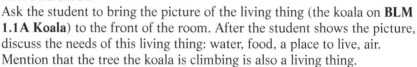

Objective

Students will classify living and nonliving things.

Materials

Introduction
• BLM 1.1A Koala, BLM 1.1B Kite

Directed Instruction
• Red crayons

Preparation

The Chapter 1 Preparation page provides a list of recommended student books about animals. Display the books in the classroom so students can access them easily.

Print and give a copy of **BLM 1.1A Koala** to one student and **BLM 1.1B Kite** to another. Color these copies first if desired. (*Introduction*)

Write the definitions of *living thing* and *nonliving thing* on the board. A definition for each word is found in the *Directed Instruction* section of the lesson as well as in the *Glossary*. (*Directed Instruction*)

Obtain a RED CRAYON for each student. (*Directed Instruction*)

Content

In the beginning God created the heavens and the earth (Genesis 1:1). He created living and nonliving things. Most living things, such as animals and plants, need sunlight, water, air, and food, and a place to live. God provided for these needs at the Creation, allowing living things to change, grow, and stay alive. Nonliving things do not need such things; they do not grow.

Introduction

Ask the student to bring the picture of the living thing (the koala on **BLM 1.1A Koala**) to the front of the room. After the student shows the picture, discuss the needs of this living thing: water, food, a place to live, air. Mention that the tree the koala is climbing is also a living thing.

Next, state that someone in the room has a picture of a nonliving thing. Ask the other student to bring the picture of a nonliving thing (the kite on **BLM 1.1B Kite**) to the front of the room. After the student displays the picture, discuss that the kite does not need what the koala needs.

Directed Instruction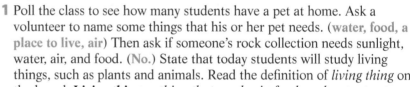

1 Poll the class to see how many students have a pet at home. Ask a volunteer to name some things that his or her pet needs. (**water, food, a place to live, air**) Then ask if someone's rock collection needs sunlight, water, air, and food. (**No.**) State that today students will study living things, such as plants and animals. Read the definition of *living thing* on the board. **Living thing**: *a thing that needs air, food, and water to stay alive. It grows and changes*. Convey that students will also study nonliving things. Read the definition of *nonliving thing*. **Nonliving thing**: *a thing that is not alive and does not grow*. State that rocks and kites are examples of nonliving things.

2 Give the class some examples of plants (rose bush, maple tree, grass) and animals (fox, buffalo, mouse). Explain that these living things need sunlight, water, air, and food so they can grow and change. Ask students why a horse is a living thing. (**It needs water and food; it needs a place to live; it grows and changes.**) Is grass living or nonliving? (**living**) What things do birds need? (**water, food, and a place to live**) Ask the class to name some things that are nonliving. (**Possible answers: carpet, concrete, cup, toothbrush**) Ask students if a pillow is living or nonliving. (**nonliving**) Does a chair need water and food? (**No.**) Why is a table nonliving? (**It does not need water and food; it does not need a place to live.**)

3 Direct students' attention to the student pages. As you go through the first page with students, read each caption and explain that the bear, fish, bird, and lemon tree need water, food, and a place to live. Continue the discussion by explaining that the planet, the rocks, the ball, and the computer do not need water, food, and a place to live. They are not alive. They do not grow and change.

Point out that when students separate the living from the nonliving things, they are classifying them. State that *classify* means *to put things that are alike in the same group*. Read the directions on the second page. One at a time, ask if each item is alive. Distribute RED CRAYONS and have students circle all the living things. Name all the items that did not get circled and explain that they are nonliving things. They are not alive; they do not need water and food; and they do not grow.

4 Discuss the questions at the bottom of the page. Help students understand that God created living and nonliving things with a purposeful design and function. For example, people need other living things (food) and nonliving things (water) to stay alive. Collect student pages.

5 Draw part of the Creation web diagrammed below onto the board. Only include the words *Living Things* and *Nonliving Things* under the heading. You will add parts to the diagram in following lessons. Clarify that *God's Purposeful Design* refers to *what He created*. Explain that God made all things with a purpose. Read **Genesis 1:1** to students. Share that during the year they will be observing, or studying and looking closely at, things that God created. Lead students to sense your enthusiasm about observing God's creation. To conclude, have students point out living or nonliving things in the classroom to a partner. If desired, collect each student page as students complete it, and compile the pages into a booklet for students to take home at the end of the chapter.

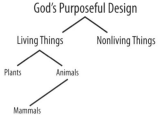

God's Purposeful Design
- Living Things
  - Plants
  - Animals
    - Mammals
- Nonliving Things

⊕ Extension

Materials
• Small toys or pictures

Create a learning center for students to classify small toys or pictures of living and nonliving things.

Living and Nonliving Things **1.1**

God created living and nonliving things. Plants and animals are living things. They need water and food to stay alive. They grow and change.

fish

bird

lemon tree

bear

Nonliving things are not alive. They do not need water or food. They do not grow.

planet

ball

rocks

computer

In the beginning God created the heavens and the earth. Genesis 1:1

© *Science Level 1*   3

Classify means **to put things that are alike in the same group**. Use a red crayon to circle the pictures of living things.

1. Why is a tree classified as a living thing? How does it help people? **needs air, food, and water; provides shade, wood and paper**
2. How does a bicycle, a nonliving thing, help people? **provides transportation and enjoyment**

4   © *Science Level 1*

1.2 Animals

Objective

Students will list the four basic needs of animals.

Materials

Introduction
• Gardener's trowel

Directed Instruction
• TM-1.2A More About Animals, globe
• BLM 1.2A Animals in Their Habitats, scissors, glue, crayons

Preparation

If possible, use a GARDENER'S TROWEL to dig a small hole outside before class. As a safety precaution, be sure to mark the hole. Plan to take students on a walk around campus and include a visit to the hole. (*Introduction*)

Write the definitions of *animal* and *habitat* on the board. (*Directed Instruction*)

Select **TM-1.2A More About Animals** for display. Obtain a GLOBE. (*Directed Instruction*)

Print **BLM 1.2A Animals in Their Habitats** for each student. Have SCISSORS, GLUE, and CRAYONS available. (*Directed Instruction*)

Content

Scientists classify living things into three main domains: Eukarya, Bacteria, and Archaea. There are four major kingdoms within the domain Eukarya: Animals, Plants, Fungi, and Protists (for example, an amoeba). This classification system is called *taxonomy*. Members of each kingdom have characteristics in common that classify them in that kingdom.

One major distinction of members of the animal kingdom is the presence or absence of a backbone. Mammals, reptiles, birds, amphibians, and fishes have a backbone; whereas worms, mollusks, and insects lack a backbone. Information pertaining to backbones and skeletons will be addressed in later lessons.

Each living thing has a habitat, the specific place where that living thing can be found. Within an ecosystem like a type of desert, stream, or forest, there are many habitats with organisms from different kingdoms. The ecosystem provides what an organism needs to stay alive; the organism has the structures necessary to obtain things it needs to stay alive. Understanding these connections helps people be good stewards of God's creation.

Introduction

Take students on a short walk around the school grounds. Instruct the class not to disturb the animals, just to observe them by looking and listening. Some observations may include insects (ants, crickets, beetles), earthworms, and spiders and their webs. Birds may also be present. If you have dug a hole, show students some of the animals, such as worms, that live in the soil. Return to the classroom.

Directed Instruction

1 Compile a class list of the animals students saw. Explain that an **animal** is defined as *a living thing that needs air, food, and water, and a place to live.* Have students apply the definition to one of the animals mentioned. (**Possible answer: A robin drinks water left from rain and finds worms and other foods.**) Express that animals are part of God's purposeful design. Inform students that animals not only need water and food, they also need air. Point to the Creation web from Lesson 1.1 on the board, and add the words *Plants* and *Animals*.

2 Inform the class that each animal they saw outside has a special place to live. Refer to the definition on the board and state that a **habitat** refers to *the place where an animal lives.* The habitat is where the animal gets the things it needs to survive.

3 Read **Genesis 1:20–21, 25**. Share that God made many different kinds of animals that live in many different places on the earth. Ask students to name some birds that fly. (**Possible answers: sparrow, blackbird**) What are some great creatures of the sea? (**Possible answers: whale, octopus**) Can you name some wild animals? (**Possible answers: lion, elk**) State that livestock live on a farm. Ask students to name some animals whose habitat is a farm. (**Possible answers: chickens, cows**) Can you name some creatures that move along the ground? (**Possible answers: snakes, ants, reptiles, insects**)

4 Direct students' attention to the first student page. Read it aloud, help students answer the question, and then convey the following information:
- Crocodile: This animal lives on river banks and in swamps. An adult is usually between 6 and 10 ft long.
- Pronghorn antelope: This interesting animal can be seen eating and running on the plains. It can run up to 60 mph!
- Raccoon: This animal can live in the city or countryside wherever there is water and food. It eats plants and animals.
- Manatee: This big, slow-moving animal eats only plants. It lives near the shore in warm waters.

Point out the skeleton of the giraffe on the second page. Clarify that the purpose of covering is for protection and warmth. Discuss ways animals might move, such as walking, flying, and crawling. Discuss the review questions and then collect the student pages.

5 Display **TM-1.2A More About Animals**. Share these additional facts:
- Lemur: These are monkey-like animals. Most lemurs live in trees. They live on Madagascar and nearby islands. (Locate Madagascar on a GLOBE.)
- Frog with eggs: Most frogs lay their eggs in water. After the eggs hatch, the tadpoles grow. Soon the tadpoles grow into adults.
- Kangaroo: The young, called *joeys*, grow in the mother's pouch.

6 Distribute **BLM 1.2A Animals in Their Habitats**, SCISSORS, GLUE, and CRAYONS to students. Complete the page with students. Allow them to take the completed page home to share with a parent what they have learned.

⊕ Extension

Materials
- *Amazing Animal Alphabet* or *National Geographic Book of Animal Poetry*

For language integration, obtain and read *Amazing Animal Alphabet* by Brian Wildsmith (Star Bright Books, 2009) or *National Geographic Book of Animal Poetry* (National Geographic, 2012) with students. Have students design an animal picture for a letter of the alphabet.

Animals **1.2**

Animals are living things. They move on their own. They grow. Animals need air to breathe. They need water to drink and food to give them energy. They also need a place to live.

Some animals eat other animals. Some animals eat plants. Some animals eat animals and plants.

crocodile

antelope

raccoon

manatee

A habitat is the place where an animal lives. What is the habitat of a manatee?

_____ water _____

© Science Level 1   5

Some animals have a skeleton that helps them move. Animals have different coverings. Animals move in different ways.

giraffe

bird

dolphin

cheetahs

bear

1. What do animals need to live? air, food, water, place to live
2. What do animals eat? plants and animals
3. What is the place called where an animal lives? habitat

6   © Science Level 1

1.3 Special Animals Called Mammals

Objective

Students will recognize hair and milk as two characteristics of mammals.

Materials

Introduction
• TM-1.3A Red the Fox

Directed Instruction
• BLM 1.3A Mammal Facts

Preparation

Select **TM-1.3A Red the Fox** for display. (*Introduction*)

Write the definition of *mammal* on the board. (*Directed Instruction*)

Print **BLM 1.3A Mammal Facts** for each student. (*Directed Instruction*)

Content

In studying the characteristics of living things, scientists observe that some different organisms have common characteristics. Animals with hair, mammary glands to produce milk for their young, and similar skeletal structures are grouped as mammals. These characteristics allow mammals to function and survive in their habitat. God created people with features of mammals. With this form, they can function in their environment to fulfill God's purposes for them. Humans share characteristics—backbones, lungs, warm-bloodedness—with some animals. However, they are uniquely eternal beings. Made in His image and likeness (Genesis 1:26), people are set apart for Him. People can delight in the fact that God formed Adam from the dust of the ground and breathed the breath of life into him and that Adam became a living being (Genesis 2:7).

Introduction 🖐

Display **TM-1.3A Red the Fox** and read the story below; cover the photos until the story mentions when to reveal them. Instruct the class to listen for two special ways God designed the fox. (**hair, milk for its young**)

Red the Fox
(*Uncover the first photo.*) Sophia and Aiden watched from the big window. "Look, there's Red!" said Sophia. Aiden grabbed his pencil and pad so he could draw Red. Sophia loved to watch Red, the red fox. Red came out during the day sometimes but hunted at night. Sophia pointed, "He is so beautiful. I love his pointed nose and white-tipped tail." The children always watched from the window and never got close to the wild animal.

During the winter months, Red was by himself. (*Uncover the second photo.*) The children were amazed at how Red pounced on animals, such as mice, to catch them. (*Uncover the third photo.*) On one very cold morning, Aiden noticed, "Look how Red keeps warm. His big, bushy tail curls around him."

(*Uncover the fourth photo.*) Red and his family live in a den, while their young, called *kits,* are small. Sophia and Aiden knew that since foxes are mammals, the mother fox makes milk. She nurses her young to help them survive and grow. After the young grow up a little, they catch food too!

Sophia said, "Isn't it amazing how God designed the red foxes to be able to live in their habitat? He designed their mother to make milk for her young. He gave them hair to keep them warm!" As Aiden finished his picture of Red, he smiled, "God made red foxes beautiful. He sure cares for them!"

Use the following questions to assess listening skills:
• What kind of animal is Red? (**a fox**)
• Does Red hunt more during the day or night? (**night**)
• What does Red's tail help him do? (**keep warm**)
• What animal does Red catch? (**mice**)
• What is a baby fox called? (**a kit**)

Directed Instruction 🖐

1 Explain that a fox is a mammal. Point out the definition of *mammal* from the board. **Mammal** refers to *an animal that has hair and can make milk to feed its young.* Convey that God's special design of mammals helps them survive. Discuss how the mammals' hair, or fur, protects them and keeps them warm and mother mammals make milk to feed their young.

Ask students about another mammal, the cow. Inquire about where a cow's habitat would be. (**on a farm**) How do you think a cow's hair feels? (**not soft, stiff**) Where does the milk you drink come from? (**cows, goats**)

2 Direct students' attention to the student pages. Read and discuss the top half of the first page. List some milk products and have students raise their hand if they like that product. State that these products are made using cow's milk. Discuss how the next mammal on the page gets its hair cut or sheared. Note products that are made of wool. Read the sentences on the second page. Restate that *identify* means *to notice a certain thing*. Reiterate that God designed these mammals to have hair and to make milk to feed their young. Point to and complete the Creation web from Lesson 1.1, and emphasize *Mammals* within God's purposeful design.

Permit students to share with a classmate two things they have learned about mammals. Complete the review questions together. Check student work for spelling accuracy and collect the pages.

3 Distribute **BLM 1.3A Mammal Facts**. Reiterate that mammals are living things designed with lungs to breathe air. The giraffe's whole skeleton helps the giraffe move. In addition, mammals keep the same body temperature, no matter how hot or cold it is outside. The body temperature of a giraffe ranges from 99°F–101.5°F, with an average of 100.5°F. A healthy giraffe keeps this temperature range, no matter how hot the air temperature is.

➕ **Extension**

Materials
• CP-1.3 Animal Habitats: Mammals and Fish, Part 1

Present **CP-1.3 Animal Habitats: Mammals and Fish, Part 1** and discuss the slides about mammals.

Share with students that people have hair and that human mothers are able to make milk for their babies. God designed people to fellowship with Him. They are made in God's image and likeness (Genesis 1:26).

Special Animals Called Mammals **1.3**

Mammals are a special group of animals. They have hair and can make milk to feed their young.

The cow has hair. How do you think the hair feels?

The mother cow makes milk to feed her young. Milk from the cow is used to make ice cream, yogurt, cheese, butter, and milk to drink.

Is the cow a mammal? Write **yes** or **no**.

_____ yes _____

This mammal makes milk for her young. It also gets its hair cut or sheared. Its hair is called **wool**.

What is this mammal? _____ sheep _____

Wool from the sheep makes socks, blankets, sweaters, and hats.

© Science Level 1   7

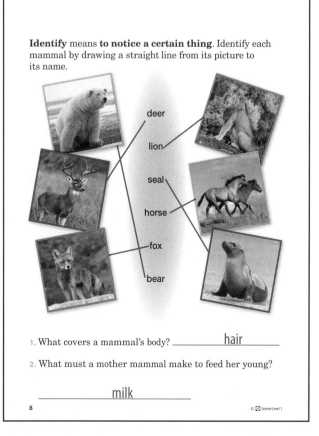

Identify means **to notice a certain thing**. Identify each mammal by drawing a straight line from its picture to its name.

deer

lion

seal

horse

fox

bear

1. What covers a mammal's body? _____ hair _____

2. What must a mother mammal make to feed her young?

_____ milk _____

8   © Science Level 1

1.4 Mammals in the Woodlands

Mammals

Content

This lesson presents a variety of mammals and the environment in which they live. The woodlands provide many types of habitats. Plants, animals, and other organisms populate the woodlands—each in their specific habitat. All parts of the woodland population interact and form a community.

Introduction 👋

Distribute copies of **BLM 1.4A "Mammals."** Sing the lyrics to the tune of "London Bridge."

Directed Instruction 👋 ➕

1 Inform students that in today's lesson they will be studying habitats in the woodlands, or the forest. These woodlands border a pond.

2 Display **TM-1.4A The Woodlands**. Discuss some of the plants found in the woodlands, such as trees, shrubs, and flowers. Point out nonliving things, such as air, rocks, and water. Share the following information:
   • Air cannot be seen, but it is in the woodlands.
   • Water, both in the pond and from the rain that falls, is important for the living things.
   • Food is everywhere. For example, an insect may eat the leaf of a plant. A frog may eat the insect. A snake may eat the frog and a hawk may eat the snake.

   Ask students to name some plants that they see in the woodlands scene. (**trees, shrubs, plants, flowers**) What other living things might you see in the woodlands? (**Answers will vary but should include animals.**)

3 Replace TM-1.4A with **TM-1.4B Animals in the Woodlands**. First, point out the mammals (porcupine, rabbit, deer, skunk, mouse, red fox, squirrel, raccoon, bear, beaver, bat, and mole). Ask students if they have ever seen any of these mammals. Which ones? Where? (**Answers will vary.**) Then point out that fish and birds are not mammals because they do not have hair; fish have scales and birds have feathers.

   Briefly mention that there are also other living things in the woodlands that are not easily seen, such as insects and tiny living things that live in the soil and in the water. Ask students what all these living things need (**All need water and food. Most need air.**) and where those items are in this picture. (*water*: **in the pond;** *food*: **all around, depending on what a certain living thing eats;** *air*: **all around the scene but cannot be seen**) Point out the dead tree near the bear. Mention that this tree is a habitat for many living things. For example, the bird finds insects in the dead tree.

   Stress the importance of appreciating the beauty of natural places for what they are—God's creation. Guide students to see the beauty of such habitats and the detail of God's purposeful design of each living and nonliving thing.

4 Have students turn to their first student page about the woodlands. State that students will play a game with their page. Explain the rules of the game What Mammal Am I? Students should listen carefully to the clues about a mammal and raise their hand when they think they might know what animal is being described. Have them circle each mammal as it is

identified. Point out each mammal on TM-1.4B as students identify it. Read the following clues to the game What Mammal Am I?

- I am a large mammal with shaggy hair. I have a short tail. I eat fruit, insects, and other animals. What mammal am I? (black bear)
- I have sharp bristles, or quills, mixed in with my hair. What mammal am I? (porcupine)
- I have long ears and a short tail. I eat grass. What mammal am I? (rabbit)
- I can squirt another animal that threatens me. When I squirt, it makes a stinky odor! What mammal am I? (skunk)
- I am the only mammal that can fly. I fly and feed mainly at night. What mammal am I? (bat)
- I eat earthworms, insects, and other small animals. I have strong front feet for burrowing. What mammal am I? (mole)
- I eat plants. I have webbed feet and a flat, scaly tail that helps me swim. I build a lodge where I can live. What mammal am I? (beaver)
- I eat leaves, berries, and bark of trees. My young are spotted. The spots help them blend in with shadows under trees. What mammal am I? (deer)
- I have a black mask and a bushy, ringed tail. I eat frogs and other animals, as well as fruits and nuts. What mammal am I? (raccoon)
- I am very small. I have a pointed nose, a long body, and a thin tail. What mammal am I? (mouse)
- I am small and have a big, fluffy tail. What mammal am I? (squirrel)
- I catch mice, earthworms, and insects. I am active mostly at night. My babies are called *kits*. What mammal am I? (fox)

5 Direct students' attention to the next page. Read the directions and complete the page together. Collect the student pages.

Extension

Compare and contrast woodland animals to those seen around the students' neighborhood or school.

Create a class graph of the animals on the first student page. Graph animals by mammals and nonmammals, fur or feathers, number of legs, size, color, or short and long tails.

Invite volunteers to pantomime a woodland mammal and encourage the rest of the class to guess.

Have students write or tell a fictional story about woodland mammals.

Mammals in the Woodlands 1.4

© Science Level 1   9

Make an **X** on the mammal that does not belong in the woodlands.

10   © Science Level 1

1.5 A Whale's Warmth

Content

The design of the whale's body allows the whale to survive in its environment and to function as it needs to. The whale exhibits many features that show this design, including the ability to hold its breath underwater, echolocation (in some species of whales), and the presence of blubber.

A whale breathes through a blowhole. After a whale inhales air, a flap that covers the blowhole closes. When the whale returns to the surface, it breathes out of its blowhole, creating an upward spout. Large whale species have unique spout shapes.

Blubber, found under the whale's skin, functions to insulate the whale and act as an energy reserve. The thickness of blubber depends on the species. A killer whale has a blubber layer that is a few inches thick, while the thickness of a bowhead whale's blubber may reach 20 inches.

Studying the details of different species helps bring understanding of how to be good stewards of the earth. It is important to see a habitat or an ecosystem as a whole, not simply as its independent parts. Any change such as adding pollutants or developing land can upset the delicate balance within an ecosystem. It is important that people make wise choices now in order to maintain ecosystems for the future.

Introduction

Ask students if they have seen a whale or pictures of one. Pick a volunteer to describe what a whale looks like and where it lives. (**Possible answer: A whale is very big; it lives in the water.**)

Read **Genesis 1:9–10**. Elaborate on the fact that God made the sea and later filled it with many animals suited for living in water. Mammals that live in the water all the time, such as whales, would not survive if God had not designed them to thrive in water.

Directed Instruction

1 Announce that the class is going to do an experiment. Use the *Scientific Inquiry* and *Senses* sections at the beginning of this book as a reference for conducting an experiment. Direct students to the student page with the experiment. Explain that an *experiment* means *a way to test, or try out, a science question to learn something*. Point out that materials are usually needed to do an experiment. In this experiment, empty CUPS and a THERMOS containing WARM WATER are needed. Use the thermos that was filled with warm water an hour ago. Students should have felt the warm water previously. The steps on the student page must be done in the order they appear. Proceed through each step. Read each bold heading and have students repeat it before discussing it.

  1. Ask a question: Read the question that students will try to answer through the experiment.

  2. Make a hypothesis: Ask students what they think has happened to the water. Have them circle their guess. (**Answers will vary.**)

  3. Plan and do a test: Explain that students will plan and do an experiment. It is a way to test their hypothesis. Pour some warm water into a cup, one for each row or group. Do not permit students to pour the water. Remind them of the scientific technique in the *Safety* sidebar that alerts

one to test a container by touching it lightly before feeling the contents. Have students feel the water in the cup to make their observations.

4. Record and analyze your results: Ask students if the water from the thermos is warm or cool. **(warm)** Give students time to record their answer.

5. Make a conclusion: Have students compare the results with their hypothesis. Reassure students that scientific inquiry is not about being right or wrong; it is about discovering something they did not know before or confirming something they do know.

6. Share your results: Have students share with a classmate what they learned about a thermos from their experiment.

Instruct students that blubber is fat under the skin of the whale. Help them understand that a whale's blubber functions like a thermos. People designed the thermos to keep its contents a certain temperature. Point to the thick, insulated walls of the thermos. Share that it is God's design that blubber helps keep the whale warm in cold waters.

2 Direct students' attention to the next page. Read the paragraph aloud and reiterate that, like all mammals, whales have hair, even though it appears they do not. Include that some whales have a special sense called *echolocation* that helps them know what is around them in the water.

3 Give adequate time for students to finish the page and share their drawing with another classmate. Check the accuracy of answers. Assign one partner to discuss why blubber is important to whales; have the other partner describe the term *spout*. If desired, collect student pages.

➕ Extension

Materials
• Bowl, ice water, bags, spoon, lard or shortening, tape

Obtain a bowl of ice water and 4 quart-sized ziplock bags. Scoop 3 spoonfuls of lard or shortening into one bag. Turn a second bag inside out and place it inside the first bag. Zip the 2 bags together. Make a second set of bags without lard. Have a volunteer place one hand inside each set. Mold the lard to insulate the hand. Secure the bags at the wrist with tape. Explain that the empty bag is like skin, but the lard bag is like blubber. Instruct the student to place the hands into the ice water and to compare how they feel. **(The hand in the empty bag feels colder.)** State that blubber is a protective layer that keeps whales warm in cold water.

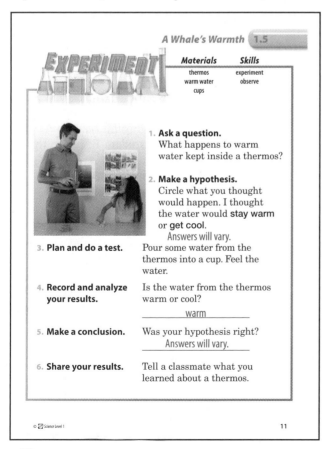

A Whale's Warmth **1.5**

EXPERIMENT

Materials	Skills
thermos	experiment
warm water	observe
cups	

1. **Ask a question.** What happens to warm water kept inside a thermos?

2. **Make a hypothesis.** Circle what you thought would happen. I thought the water would **stay warm** or **get cool**.
Answers will vary.

3. **Plan and do a test.** Pour some water from the thermos into a cup. Feel the water.

4. **Record and analyze your results.** Is the water from the thermos warm or cool?
_____ warm _____

5. **Make a conclusion.** Was your hypothesis right?
Answers will vary.

6. **Share your results.** Tell a classmate what you learned about a thermos.

© Science Level 1   11

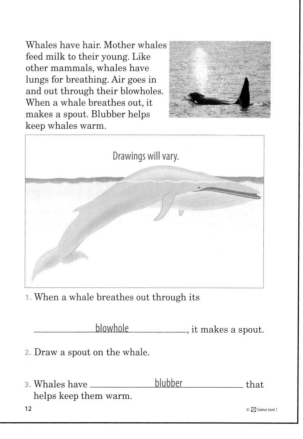

Whales have hair. Mother whales feed milk to their young. Like other mammals, whales have lungs for breathing. Air goes in and out through their blowholes. When a whale breathes out, it makes a spout. Blubber helps keep whales warm.

Drawings will vary.

1. When a whale breathes out through its
_____ blowhole _____, it makes a spout.

2. Draw a spout on the whale.

3. Whales have _____ blubber _____ that helps keep them warm.

12   © Science Level 1

1.6 Tech Connect

Objective

Students will relate how the animal characteristic of echolocation is used in technology.

Materials

Directed Instruction
• Large ball

Preparation

Arrange a location for the activity What's Out There? Select a large area, perhaps outdoors or a gymnasium. Obtain a LARGE BALL. (*Directed Instruction*)

Content

Some details in the *Content* section of Lesson 1.5 make evident the design of the killer whale. Echolocation is another ability that this marine mammal uses in order to survive in its habitat. This ability allows the killer whale to know what is around it. Other marine mammals and bats have this capability too. The killer whale sends out sound signals, which bounce off a nearby object. The whale receives an echoing sound back from this nearby object. The echo provides information about the shape and size of the object, as well as its direction, distance, and speed. In essence, the echo helps the whale locate, with pinpoint accuracy, an object it cannot see.

It is amazing to understand how God has equipped living things, such as killer whales, to function by design. God also equips people for tasks that are before them, through one or more obvious gifts and also through Scripture. This is His plan for His people. All Scripture is God-breathed and is useful for teaching, rebuking, correcting, and training in righteousness, so that the believer may be thoroughly equipped for every good work (2 Timothy 3:16–17). God equips believers to do His work and to rely on Him to show them how to be all He created them to be.

Introduction

Ask the class if they have ever clapped their hands while in a tunnel. (**Answers will vary.**) What happens? (**The clap is heard again.**) The echo is the sound that is heard again; the sound bounces off the tunnel walls.

Directed Instruction

1 Direct students to the *Senses* section at the beginning of the student book and state that you will be doing an activity that will demonstrate a particular use of hearing. Pick two volunteers to participate in the What's Out There? activity. Direct the volunteers to sit on the floor where the class can easily see them. Direct student A to gently roll a LARGE BALL to student B and student B to roll it back to A.

Ask student A to close his or her eyes. Have student A gently roll the ball several times in different directions. Have student B roll it back to A when it comes to him or her. (If the ball does not roll to student B, return the ball to student A and inform student A that the ball missed student B.) Explain that student A learned student B's position because student B returned the ball.

2 Explain that the ball coming back to student A demonstrates how an echo works. The ball being returned to student A was a clue to the location of student B. Expound that this is like something that God designed for some animals. It is called *echolocation* because echoes help the animal locate, or find, something. Animals use sound, not a ball. Write *echolocation* on the board. State that this long word is made up of two shorter words that students know. Write *echo* and *location* as two words.

3 Convey that people use something on boats and ships that is like echolocation. It is called *sonar*. Like echolocation, sonar is a way to find out if something is nearby. Ships send out a special sound and get sound in return. This helps them know if something is nearby in the water.

4 Have students turn to their first page. Read the top paragraph and discuss the information about the echo that the child heard. Guide students to look at the picture and fill in the blank. Check to see that *echo* has been written on the correct line. Read through the rest of the page and lead students to the correct answers. In discussing the two words in *echolocation*, mention that *locate* has a different ending than *location*.

Read the paragraph about sonar on the second student page. Have the class give a phrase that suggests warning as they pretend they are on a ship that is detecting objects in the water by sonar. Have students act out the call of warning as though they were on the ship.
Possible phrases:
• Island (**Be careful!**)
• Iceberg (**Look out!**)
• School of fish (**Let's catch fish!**)
• Submarine (**It's a submarine!**)
• Seafloor (**It's deep here!**)
Collect student pages.

Notes:

➕ **Extension**

Materials
• BLM 1.6A Mammal Maze
• Blindfold

Have students complete **BLM 1.6A Mammal Maze**.

In an open space, have students stand in a circle. Choose two volunteers to play a whale and a fish in the center. Blindfold the "whale" and state that he or she must find the "fish" through echolocation. Have the whale say *echo* and the fish respond *location*. The whale must listen for the fish's response and catch the fish by tagging him or her. Advise students to walk inside the circle and not run. Once the whale catches the fish, select new volunteers. Adjust the size of the circle to make the game more challenging for the whale or the fish.

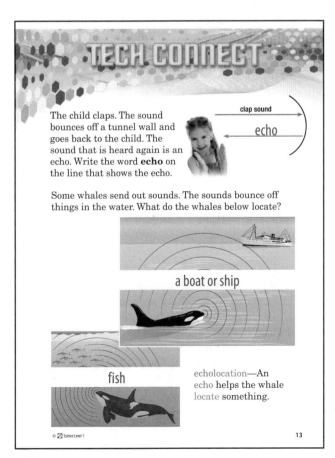

TECH CONNECT

The child claps. The sound bounces off a tunnel wall and goes back to the child. The sound that is heard again is an echo. Write the word **echo** on the line that shows the echo.

clap sound

echo

Some whales send out sounds. The sounds bounce off things in the water. What do the whales below locate?

a boat or ship

fish

echolocation—An echo helps the whale locate something.

© *Science* Level 1   13

TECH CONNECT

Sonar is like echolocation. People use sonar on ships and boats to find out what is nearby.

14

How does sonar help people? by locating objects, finding food, and helping them be safe © *Science* Level 1

Introduction
• TM-1.7A Meet More Mammals

Directed Instruction
• BLM 1.7A Chapter 1 Test, crayons

Preparation

Select **TM-1.7A Meet More Mammals** for display. (*Introduction*)

Draw the complete Creation web from Lesson 1.1 onto the board. (*Introduction*)

Print **BLM 1.7A Chapter 1 Test** for each student. Have CRAYONS available. (*Directed Instruction*)

Introduction

Display **TM-1.7A Meet More Mammals**. Present one mammal at a time and read the following facts about that mammal. After each mammal is introduced, allow a few students to act out that mammal for the class.
• The elephant is the largest living land mammal. Its habitat is in Africa and Asia. It is known for its trunk that helps it eat hundreds of fruits, leaves, and plants every day. It can drink up to 50 gallons of water a day. That is like drinking 800 bottles of water. Elephants travel in herds and swim well.
• A zebra is a mammal. It is known for its black and white stripes. It is related to horses, and most kinds live in herds. The zebra is a plant eater.
• The prairie dog is a mammal. It lives in groups with other prairie dogs. It is known for digging and making its home in underground tunnels. A prairie dog grows to about as tall as a ruler and feeds mostly on the grasses of the plains, which is its habitat.
• The grizzly bear is a mammal. It grows taller than a person and weighs about as much as 16 first graders! A grizzly bear eats some kinds of mammals, fish, insects, plants, and berries. Its habitat can be in forests, grasslands, or river valleys. It is known for digging dens, or hollows.
• A coyote is a mammal. A coyote looks like a medium-sized dog. Its habitat can be forests, grasslands, mountains, deserts, or even near cities. It is known for its howl, or cry.

Direct students' attention to the Creation web drawn on the chalkboard. Explain that this graphic shows that God made each living and nonliving thing in a special way. Ask a student to place a finger on *living things* and another student to point to *nonliving things*. Teach that God made two groups of living things—plants and animals. Have the first student move his or her finger accordingly. Ask students to name the animal group that they have studied this week. (**mammals**) What are two specials ways that God made mammals? (**He gave them hair and made them able to make milk for their young.**)

Directed Instruction

1 Review the definitions of *living thing* and *nonliving thing*. (***Living thing**: a thing that needs water and food to stay alive. It grows and changes. **Nonliving thing**: a thing that is not alive and does not grow.*) Inform students that you will name a thing. If it is living, they are to stand. If it is nonliving, they should stay seated or be seated. Name several things such as lizard (**stand**), motorcycle (**sit**), bluebird (**stand**), oak tree (**stay standing**), jet (**sit**), ant (**stand**), ice cream (**sit**), flower (**stand**), kitten (**stay standing**), and phone (**sit**).

2 Review the definitions of *animal* and *habitat*. (***animal**: a living thing that finds its own food; **habitat**: the place where an animal lives*) Invite volunteers to draw a picture on the board of something an animal needs to survive. (**water, food, a place to live, air**) Ask students to name some habitats where an animal could live. (**Possible answers: woodlands, ocean, desert**) Remind students that mammals have hair and make milk for their young.

3 Use the student pages as a review or a pretest. Distribute CRAYONS to students. Complete the pages with the class. Refer to the diagram on the board for reading the Creation web.

4 You may choose to use **BLM 1.7A Chapter 1 Test** for individual assessment. Provide support by reading it through with the class. Let the reading level of your students determine how you use the test. If your class is not ready for this level of independent work, you may use it as an oral assessment or choose not to do it at all.

5 Chapter 1 Mammals has been completed. If you decided to collect the pages of the chapter, staple and send them home as a booklet. Encourage students to share their booklets with a parent.

Notes:

+ Extension

Materials
• Aluminum pie pan, paper-towel tubes

Create a learning center about echolocation. Stand a pie pan on a desk by leaning it against books or a wall. Tape 2 paper-towel tubes to the desk, angled toward each other and facing the pan. Direct one student to whisper into one of the tubes. Have a second student listen for the sound to bounce off the pie pan into the other paper-towel tube.

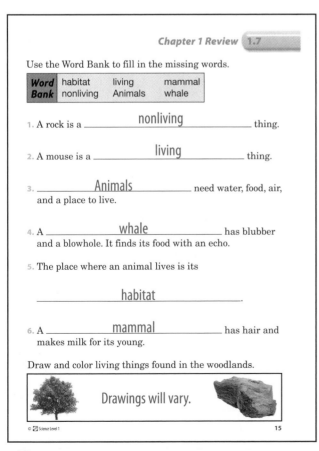

Chapter 1 Review 1.7

Use the Word Bank to fill in the missing words.

Word Bank	habitat	living	mammal
	nonliving	Animals	whale

1. A rock is a _____ nonliving _____ thing.

2. A mouse is a _____ living _____ thing.

3. _____ Animals _____ need water, food, air, and a place to live.

4. A _____ whale _____ has blubber and a blowhole. It finds its food with an echo.

5. The place where an animal lives is its

_____ habitat _____.

6. A _____ mammal _____ has hair and makes milk for its young.

Draw and color living things found in the woodlands.

Drawings will vary.

© Science Level 1   15

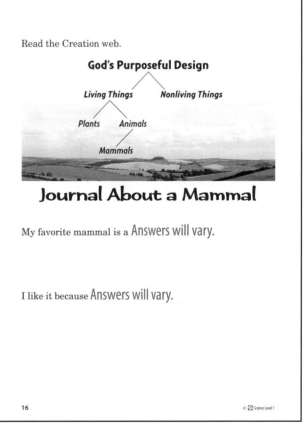

Read the Creation web.

God's Purposeful Design

Living Things   Nonliving Things

Plants   Animals

Mammals

Journal About a Mammal

My favorite mammal is a Answers will vary.

I like it because Answers will vary.

16   © Science Level 1

Fish

Chapter 2

Key Ideas

- The kingdom of animals is further classified into the class of fish.
- Fish have fins, gills, and scales and live in water.
- God designed many fish with camouflage and other methods of defense against predators. Camouflage also helps fish when they are seeking prey.

2.0 Chapter Preparation

Vocabulary

fish
school of fish

Looking Ahead

- For **Lessons 2.6** and **2.7**, cut out a total of 15 fish from **BLM 2.6A Make a Fish** on various colors of construction paper. Laminate for durability.
- For the *Extension* activity in **Lesson 3.2**, invite an employee of a local sports store or a member of a nearby bird-watching club to visit and demonstrate the use of bird calls.

Introduction

Welcome to the fascinating underwater world of fish! By studying fish, students will see that fish can be categorized as having either a skeleton made of bone or a skeleton made of cartilage. During the classification process, students will also see common features, such as skeleton types, habitats, means of obtaining food, and life cycles. Students will correlate the design of fish to the habitat God made for them. Students will discover differences in saltwater and freshwater environments. They will also observe various physical characteristics for protection and defense. As they see the effects of humans on fish, they will begin to acknowledge the significance of being good stewards of God's creation.

About This Chapter

Lesson 2.1 – What Fish Are

Materials
- Plates
- Crayons
- Smocks
- Paint
- Cups of water
- Paintbrushes
- Scissors
- Plastic wrap
- Tape
- Glue
- Optional items
- Stapler

Lesson Content
Fish are a special group of animals that live in the water. Just as God created people with arms and legs to move, He created fish with fins to swim. People have lungs to breath and skin to cover their body; fish have gills for breathing and a covering of scales. God also designed fish to swim in schools for protection from larger fish.

Lesson 2.2 – Parts of a Fish

Materials
- Thermometer
- Bowl of water
- Box
- Glue sticks
- Glitter

Lesson Content
Dorsal fins and tail fins help fish move easily through the water. The dorsal fin assists the fish in staying upright, and the tail fin guides the fish to move forward. A lining of mucus over the scales allows the fish to glide through the water, and the mucus coating also resists germs. Other body parts such as eyes, nostrils, ears, and a mouth help fish thrive in their environment. A fish uses its senses to get food and stay safe.

Lesson 2.3 – Differences in Fish

Materials
- Yarn
- Clay
- Ziplock bags
- Waxed paper

Lesson Content
The size difference between the smallest and largest fish is more than 44 ft. Fish vary in size and shape in order to survive in their habitat. A fish's shape may affect how it moves, how it blends in with its surroundings, and how it keeps other fish away or attracts them. Some types of fish, such as tuna, have bones and cartilage that make up their skeleton and give them a shape. Other types of fish, such as sharks and rays, have a skeleton made of cartilage only.

Lesson 2.4 – Fish Grow
Materials
- Envelopes
- Crayons
- Scissors
- Tape

Lesson Content

Most fish lay eggs. Some eggs float in the water; some are encased or hidden in nests. A female sea horse puts her eggs in the male's pouch. Fish emerge from their eggs and grow from young fish to adult fish. Some fish grow up in different ways, but they all are part of God's design.

Lesson 2.5 – Habitats and Food
Materials
- Goggles
- Hand lenses
- Salt
- Construction paper
- Jars of water
- Teaspoon
- Stirrer
- Paper towels

Lesson Content

Fishes can be found in saltwater and freshwater environments. Saltwater is characteristic of oceans and seas. Freshwater habitats include lakes, swamps, ponds, rivers, and streams. God designed different types of fish to live in different types of water. He also created them to eat different things, such as plants and other animals. God's design of each fish enables it to live in its specific habitat.

Lesson 2.6 – Camouflage and Defense
Materials
- Construction paper
- Crayons

Lesson Content

God designed some types of fish to have camouflage, the ability to blend in with the surroundings. Camouflage helps fish hide from other fish that want to eat them, or hide so they can catch fish without being seen. Other methods of defense that fish have include an ability to puff up, sting, or make mucus to protect themselves from predators.

Lesson 2.7 – Chapter 2 Review
Materials
- Paper clips
- Fishing pole
- Magnet
- Bulletin board paper (optional)

Teacher Resources

Aquarium Care of Bettas by David E. Boruchowitz. TFH, 2006.

The Illustrated Encyclopedia of Fish and Shellfish of the World by Daniel Gilpin, Amy Jane Beer, and Derek Hall. Lorenz, 2010.

Student Resources

Fishy Tales. DK, 2011.

How Many Fish in the Sea? by Linda Tagliaferro. Capstone, 2007.

Lots of Spots by Lois Ehlert. Beach Lane Books, 2010.

Supplemental Materials

Blackline Masters
2.1A About a Trout
2.2A Parts of a Fish
2.3A Fish Facts
2.4A Puzzle: Fish
2.4B Cycle of Life
2.5A Making a Betta Fish Bowl

2.6A Make a Fish
2.7A Chapter 2 Test

Transparency Masters
2.2A Fish
2.7A Amazing Fish

Computer Presentation
1.3 Animal Habitats: Mammals and Fish, Part 2

2.1 What Fish Are

Objective

Students will describe fish and their features.

Materials

Introduction
• BLM 2.1A About a Trout

Directed Instruction
• Uncoated paper plates; crayons; smocks; blue watercolor paint; cups of water; paintbrushes; scissors; plastic wrap; tape; glue; rocks, sand, or shells (optional); stapler

Preparation

Print **BLM 2.1A About a Trout** for yourself. (*Introduction*)

Write the definitions of *fish* and *school of fish* on the board. (*Directed Instruction*)

Draw the following Creation web on the board. (*Directed Instruction*)

For a craft activity, prepare for each student to have 2 UNCOATED PAPER PLATES; CRAYONS; a SMOCK; BLUE WATERCOLOR PAINT; a CUP OF WATER; a PAINTBRUSH; SCISSORS; a sheet of PLASTIC WRAP; TAPE; GLUE; SMALL ROCKS, SAND, OR SHELLS (OPTIONAL); and a STAPLER. (*Directed Instruction*)

Content

The term *fishes* refers to many species of fish; the term *fish* refers to many individuals of a single species. Because first graders might have difficulty understanding the difference, the term *fish* is used with these students.

Fishes are identified by three main distinctions:
• Gills: Most fishes breathe through gills that are located in a special chamber just behind the mouth. When a fish takes water in through its mouth, the water flows over its gills. Gills take oxygen out of the water and pass it into the fish's bloodstream. Carbon dioxide is expelled through the gills and into the water. The oxygen present in water provides the necessary amount to sustain aquatic life. In bony fishes, the gills are covered by a gill cover.
• Scales: Most fishes have scales that serve to protect them. Scale type and the number of rows of scales help identify a fish. The body of the fish is also covered with mucus, which protects the fish from infection and helps it glide easily through water.
• Fins: Fishes have fins that help them swim. Fins are tissue supported by cartilage or bone. Fins help a fish with movements such as swimming forward, turning, balancing or remaining upright, and moving slowly.

Schooling behavior serves to protect fish from predators. This behavior confuses predators and gives the appearance of one large organism.

Introduction

Ask students to share about a pet fish they may have at home. (**Answers will vary.**) Direct the class to listen carefully to a story about Jacob's family observing fish. Read the story on **BLM 2.1A About a Trout** and stress the importance of the three parts of a fish mentioned—gills, scales, and fins.

After the story, use the following questions to assess listening skills:
• God designed fish. What did He design for fish to breathe with? (**gills**)
• What covers and protects a fish's body? (**scales and mucus**)
• What helps a fish swim? (**fins**)

Directed Instruction

1 Read the definition from the board—**fish:** *an animal that lives in water.* Convey that there are many different types of fish, but they all live in the water. Inform students that God purposefully designed fish to get all the things that they need to live. Make parallels between people and fish. Just as God created people with arms and legs that help them move, God gave fish fins. A *fin* refers to *a part of a fish that helps it swim.* God designed people with lungs and fish with gills. A *gill* is defined as *a part of a fish that helps it breathe.* God designed people with skin and fish with scales. A *scale* refers to *a part of a fish that protects it.*

2 Have students look at the first student page. Read the sentences at the top. Direct students to look at the photo and labeled parts. Discuss the question and the answers about fins, gills, and scales. As you discuss fins, have students put a finger on each one. Have them find the gill cover and scales in the same manner. Allow time for students to draw the fins and scales on the fish at the bottom of the page. Check students' work.

3 Point out the definition on the board—**school of fish**: *a large number of one kind of fish swimming together.* Have a volunteer read the paragraph at the top of the second page. Discuss how God designed some fish to swim in a group. Ask students how swimming in a school protects fish. (**A bigger fish might be scared off by a large number of fish swimming together.**) Allow students time to estimate the number of fish in the picture.

4 Have students answer the first review question. Give instruction on how to complete the second one. Have them work in pairs to explain the function of fins, gills, and scales. If desired, collect the student pages each day for students to take home as a booklet at the end of the chapter.

5 Read **Genesis 1:21**. Explain that the idea of water teeming with living creatures means that the water was filled with fish and other living things. Refer to the Creation web on the board and point out God's design for fish.

6 For each student to create a fishbowl habitat craft, distribute as needed: 2 PAPER PLATES; CRAYONS; a SMOCK; WATERCOLOR PAINT; a CUP OF WATER; a PAINTBRUSH; SCISSORS; PLASTIC WRAP; TAPE; GLUE; ROCKS, SAND, OR SHELLS (OPTIONAL); and a STAPLER. On a plate placed faceup, have students draw and color fish. Advise them to press down when they color. Then have them paint the entire plate with blue paint. The fish will show through the paint. While the paint dries, direct students to draw and cut out a large circle in the center of the second plate. Then have them stretch and tape the plastic wrap over the top side of the circle. When the paint on the first plate dries, allow students to glue on rocks, sand, or shells. Staple the plates together with the edges facing each other.

 Extension

Materials
• Ocean video

Obtain a video about ocean life, such as *Disneynature: Oceans* (Walt Disney Video, 2009) or *Turtle: The Incredible Journey* (Hannover House, 2009). Show a segment of the video each day or just play a selection.

Discuss the importance of learning to swim. Have students who can swim demonstrate or discuss their technique with the class. Compare how swimmers use their arms or legs to how fish use their fins.

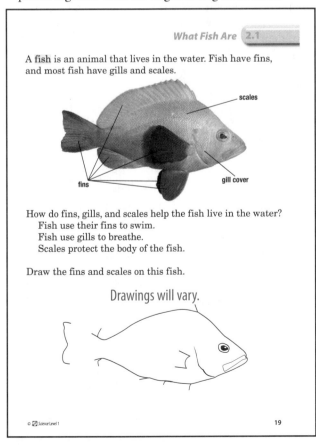

What Fish Are 2.1

A **fish** is an animal that lives in the water. Fish have fins, and most fish have gills and scales.

scales
fins
gill cover

How do fins, gills, and scales help the fish live in the water?
Fish use their fins to swim.
Fish use gills to breathe.
Scales protect the body of the fish.

Draw the fins and scales on this fish.

Drawings will vary.

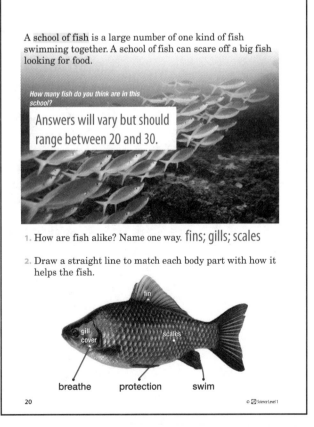

A **school of fish** is a large number of one kind of fish swimming together. A school of fish can scare off a big fish looking for food.

How many fish do you think are in this school?

Answers will vary but should range between 20 and 30.

1. How are fish alike? Name one way. fins; gills; scales

2. Draw a straight line to match each body part with how it helps the fish.

fin
gill cover
scales

breathe   protection   swim

2.2 Parts of a Fish

Fish

Objective

Students will identify features of a fish that help it survive in its habitat.

Materials

Directed Instruction
- Thermometer, bowl of water
- BLM 2.2A Parts of a Fish, TM-2.2A Fish, paper box, glue sticks, glitter

Preparation

Gather a THERMOMETER and a BOWL OF WATER. Obtain the thermometer from the ACSI Science Equipment Kit or borrow one from a local high school or college. (*Directed Instruction*)

Print **BLM 2.2A Parts of a Fish** for each student and select **TM-2.2A Fish** for display. Designate an EMPTY PAPER BOX as a GLITTER station. Obtain GLUE STICKS for students. (*Directed Instruction*)

Content

Depending on the species of fish, the occurrence, location, and function of the fins vary. In many species the dorsal and anal fins help the fish remain upright, while the caudal fin, or tail, helps forward motion. Pectoral fins and pelvic fins function to steer or maintain balance. The role of fins may depend on the shape of the fish. The fins of the sea horse have different roles. Its dorsal fin works to move it forward, while the pectoral fins serve to help it turn.

Fishes also have different senses. Most fish eyes are well developed and do not have lids. The water keeps the eyes moist. God designed fish eyes to see in many directions. Nostrils assist the sense of smell and are not associated with breathing. In migrating fishes, such as salmon, this sense of smell allows them to complete the species' life cycle, directing them to the location where they will spawn. Moray eels cannot find food without their sense of smell. Their taste buds are located in the mouth and on the tongue. They also occur on other parts of the body—feelers, lips, and on the surface of the whole body. In addition, fish can hear. A fish's ears are inside its skull; they help the fish detect sounds as well as maintain balance. A fish's body actually helps the fish hear sounds by transmitting sound waves from the environment. In some fishes, the swim bladder, which may be near the ear, helps the fish hear. The line on the side of the fish, called *the lateral line*, helps this animal sense movement.

Introduction

Ask student volunteers to describe or act out the movement of some animals such as a frog (**hops with its legs**), sparrow (**flies with its wings**), elephant (**lumbers with all four limbs**), snake (**slithers with no limbs**), and monkey (**swings through tree branches with its arms**). Ask the class what helps fish swim. (**their fins**) Have students press their palms together and move their hands back and forth in a fishlike swimming motion.

Directed Instruction

1 Review what students learned about fish in Lesson 2.1. Ask volunteers to name some body parts God designed so fish can live in the water. (**God designed fish with gills that help them breathe, scales that protect their body, and fins that help them swim.**)

Direct students' attention to the first student page. Have a volunteer walk slowly across the room with a book on his or her head. Ask the class how the volunteer must walk to keep the book balanced. (**Answers will vary, but should include that the student must keep his or her head up straight.**) Explain that God designed fish with different fins to help the fish move well. Explain that the fin on the back of the fish is called *the dorsal fin*, which helps a fish stay upright. Point out the dorsal fin on the page. Relate the book on the child's head to the dorsal fin of the fish. Have the class pronounce the word *dorsal*.

2 Ask students if they have ever seen swimmers kick their feet as they swim. (**Answers will vary.**) How does this motion help swimmers? (**It helps them go forward.**) Guide students to analyze the fish picture and to name the fin that helps a fish move forward. (**tail fin**)

3 Read the paragraphs in the center of the page. Convey that God designed the fish with many other things that help it live and move in its habitat. Ask students why God designed fish to have mucus. (**Mucus helps the fish move well through the water and keeps away germs.**) Read the last paragraph and have students place a finger on the sea horse's back fin.

Remind the class that gills help fish get the air they need. Elaborate on the fact that God designed some fish with a special cover that protects their gills. This flap is called *a gill cover*.

Explain that another special design that fish and some other animals have is that they change their body temperature to match the temperature of what is around them. To demonstrate this, place a THERMOMETER inside a BOWL OF WATER. Read the temperature. Clarify that if you were to put a fish inside the bowl, its temperature would change to match the water temperature.

4 Direct students' attention to the second student page. Read through the information and relate the pictures to the information. Assist students in answering the questions at the bottom of the page.

5 Distribute copies of **BLM 2.2A Parts of a Fish**. Display **TM-2.2A Fish** to help students label the parts of the fish. As students finish, instruct them to rub glue over the fish's scales with a GLUE STICK. One at a time, direct students to bring their paper to the glitter station. Have them place their paper inside the EMPTY PAPER BOX and sprinkle GLITTER over the page. Set the pages aside to dry and then allow students to take them home.

➕ Extension

Materials
• Beginner's Bible or storybook

Draw a fish symbol (✡) on the board. Ask students if and where they have seen one. (**Answers will vary.**) Explain that fish are mentioned many times in the Bible. Several of Jesus' disciples were fishermen who made their living catching fish. Jesus fed over 5,000 people using only two fish and five loaves of bread. Some of the early Christians used the symbol of a fish to let others know that they were followers of Christ.

Share with students the Bible truth of Jonah and the big fish from a Bible storybook or a beginner's Bible.

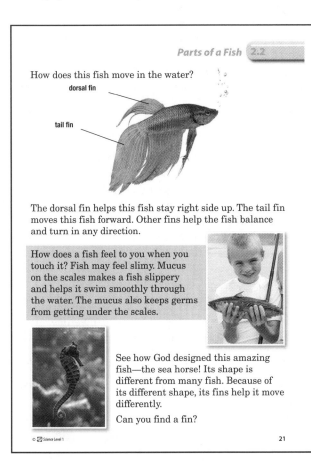

Parts of a Fish 2.2

How does this fish move in the water?

dorsal fin

tail fin

The dorsal fin helps this fish stay right side up. The tail fin moves this fish forward. Other fins help the fish balance and turn in any direction.

How does a fish feel to you when you touch it? Fish may feel slimy. Mucus on the scales makes a fish slippery and helps it swim smoothly through the water. The mucus also keeps germs from getting under the scales.

See how God designed this amazing fish—the sea horse! Its shape is different from many fish. Because of its different shape, its fins help it move differently.

Can you find a fin?

© *Science* Level 1   21

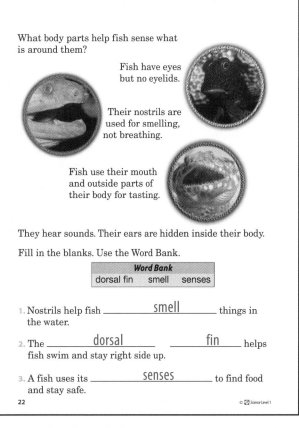

What body parts help fish sense what is around them?

Fish have eyes but no eyelids.

Their nostrils are used for smelling, not breathing.

Fish use their mouth and outside parts of their body for tasting.

They hear sounds. Their ears are hidden inside their body.

Fill in the blanks. Use the Word Bank.

Word Bank		
dorsal fin	smell	senses

1. Nostrils help fish _____smell_____ things in the water.

2. The ____dorsal_____ _____fin____ helps fish swim and stay right side up.

3. A fish uses its ____senses____ to find food and stay safe.

22   © *Science* Level 1

2.3 Differences in Fish

Objective

Students will compare and contrast fish design.

Materials

Introduction
• Yarn

Directed Instruction
• Clay, ziplock bags, waxed paper
• BLM 2.3A Fish Facts

Preparation

Cut **2 PIECES OF YARN**. One should measure ½ in.; the other strand should measure 45 ft and be rolled into a ball. (*Introduction*)

Prepare a small ball of CLAY in a ZIPLOCK BAG and a small sheet of WAXED PAPER for each student. (*Directed Instruction*)

Print **BLM 2.3A Fish Facts** for each student. (*Directed Instruction*)

Content

There are many differences in the numerous species of fish, including size, shape, color, and pattern, as well as life cycle, parenting behavior, and defense mechanisms:

• Size: One of the smallest fish, the goby, can measure less than ½ in. long, while the largest fish, the whale shark, may attain a size of over 45 ft in length.

• Shape: While most fishes exhibit the typical streamlined shape, there are more varieties of shapes than this. One fish known for its unique shape is the sea horse. Also, the flounder appears flat, the ray appears oval, the puffer fish is boxlike, and the eel looks like a snake.

• Color and pattern: Colors and patterns of fishes vary greatly, and sometimes these features reflect an unexpected purpose. For example, types of fishes that God designed with beautiful stripes may be fascinating; however, these stripes serve to help the fishes blend in with their surroundings. To a predator, a fish's outline is visually broken up by its stripes. Eyespots of some fishes are another example of an unexpected design. These large spots serve to protect this animal from a predator. The predator thinks these spots are true eyes and attacks the wrong place, allowing the fish to get away.

• Skeleton type: Bony fishes have a skeleton made of bone and cartilage; cartilaginous fishes, such as sharks, have a skeleton made of thick, soft cartilage that is lightweight and flexible.

Introduction

Display the ½ in. piece of YARN and explain that this is about the size of the goby—one of the smallest fish. Have a volunteer hold the free end of the ball of yarn. Unwind the yarn and ask students to raise their hand when they think the length of the yarn shows the correct length of the largest fish, a whale shark. (Be sure to emphasize that this fish is not a whale.) When the length of the yarn is rolled out to 45 ft, announce that this is the length of the largest fish. Contrast the ½ in. piece of yarn with the 45 ft length of yarn.

Directed Instruction

1 Convey to the class that today's lesson compares differences in types of fish. Mention that just as God created fish to be certain sizes, He also created them to be various shapes. Note that the size and shape of a fish help it stay protected from other fish or other animals that might want to eat it. A fish's shape may affect how it moves, how it blends with its surroundings, and how it avoids or attracts other fish. Clarify that although God designed fish to be very different in size and shape, they still have the same important characteristics that make them fish: gills, fins, and scales.

2 Direct students' attention to the first student page. Compare the sizes of the goby and the shark. Comment about how much larger the whale shark is in real life. Read each direction and caption. Give students time to circle their answer. Follow this format for shape, color, and pattern.

Ask students if there are any fish that have shapes that are alike. (angelfish and moorish idol) Do any fish have colors that are alike? (sea horse, yellow perch, bluegill, and moorish idol; red snapper and rainbow trout)

3 Have students gently squeeze their arm, and ask what makes the hard part under the skin. (**bones**) Then have them gently wiggle their nose, and explain that their nose can wiggle because of cartilage, which is softer and more flexible than bone. Inform the class that some types of fish, such as tuna, have bones and cartilage that make up their skeleton and give them a shape. Other types of fish, such as sharks and rays, have a skeleton made completely of cartilage.

Direct students' attention to the picture of the fish skeleton on the second page. Explain that the skeleton gives fish their shape and helps them move. Point out that some of the ribs and small bones in a fish's back help protect its insides. A shark's flexible skeleton helps the shark move in special ways. Its skeleton, as well as the stingray's, is made of cartilage. Have students put a finger on the picture of the stingray and ask them to share how they think the stingray swims in the water. (**Answers will vary.**) Explain that it appears to flap slowly in the water in order to move. Its unique design allows it to move in a unique way. Direct students to answer the review question.

4 Give each student a ball of CLAY in a ZIPLOCK BAG and a sheet of WAXED PAPER. Allow time for students to make a fish from the clay on the waxed paper. Encourage them to refer to the fish on their student pages. Allow students to take their clay fish home and share what they learned with a family member.

5 Use **BLM 2.3A Fish Facts** to reinforce the information studied about fish.

+ Extension

Materials
- *Rainbow Fish Discovers the Deep Sea*
- Colored goldfish crackers

Read *Rainbow Fish Discovers the Deep Sea* by Marcus Pfister (North-South Books, 2009). Share the colorful illustrations with students. Remind students that just as all fish are different, people are all unique and special, created in God's image. They should love and care for each other.

Give each student a handful of colored goldfish crackers and have them sort and graph the fish by color.

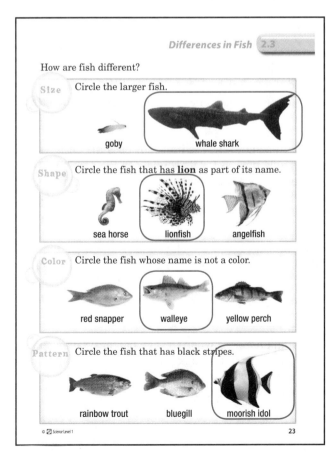

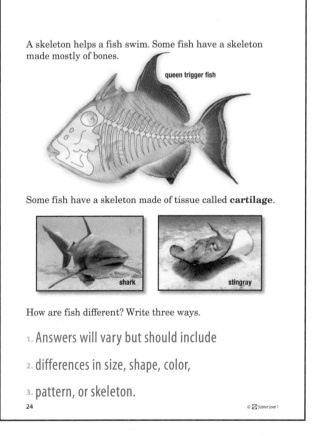

2.4 Fish Grow

Objective

Students will identify the life cycle of fish.

Materials

Introduction
• Envelopes, BLM 2.4A Puzzle: Fish

Directed Instruction
• BLM 2.4B Cycle of Life, crayons, scissors, tape

Preparation

Print **BLM 2.4A Puzzle: Fish** for every three to four students. Cut apart each puzzle and place each puzzle's pieces into an ENVELOPE. (*Introduction*)

Print **BLM 2.4B Cycle of Life** for each student. Obtain CRAYONS, SCISSORS, and TAPE. Cut out large paper circles for students to make their fish life cycle. (*Directed Instruction*)

Content

The life cycle of many fishes begins when eggs are laid that then develop into young fish. The young fish mature to adult fish. Other kinds of fish—for example, some sharks—reproduce by internal fertilization and some give birth to live young.

Some types of sharks bear live young, yet others lay eggs in protective cases. One example of a shark's egg case is called *a mermaid's purse* that may be anchored to seaweed as the embryo develops.

Most fishes spawn: the female produces and deposits eggs in the water and then the male fertilizes them. Some types of fish may lay millions of eggs, many of which may be eaten as they float in the water. In other species, an adult parent may build and even guard a nest.

The involvement of the female and male may simply be the deposition and fertilization of the eggs. However, the sea horse has a more lengthy parenting process. The female lays eggs (sometimes over 1,000 in number) and deposits them in the male's abdominal pouch. Here they are fertilized, and then hatch and develop into young. The young then care for themselves.

Introduction

Distribute the ENVELOPES containing puzzle pieces from **BLM 2.4A Puzzle: Fish** to groups of three or four. Have students work in their group to find out the mystery sentence. (**Most fish lay eggs.**) After students return to their seat, discuss that many kinds of fish lay eggs; some kinds of fish are designed to care for their eggs, while others are not.

Directed Instruction

1 Direct students' attention to the student pages. Read the information regarding what happens to fish eggs—God designed some to float in the ocean, providing food to other fish. Some kinds of fish, mostly those that live in freshwater, hide their eggs in nests; in some species, the nests are guarded.

   After reading the information about the sea horse, discuss the design of this fish's body as well as how it cares for its young. On the next page, read the information about sharks and ask the class why they think that an egg case of some sharks is known as *a mermaid's purse*. (**Possible answer: It looks like a purse that a fanciful mermaid may have left.**)

2 Read the question about how fish grow up. Have the class look at the diagram of the fish life cycle. Direct students to put a finger on the picture of an egg. They should then slide their finger along the arrow from the egg to the young fish. Finally, have them slide a finger along the arrow again to reach the adult.

   Ask the class what they think happens when the egg hatches. (**It becomes a young fish.**) Continue the discussion to talk about how the young fish grows into an adult and the adult fish may then lay eggs, starting the cycle over again. Mention that some fish grow up in different ways.

3 Complete the exercises together. Read "Egg Journey" on the next page and draw ten eggs on the board to help students visualize the story. Erase eggs as they get eaten and add the young fish and adult fish as they emerge in the story. Emphasize that although some fish eggs get eaten, some survive to grow up and lay eggs. The eggs that are eaten serve as food for other fish; this is all part of God's plan.

Egg Journey
The ten little eggs were laid in a nest,
So for a little while, they had a little rest.
A hungry group of fish looking now to dine
Ate four of the eggs, and then they felt so fine.

Six eggs were left and the hungry fish were fed;
Soon came another fish, and it was very red.
The six eggs left had changed into young fish;
Red fish ate three of them, and ate without a dish!

Three young fish were left; a fisherman caught two.
There was one fish left; can you guess what she would do?
She grew into an adult and did so fine;
She laid many eggs, just as God had designed.

4 Distribute the copies of **BLM 2.4B Cycle of Life,** the paper circles, CRAYONS, SCISSORS, and TAPE. Guide students through the activity by having them create a life cycle similar to the one on their student page. Instruct students to take their craft home and to share what they have learned.

➕ Extension

Materials
• Paper plates, peanuts or raisins, goldfish crackers, gummy fish

Allow students to retell "Egg Journey" on a paper plate. Supply each student with 10 peanuts or raisins for eggs, 6 goldfish crackers for young fish, and 1 gummy fish for the adult. Check student records for possible allergies.

Create several math story problems about fish. Allow students to act out the stories or to use food items to work the problems.

Fish Grow **2.4**

Most fish lay eggs. What happens to the eggs?

Some eggs float in the ocean and are eaten by other fish.

Some fish hide their eggs.

Some fish guard their eggs.

eggs

This clown fish lays its eggs in the coral reef.

Sea horse mothers lay their eggs and put them in the father sea horse's pouch. When the eggs hatch, the baby sea horses come out of the father's pouch.

sea horse

The mother can make over 1,000 eggs. The sea horse is about one centimeter long when hatched.

⊢——⊣ = 1 centimeter

© Science Level 1   25

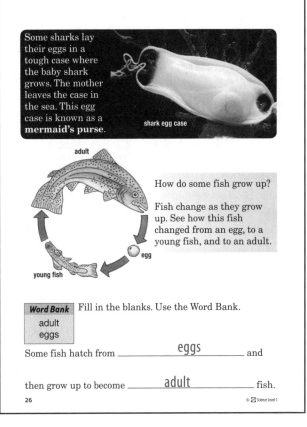

Some sharks lay their eggs in a tough case where the baby shark grows. The mother leaves the case in the sea. This egg case is known as a **mermaid's purse**.

shark egg case

adult

How do some fish grow up?

Fish change as they grow up. See how this fish changed from an egg, to a young fish, and to an adult.

egg

young fish

Word Bank   Fill in the blanks. Use the Word Bank.
adult
eggs

Some fish hatch from _____eggs_____ and

then grow up to become _____adult_____ fish.

26   © Science Level 1

2.5 Habitats and Food

Fish

Objective

Students will compare saltwater and freshwater.

Materials

Directed Instruction
- Goggles, hand lenses, salt, construction paper
- Jars of water, teaspoon, salt, stirrer, paper towels

Preparation

Create four to five stations in the room. Gather enough GOGGLES and HAND LENSES from the ACSI Science Equipment kit for each student. You may also borrow them from a local high school or college, or purchase them from an online science supply catalog. Set up a pinch of SALT on a sheet of BLACK CONSTRUCTION PAPER for each station. (*Directed Instruction*)

Obtain 2 GLASS JARS OF WATER. Mark the letter *S* on one jar. Provide a TEASPOON, SALT , a STIRRER, and PAPER TOWELS. Find the jars and measuring spoon in the ACSI Science Equipment Kit or bring them from home. (*Directed Instruction*)

Alternatives

If goggles and hand lenses are not available for every student, have students rotate between the first and second stations. Be sure to walk around and monitor every group.

Content

Fishes can be found in many saltwater and freshwater environments. Saltwater is characteristic of oceans, seas, and some lakes. Tide pools, coral reefs, and different zones or depths of the ocean are considered marine habitats. Freshwater habitats include lakes, swamps, ponds, rivers, and streams. An important nursery for young fish and other organisms is an estuary—a body of water found at the coast that consists of saltwater from the ocean mixed with freshwater from inland sources.

The design of fish allows them to live in their unique environment and obtain things needed for survival. Each living and nonliving thing is a vital part of the ecosystem's health. The delicate balance between all living and nonliving things becomes obvious when changes in the ecosystem occur. As stewards, it is important for people to recognize that any change in an ecosystem, even one that seems minor, can cause major problems. Because of such factors as run-off, an estuary can be flooded with too many nutrients, causing an overgrowth of plants and a decrease of oxygen.

In this lesson, students will practice some forms of observation to discover the differences between saltwater and freshwater. It is important to reinforce that God designed fishes and other organisms to thrive in the habitat in which they live. If this habitat is changed too much, the fishes will have difficulty surviving. The means by which these changes occur may be natural or caused by people.

Each environment contains producers (those producing food), consumers (those consuming producers and/or other consumers), and decomposers (those breaking down dead organic matter). Each role is important, and it needs to function well in order for the ecosystem to be healthy. To function successfully, food sources must be available in the correct quantities.

Introduction

Have students name bodies of water. (**Possible answers: ocean, lake, river, stream**) Give an opportunity for students to describe an experience they have had visiting bodies of water; you may choose to name some of your experiences. (**Possible answers: deep-sea fishing, going on a cruise, swimming, boating, tubing**) Note that students will study two types of water—saltwater and freshwater.

Directed Instruction

1 State that students will compare saltwater and freshwater by observing them. Explain that *compare* means *to study things to see what is alike about them*. Reiterate that to observe is to study and watch carefully. Refer to the *Senses* section at the beginning of the student edition.

2 Have students turn to the first student page, and assign them to a station. Direct students to wear GOGGLES for safety. Point out the SALT on the CONSTRUCTION PAPER and guide students on how to observe the salt with the HAND LENSES. Demonstrate how to use a hand lens. Guide students to lean slightly forward and to hold the hand lens approximately 3 in. from the salt. Have them draw their observation in the box provided on their page.

Next, display the 2 JARS OF WATER at a demonstration area. As you supervise, ask a volunteer to put 2 TSP OF SALT in the container with an

32

S marked on it. Have another volunteer use a STIRRER to mix the salt until it is dissolved. At this point, students can compare the saltwater to the freshwater by making three observations—by looking at, smelling, and feeling both kinds of water. Allow students time to make these comparisons. Instruct students to use a different hand for each container. Let students use a PAPER TOWEL to wipe their hands. Read the questions on the page and discuss the observations as a class. Mention that sometimes during observation, things may look alike but can be very different.

3 Direct students' attention to the bottom section of the page. Ask the question about fishing and allow for responses. (**Answers will vary.**) Read the information about saltwater and remind students that God designed different fish to live in different places; some fish live in saltwater, some in freshwater. Observe that the salt in saltwater is a little different from the table salt they observed. When God created different kinds of fish (Genesis 1:20), He equipped them to be able to live in a certain kind of water. His design for all creation is amazing! Continue on the next student page with a discussion of freshwater.

God also designed what each kind of fish would eat so they would all have the food they need. Point out what fish eat and connect the photos and captions with the sentences.

4 Conclude by completing the review questions together. Have students discuss with a partner what they have learned.

⊕ Extension

Materials
• BLM 2.5A Making a Betta Fish Bowl
• Maps

Follow the steps in **BLM 2.5A Making a Betta Fish Bowl** to set up a class fish bowl. Assign students the responsibilities of feeding the betta 1 pellet every other day and cleaning the bowl once a week. Provide supervision. Let students vote on a name. Encourage appreciation of the beauty and fascinating movements of a betta.

To reinforce map skills, have students locate freshwater and saltwater bodies of water on city, country, or world maps.

Discuss water pollution and the way it affects fish.

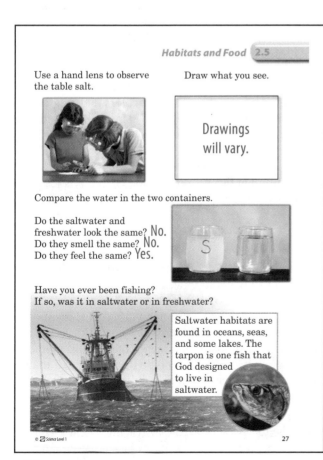

Habitats and Food 2.5

Use a hand lens to observe the table salt.

Draw what you see.

Drawings will vary.

Compare the water in the two containers.

Do the saltwater and freshwater look the same? No.
Do they smell the same? No.
Do they feel the same? Yes.

Have you ever been fishing? If so, was it in saltwater or in freshwater?

Saltwater habitats are found in oceans, seas, and some lakes. The tarpon is one fish that God designed to live in saltwater.

Freshwater habitats are found in rivers, ponds, and most lakes. The carp is one fish that God designed to live in freshwater.

What do fish eat?

clown fish

eel

Some fish eat plants.

Some fish eat other animals.

1. What are two kinds of water God designed fish to live in?
   saltwater; freshwater
2. What are some things fish eat?
   plants; other animals

2.6 Camouflage and Defense

Content

Fishes are both prey and predator. God designed them with camouflage so they could blend in with their surroundings. Fish that exhibit camouflage include the flounder, which can change the color of its upper body to match the color of its environment, and the moray eel, which is camouflaged by color patterns. Even the inside of this snakelike animal's mouth is camouflaged because its mouth is open most of the time. The body of some moray eels is actually dark blue, but the yellow mucus that covers their body makes them appear green—so they are camouflaged.

The design of the butterfly fish allows it to confuse predators with its eyespot. This dark spot on its posterior area may appear to predators as a large eye. The puffer fish surprises its predator. When a predator attempts to eat it, the puffer puffs up and the predator spits it out. The lionfish defends itself with a poisonous sting. The clown fish hides amid the tentacles of the sea anemone; the fish produces mucus, which protects it from the stinging tentacles. (The sea anemone is an invertebrate, not a fish.)

The oyster toadfish may be mistaken for a tadpole, but this amazing animal is a fish. Camouflage helps it blend in with its surroundings and wait for prey. A different type of fish, the frogfish, actually has a spine above its mouth that it uses as a lure. Opening to a size 12 times larger than normal, its mouth catches the food in less than one second.

Introduction

Ask students to raise their hand if they have ever played the game Hide and Seek, and have one student explain the rules of this game. (**Everyone hides and one person who is "it" tries to find everyone else.**) What are some places you like to hide? (**Answers will vary.**) Mention that many fish seem to play a game of hide and seek. They can do this because they are camouflaged. *Camouflage* refers to *the ability an animal has to blend in with its surroundings*. God gave fish the ability to hide from other fish that want to eat them! He did this by making fish different colors and by making unusual patterns on their bodies. State that unlike the game of Hide and Seek, in which people hide out of sight, many fish can remain in plain view because God gave them camouflage to blend in with their surroundings. When God made fish (Genesis 1:20), He purposefully created them to be able to protect themselves. Although fish share common characteristics, camouflage is one way that God designed many kinds of fish to be different from each other.

Directed Instruction

1 Explain that fish shapes cut out of **BLM 2.6A Make a Fish** are hidden around the classroom. Direct students to move around the classroom and to silently notice where the fish are. After everyone has had a chance to notice the fish, invite various students to point them out. Ask students what made it hard to see the fish. (**The fish were the same color as the objects they were placed beside.**) Explain that one of the reasons God made some fish different colors is to help them hide from other fish that want to eat them or to hide so they can catch fish without being seen.

2 Direct students' attention to the first student page. Instruct students to follow along as you read the top paragraph, the instructions, and the photo descriptions. Allow time for students to look at each picture and

to discuss it before writing their answer. Review the answers so students can check their work. Include the caption of each fish with the answer number. State that the picture at the bottom of the page is that of a moray eel. The color of this fish is dark blue, but it appears green when seen in the water. Elaborate on the fact that the eel makes mucus that covers and protects its body. The mucus is yellow; the blue body and the yellow mucus make the eel appear green. Give the class time to color the blue eel with a yellow crayon and to observe the green color. Lead students to understand that it is better for the eel to be green than blue because this method of camouflage is a source of protection. Explain that camouflage is an animal's coloring that blends in with the animal's habitat.

3 Direct students' attention to the next page and encourage students to observe and enjoy the beauty of each fish. Before you read each sentence, allow students to make observations and to guess how these fish protect themselves. Encourage students to listen attentively as you read each sentence about the butterfly fish, puffer fish, lionfish, and clown fish. Instruct students to listen for words that name the defensive characteristic. Pitch your voice higher on the answer words as an element of meaning. Have students circle their answers. Check for accuracy. Conclude by discussing the question at the bottom.

4 Distribute CRAYONS and each student's blank fish from **BLM 2.6A Make a Fish**. Have students design a fish that would be camouflaged in a certain room in their house, such as a kitchen or a bedroom. Encourage them to take their camouflage projects home and to share with an adult how the fish they designed is camouflaged for a designated place.

➕ Extension

Materials
• BLM 2.6A Make a Fish, marker

Discuss ways some people such as hunters or soldiers use camouflage to blend in with their surroundings. Ask students why the camouflage pattern includes green and brown. (**so a person would blend in with the ground and trees**)

Print several copies of **BLM 2.6A Make a Fish** and write each letter of *fish* and *school* on the fish cutouts. Or use the laminated fish and a wet-erase marker so they can be reused in Lesson 2.7. In a learning center, have students practice spelling their vocabulary words with the fish. Then, add more letters and challenge students to spell other science words they have learned.

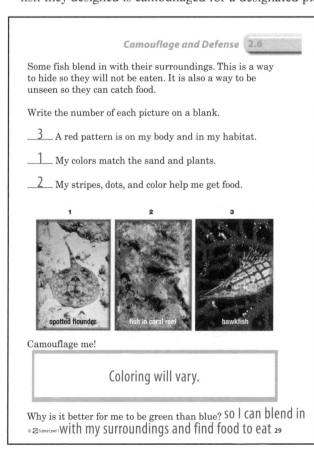

Camouflage and Defense 2.6

Some fish blend in with their surroundings. This is a way to hide so they will not be eaten. It is also a way to be unseen so they can catch food.

Write the number of each picture on a blank.

___3___ A red pattern is on my body and in my habitat.

___1___ My colors match the sand and plants.

___2___ My stripes, dots, and color help me get food.

1   2   3

spotted flounder   fish in coral reef   hawkfish

Camouflage me!

Coloring will vary.

Why is it better for me to be green than blue? so I can blend in with my surroundings and find food to eat 29

These fish are designed to protect themselves from harm. Circle the words that tell what each fish uses as defense.

A butterfly fish has a (false eyespot) near its tail to trick a predator.

A puffer fish puffs up and gets spit out of a predator's (mouth.)

The lionfish uses (its poison) to sting a predator.

The clown fish makes (mucus) to protect itself from the sea anemone's poison.

How does the design of some fish help them stay alive?
serves as a camouflage and defense
30

2.7 Chapter 2 Review

Fish

Materials

Introduction
• TM-2.7A Amazing Fish

Directed Instruction
• Fish from BLM 2.6A Make a Fish from Lesson 2.6, paper clips, fishing pole, magnet, bulletin board paper (optional)
• BLM 2.7A Chapter 2 Test

Preparation

Select **TM-2.7A Amazing Fish** for display. (*Introduction*)

Draw the Creation web from Lesson 2.1 on the board. (*Directed Instruction*)

Obtain the 15 fish from **BLM 2.6A Make a Fish** in Lesson 2.6. Write the numbers 1–15 on the back of the fish and attach a PAPER CLIP to each one. Provide a FISHING POLE and attach a MAGNET (available in the ACSI Science Equipment Kit) to the end of the line. Lay the fish on the floor of an open area in the classroom or cut out a small pool from BLUE BULLETIN BOARD PAPER. (*Directed Instruction*)

Print **BLM 2.7A Chapter 2 Test** for each student. (*Directed Instruction*)

Alternatives

Instead of obtaining a fishing pole, tie a piece of yarn to a long stick or rod.

Introduction

Display **TM-2.7A Amazing Fish**. Read the sentences and share the following additional information:
• Flying fish: Imagine traveling on a ship in the ocean. When you look out at the water, you see several fish that look like they are flying. These fish do not really fly—they glide. They are able to come out of the water and use their fins to glide through the air at the surface of the water.
• Batfish: These fish are not great swimmers, but they can use their fins for something special. They move by walking with their fins!
• Frogfish: They have a special design—a secret built-in fishing lure that looks like bait. Part of their dorsal fin is long and attracts other fish. When these other fish come near to see the bait, they become dinner.
• Parrot fish: The teeth of these amazing fish look like the beak of a parrot. Parrot fish like water plants and actually eat coral, which is very hard. Part of the coral is used for food; other parts of the coral are broken down into tiny pieces by parrot fish's special teeth located in their throat.
• Trumpet fish: God gave these fish an amazing shape. They sometimes hunt for other fish while in an up-and-down position.
• Sharks: Imagine having several rows of teeth. Sharks use these teeth to tear food, not to chew. Front teeth wear out and back teeth move forward to replace them. Gills on a shark are easily seen.

Directed Instruction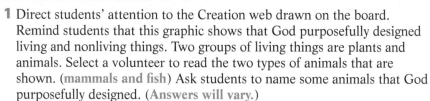

1 Direct students' attention to the Creation web drawn on the board. Remind students that this graphic shows that God purposefully designed living and nonliving things. Two groups of living things are plants and animals. Select a volunteer to read the two types of animals that are shown. (**mammals and fish**) Ask students to name some animals that God purposefully designed. (**Answers will vary.**)

2 Review the definitions of *fish* and *school of fish*. (*fish*: **an animal that lives in the water**; *school of fish*: **a large number of one kind of fish swimming together**) Review that fins help a fish swim, gills are used for breathing, and scales protect a fish's body.

3 Engage the class by stating that they will be doing some fishing today. Show them the FISHING POLE. Explain that a MAGNET is attached to the end of the line, and a PAPER CLIP is attached to each fish. Since the magnet on the line pulls the paper clip, it will pull the paper fish. Demonstrate the use of the pole and assist the first volunteer. Have the volunteer read the number on the fish that he or she catches. Read the question below that has the same number as the one on the fish. If the student does not know the answer, let him or her choose someone to help.
   1. What is a kind of animal that lives in the water? (**fish**)
   2. What do fins help fish do? (**swim**)
   3. What do fish use to breathe? (**gills**)
   4. What protects the body of the fish? (**scales and mucus**)
   5. What is a large number of the same kind of fish swimming together? (**school of fish**)
   6. What does the gill cover protect? (**gills**)
   7. Do fish have eyelids? (**No.**)
   8. Do fish hear sounds? (**Yes.**)
   9. Do fish have skeletons? (**Yes.**)

10. Can fish lay eggs? (**Yes.**)
11. What does the young fish grow up to become? (**an adult fish**)
12. What is the way some fish use their color and design to hide so they will not be eaten? (**camouflage**)
13. Name a place where fish can be found. (**Possible answers: freshwater, saltwater, lake, river, stream, pond, marsh, swamp, ocean, sea, aquarium, fish bowl**)
14. Do some fish eat other fish? (**Yes.**)
15. Does the fish's body temperature change to match the water temperature or stay the same? (**It changes.**)

4 Use the student pages as a review or pretest. Complete these pages with the class.

5 Test students by using **BLM 2.7A Chapter 2 Test** for individual assessment. Read through this page with the class. Provide as much reading support as necessary. If your class is not ready for this level of independent work, you may use this test as an oral assessment or choose not to do it at all.

6 Chapter 2 Fish has been completed. Staple student pages and send them home as a booklet for students to share with a family member.

Notes:

Extension

Materials
• CP-1.3 Animal Habitats: Mammals and Fish, Part 2

Present and discuss the slides about fish from **CP-1.3 Animal Habitats: Mammals and Fish, Part 2**.

In an open area, lead the game Sharks and Minnows. Select several students to be sharks and line the other students, who will act as minnows, along one side of the area's perimeter. On your command, the minnows must run to the opposite side without getting tagged by a shark. After the game, discuss the difficulties that minnows have in crossing the stream. Inquire about ways that minnows could be more successful. (**Possible answers: camouflage, a defense such as poison or a stinger, swimming in a school**)

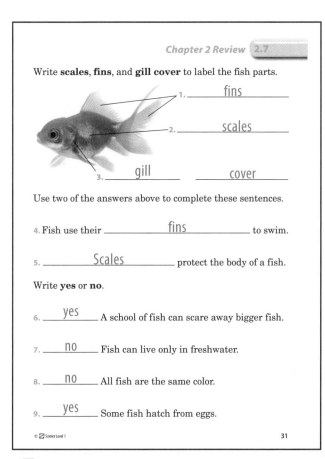

Chapter 2 Review 2.7

Write **scales**, **fins**, and **gill cover** to label the fish parts.

1. _____fins_____
2. _____scales_____
3. ___gill___ ___cover___

Use two of the answers above to complete these sentences.

4. Fish use their _____fins_____ to swim.

5. _____Scales_____ protect the body of a fish.

Write **yes** or **no**.

6. ___yes___ A school of fish can scare away bigger fish.

7. ___no___ Fish can live only in freshwater.

8. ___no___ All fish are the same color.

9. ___yes___ Some fish hatch from eggs.

© Science Level 1   31

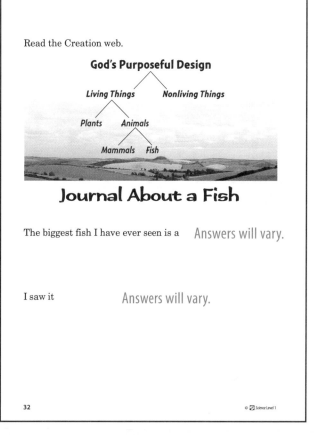

Read the Creation web.

God's Purposeful Design

Living Things   Nonliving Things

Plants   Animals

Mammals   Fish

Journal About a Fish

The biggest fish I have ever seen is a   Answers will vary.

I saw it   Answers will vary.

32   © Science Level 1

Birds
Chapter 3

Key Ideas
- The kingdom of animals contains groups, or classes, of animals, one of which is the class of birds.
- Birds lay eggs and have feathers and wings.
- God designed birds with different beaks, feathers, and feet to enable them to survive and obtain food in their habitat.

3.0 Chapter Preparation

bird
migration

Looking Ahead

- Plan to take students outdoors in **Lesson 3.5** for bird-watching.
- For the *Extension* activity in **Lesson 3.2**, invite an employee of a local sports store or a member of a nearby bird-watching club to visit and demonstrate the use of bird calls.
- For an *Extension* activity in **Lesson 4.1** or sometime during the teaching of Chapter 4, invite a guest speaker from a local museum to speak to the class about insects.
- In **Lesson 4.3**, you will need to take the class outside to a place with many insects. Arrange for parent volunteers to assist. Or, obtain some insect specimens from your local area for students to observe with a hand lens.

Introduction

God made the earth and filled it with a variety of living creatures. In Genesis 1:20, God said, "Let the water teem with living creatures, and let birds fly above the earth across the expanse of the sky." By studying how certain characteristics help birds live, students will learn about God's purposeful design. They will practice the skills of classification and analysis with such characteristics as beaks, feet, egg types, and habitats. Students are encouraged to ask questions and draw conclusions. Focusing on a special area of interest for first graders—eggs and baby birds—will help students gain an appreciation for birds. They will connect what they know about birds with advances in aviation. In doing so, students can relate to technology as part of their world and future.

About This Chapter

Lesson 3.1 – What Birds Are

Materials
- Decorative birds (optional)
- String or yarn
- Binoculars

Lesson Content
Birds are a class of animals that lay eggs and have feathers and wings. God designed birds to be fed and cared for through nature. Many people enjoy bird-watching.

Lesson 3.2 – Parts of a Bird

Materials
- Down feather
- Flight feather
- Paper bags
- Straws
- Sugar
- Tape
- Scale
- Crayons

Lesson Content
The parts of a bird include its eyes, crown, beak, throat, breast, wings, feet, and feathers. Feathers provide camouflage, attract other birds, enable a bird to fly, and help maintain a bird's temperature.

Lesson 3.3 – Beaks and Food

Materials
- Fork
- Foods
- Bowls
- Rice
- Beans
- Slotted spoons
- Goggles
- Water
- Food coloring
- Strainer

Lesson Content
God did not create birds to have teeth; He gave them a variety of beaks, or bills, uniquely designed to process the food He provides for them. The design of some beaks allows for grinding or cracking food, others for catching food, some for tearing, and some for pecking.

Lesson 3.4 – Feet

Materials
- Tracing paper
- Clay

Lesson Content
The design of birds' feet serves many functions, such as climbing, grasping, swimming, and perching. God designed each foot type for a specific habitat and way of life.

Lesson 3.5 – Habitats

Materials
- Scissors
- Glue
- Crayons

Lesson Content

Birds are found in all different places of creation, including in the sky, on land, and by the water. Certain physical characteristics about birds enable them to dwell in their habitat.

Lesson 3.6 – Birds Grow

Materials
- Plastic eggs
- Balls
- Globe
- Crayons
- Scissors
- Glue
- Construction paper

Lesson Content

Birds lay eggs. The eggs hatch and the young birds grow into adult birds. Bird eggs have different shapes to best stay in the nest. Some birds migrate, or move from one place to another.

Lesson 3.7 – Tech Connect

Materials
- Balloon

Lesson Content

After having watched birds, some people have been inspired to invent vehicles that fly. Studying birds' wings provides scientists with designs and techniques for building aircraft.

Lesson 3.8 – Chapter 3 Review

Materials
- Scissors

Teacher Resources

The Audubon Backyard Birdwatcher: Birdfeeders and Bird Gardens by Robert Burton and Stephen Kress. Thunder Bay, 2012.

National Geographic Backyard Guide to the Birds of North America by Jonathan Alderfer and Paul Hess. National Geographic Society, 2011.

A Year of Hands-On Science by Lynne Kepler. Scholastic Teaching Resources, 2008.

Student Resources

Sounds of the Wild: Birds by Maurice Pledger (illustrator). Silver Dolphin Books, 2010.

Wildlife Gardening by Martyn Cox. DK, 2009.

Supplemental Materials

Blackline Masters

3.1A Bird Cutouts
3.2A A Quill
3.5A Bird Shapes
3.6A Robin
3.6B Recipe: Bird Nest
3.7A Airplane
3.8A Bird Names
3.8B Bird Facts
3.8C Chapter 3 Test

Transparency Master

3.2A Parts of a Bird

Computer Presentation

3.5 Animal Habitats: Birds and Insects, Part 1

3.1 What Birds Are

Objective

Students will identify three features of birds and describe different kinds of birds.

Materials

Introduction
- BLM 3.1A Bird Cutouts or decorative birds, string or yarn

Directed Instruction
- Binoculars

Preparation

Print 3 copies of **BLM 3.1A Bird Cutouts**. Cut out the bird shapes and place them around the room. Or, purchase several DECORATIVE BIRDS from a craft store. Use STRING or YARN to suspend the bird cutouts or the decorative birds from objects. (*Introduction*)

Obtain a pair of BINOCULARS. (*Directed Instruction*)

Write the definition of *bird* on the board. (*Directed Instruction*)

Safety

Caution students to never look at the sun through binoculars.

Content

There are over 9,700 species of birds in the world, living in nearly every habitat on the earth. Birds are found not just in rural areas, but also in suburban neighborhoods and cities. Bird-watching is a popular activity; people enjoy identifying the common birds of their area. Developing a familiarity with bird shape, size, and behavior allows people to determine what type of bird they are observing. For example, a bald eagle is considered a bird of prey because it has a strong beak and grasping feet with claw-like talons.

While features of birds include wings, lungs, warm-bloodedness, a beak, and reproduction involving egg-laying, the one feature unique to birds is feathers. Although this feature is typically associated with flight, feathers serve several functions. Most birds fly, but some do not. The penguin, for example, uses its wings to aid in swimming instead of in flight.

God designed and equipped birds to be able to function within their habitat in order to find shelter and obtain food, water, and air. Most birds also defend their territory, build a nest, and protect their young from predators.

Introduction

Ask students where they have seen birds. (**Possible answers: in my backyard, on a camping trip in the woods, downtown, in the mountains, at the ocean**) Encourage students to share their observations of birds. (**Answers will vary.**)

Inform students that they will now pretend to bird-watch the BIRDS in their classroom. Separate the class into small groups of three or four students. Have each group count and record how many birds it observes. Choose one student from each group to report the number as well as one way the student's group noticed the birds. (**Possible answers: by color, by shape**) State that other ways to notice birds are by their movements and sounds.

Directed Instruction

1 Point out that many times students will notice birds in the sky. Read **Genesis 1:7–8a**. State that God designed the earth and sky before designing the birds so that the birds would have a place to live and fly. Read **Genesis 1:20**. Convey that in order for birds to fly in the sky, God designed them to have feathers and wings.

2 Encourage students to observe birds at home. Point out that bird-watching can be a fun adventure. Then direct students' attention to the first student page. Read the verse at the top. Convey that God planned to feed the birds through nature. Just as He provides for His birds, He also cares for His children. Share how special each child of God is and that God is faithful to meet His children's needs.

Point out the pictures of the birds at the top of the page. Explain that the child in the photo is using a tool called *binoculars* that magnifies objects at a distance. Display a pair of BINOCULARS. Model how to use them. Ask if any students have seen or used binoculars. (**Answers will vary.**) Inform students that people sometimes use binoculars at a ball game to see a player up close, or at scenic areas to get a better view. Comment that the chart at the bottom of the page shows the same birds pictured at the top of the page. On the chart, have students draw the place where each bird is shown. Allow students time to complete the assignment.

3 Read the definition of *bird* from the board—**bird**: *an animal that lays eggs and has feathers and wings.* Explain that there are many types of birds, but they all have feathers and wings, and the female birds lay eggs. On the second page, have students read the definition together from the text. Refer to the gull in the photo near the sentence. Point out the wing and explain that feathers cover almost the entire body of a bird. Have students point to the wing and feathers. Direct them to count the number of eggs in the nest. (**three**)

Relate that many people who enjoy bird-watching keep a checklist that tracks the birds they have seen. The four birds shown in Exercise 1 are the cardinal, owl, turkey, and pigeon. Allow students time to make a check mark by the birds they have seen. Have students share an experience they have had with any of these birds. (**Answers will vary.**)

4 Read Exercise 2 at the bottom of the page. Instruct students to circle each word that in some way pertains to the subject of birds. To check for understanding, read each word listed and have students flap their arms like wings when you say a word they circled. Encourage students to share with their family what they have learned in this lesson. Have them ask family members to describe their favorite bird and any special bird-watching adventures.

➕ **Extension**

Materials
• Field guide about birds

Display a field guide about birds or an online guide of birds. Explain that these resources give general information about many types of birds. A few resources are listed below.

National Geographic Field Guide to the Birds of North America by Jon L. Dunn and Jonathan Alderfer. National Geographic, 2011.
National Wildlife Federation Field Guide to Birds of North America by Edward S. Brinkley. Sterling, 2007.
The Stokes Field Guide to the Birds of North America by Donald and Lillian Stokes. Little, Brown, 2010.

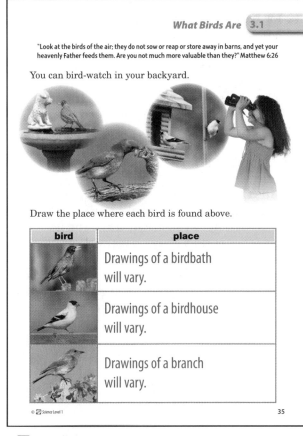

What Birds Are 3.1

"Look at the birds of the air; they do not sow or reap or store away in barns, and yet your heavenly Father feeds them. Are you not much more valuable than they?" Matthew 6:26

You can bird-watch in your backyard.

Draw the place where each bird is found above.

bird	place
	Drawings of a birdbath will vary.
	Drawings of a birdhouse will vary.
	Drawings of a branch will vary.

35

A **bird** is an animal that lays eggs and has feathers and wings.

gull
wing
feathers (all over)
eggs

1. Make a check mark beside the birds you have seen.
   Answers will vary.

2. Circle the words that tell something about birds.
   (fly) (bird-watching) fin (animals)
   (feathers) pencil shoe (wings)

36

3.2 Parts of a Bird

Students will identify the parts of a bird and explain the purpose of feathers.

Materials

Introduction
• Down feather, flight feather, paper bags

Directed Instruction
• TM-3.2A Parts of a Bird
• Straws, sugar, tape, scale
• BLM 3.2A A Quill, crayons

Preparation

Obtain a DOWN FEATHER and a FLIGHT FEATHER. Place each in its own PAPER BAG. (*Introduction*)

Select **TM-3.2A Parts of a Bird** for display. (*Directed Instruction*)

Obtain 2 STRAWS. Fill one straw with SUGAR and use TAPE to close both ends of that straw. Leave the other straw empty. Find a SCALE in the ACSI Science Equipment Kit, or borrow one from a local high school or college. (*Directed Instruction*)

Print **BLM 3.2A A Quill** for each student. Gather CRAYONS for students' use. (*Directed Instruction*)

Content

God's design allows birds to acquire food, air, and water from their habitat. Their design includes both similarities and diversity among the species. Features of birds include the following:

• Sight—The eyes of a bird are large compared to its overall size. Sight is a bird's most acute sense; it aids in finding food and shelter and in avoiding danger. Scientists believe that the golden eagle can identify the movement of prey approximately a mile away!
• Hearing—A bird's ears are located just below the eyes and away from the beak.
• Beak and feet—God designed the bill, or beak, and feet of bird species to fit their environment. A hummingbird has a long, slender bill to enable it to reach nectar; a duck has webbed feet to allow it to move in water.
• Feathers—This unique feature provides protection, warmth, and camouflage; attracts other birds; and enables flight. Different feathers have different purposes. Flight feathers help a bird fly; down feathers give insulation.

Several other features, including hollow bones and air sacs, allow a bird to fly. Like mammals, birds use lungs to breathe.

Introduction

Select a volunteer to feel the FEATHER in each PAPER BAG, describe what he or she feels, and guess what they are. Point out the different shape of each feather. Reiterate that birds are the only animals to have feathers. Pass the bags around so all students can feel the feathers.

Directed Instruction

1 Read the sentence at the top of the first student page, and have students place a finger on each part of the bird as you name it. Display **TM-3.2A Parts of a Bird** and point to the corresponding bird part. Stress some important information about these features:
• Birds have very good eyesight.
• There are several kinds of feathers; each serves a special purpose. Feathers cover almost all of a bird's body except the beak and, in some birds, parts of the legs.

Read the student text about the function of feathers. You may choose to add a few of the following details:
• Chickadee: When this bird gets cold, it "puffs out" its feathers, allowing it to be insulated by a layer of air between the feathers and the skin.
• American bittern: Camouflage allows an animal to blend with its surroundings. God designed this bird's feathers to resemble plants of the marsh habitat in which the bird lives. Camouflage is especially apparent when this bird is startled and moves its head into an upright position.
• Parrot: Male and female birds of the same species sometimes have the same feather coloration. In other species, the two are different.
• Swan: The design of its wings allows it to fly.

Read and discuss the information about feather differences on the second page. Point out the blue jay's flight feather and explain that this feather type helps the bird fly. Have students put a finger on the goose down feather and explain that this type of feather helps keep the goose warm.

2 Discuss that, just like mammals, birds have lungs with which to breathe. Point out the hummingbird's backbone and the rest of the bird's skeleton. Clarify that God designed the bird skeleton to help it fly. Ask students what the skeleton helps the mammal do. (**Possible answers: move, walk, run**) What does the skeleton help the fish do? (**swim**) Convey that in the following activity, students will discover a special design that God made for birds so that they can fly.

Display **2 STRAWS**: one empty and one filled with SUGAR. Ask a volunteer to hold up both straws and to describe the difference. (**One is heavier than the other.**) Weigh the two straws on a SCALE and allow students to observe which is heavier. Explain that the heavier straw is filled with sugar. It is like the bones of mammals. The light straw is like the bones of a bird. The design of the bird's hollow bones helps the bird be light enough to fly. Read and discuss the sentences about hollow bones.

3 Read the exercises orally. Give students time to complete the blanks independently. Provide assistance when needed. Check accuracy of student answers.

4 Distribute **BLM 3.2A A Quill** and CRAYONS. Read the information and help students complete the activity. Ask if they have ever seen a pen similar to this one with a guest book at a wedding or at a museum. Encourage students to share with an adult what they have learned about writing with a feather.

Extension

Materials
- Bird-sound sample, bird pictures
- Guest speaker

Find a sample of bird sounds from an online resource. Allow students to listen to sounds of different birds. If possible, display the picture of that bird to boost student recognition. Explain that many bird-watchers can identify a bird by its sound.

Have the employee of a local sports store or the member of a nearby bird-watching club you have already invited demonstrate the use of bird calls.

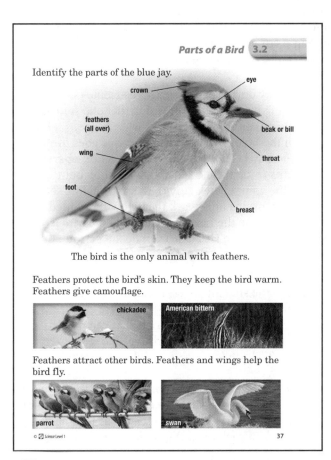

Parts of a Bird 3.2

Identify the parts of the blue jay.

crown
eye
feathers (all over)
beak or bill
wing
throat
foot
breast

The bird is the only animal with feathers.

Feathers protect the bird's skin. They keep the bird warm. Feathers give camouflage.

chickadee
American bittern

Feathers attract other birds. Feathers and wings help the bird fly.

parrot
swan

© Science Level 1   37

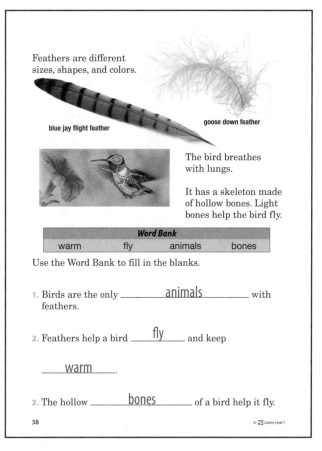

Feathers are different sizes, shapes, and colors.

blue jay flight feather
goose down feather

The bird breathes with lungs.

It has a skeleton made of hollow bones. Light bones help the bird fly.

Word Bank			
warm	fly	animals	bones

Use the Word Bank to fill in the blanks.

1. Birds are the only _____animals_____ with feathers.

2. Feathers help a bird ___fly___ and keep

    ___warm___ .

3. The hollow ___bones___ of a bird help it fly.

38   © Science Level 1

3.3 Beaks and Food

Objective

Students will analyze the varied designs of birds' beaks.

Materials

Introduction
• Fork, variety of foods

Directed Instruction
• Bowls, rice, dried kidney beans, slotted spoons, goggles
• Bowls, water, food coloring, spoon, dried beans, strainer

✋ Preparation

Collect a FORK and a VARIETY OF FOODS. (*Introduction*)

Prepare a LARGE CLEAR BOWL filled with UNCOOKED RICE and DRIED KIDNEY BEANS. For every group of three to four students, obtain 2 BOWLS and a SLOTTED SPOON. Have GOGGLES available for each student. Obtain goggles from the ACSI Science Equipment Kit or borrow them from a local high school or college. (*Directed Instruction*)

In a BOWL, tint some WATER with GREEN FOOD COLORING. Have available the LARGE CLEAR BOWL, a spoonful of BEANS, and a STRAINER. (*Directed Instruction*)

↻ Alternatives

Instead of displaying a variety of foods, use pictures of food or plastic food items.

Content

The design of the bird's beak, or bill, fits the function for which it is used. This is another example of God's design of form for function.

Many birds, such as the seed-eating sparrow, use their beaks to obtain food. A bird of prey, like the bald eagle, uses its beak to tear the food it catches with its feet, or talons. With no teeth to grind and tear food, the bird's gizzard grinds food. Some birds of prey, such as owls, cannot digest bones and fur. God's design for ridding the bird of these indigestible wastes is the formation of a pellet in the stomach that the bird regurgitates.

Introduction

Ask students to name some of their favorite foods. (**Answers will vary.**) What do you use to help you eat these foods? (**Possible answers: fingers, a spoon, a fork, a knife, chopsticks, a straw**) Hold up a FORK and explain that it is a tool people use to help them eat. Display a VARIETY OF FOODS and ask how a fork, knife, or spoon helps people eat each food. (**Answers will vary.**) Emphasize that the design of each utensil is intended to help people eat a different type of food.

Directed Instruction

1 Present the following scenario. Explain that Mother wants to cook rice for dinner. She has a bowl with a mixture of rice and beans. Display a LARGE CLEAR BOWL of UNCOOKED RICE and DRIED KIDNEY BEANS. Ask students how Mother can separate the rice from the beans. (**Answers will vary.**) State that to pick each grain of rice out would take a lot of time. Convey that students will use a tool to help Mother separate the rice from the beans. Arrange students into small groups of three to four students. Scoop the rice and bean mixture into BOWLS, one per group. Give each group a bowl of rice and beans, a SLOTTED SPOON, and an empty bowl.

2 To encourage a habit of safety during experiments, distribute GOGGLES to prevent particles from getting into students' eyes. Instruct one student in each group to scoop up the mixture and to observe what happens. (**The beans will not go through the holes of the spoon. The rice goes through the holes and back into the bowl. The rice and the beans are separated.**) Direct students to take turns using the slotted spoon to scoop out the beans and to put them in the empty bowl. Advise them to slightly shake their spoon if needed. When groups finish, ask them how the slotted spoon—a tool—is able to separate the rice from the beans. (**The beans cannot go through the holes, but the rice can.**) Conduct a cleanup of the materials.

3 Direct students' attention to the student pages. Read and discuss the picture at the top of the first page to review how people use eating utensils. Share that people have designed many tools that can be used for different purposes. Point out to students that birds have no teeth. Yet, God designed birds' bodies with beaks that are best suited to eat certain foods.

Read each sentence about the birds and their beaks on both student pages, then ask volunteers to describe how the shape of each bird's beak is suited for the kind of food it eats. Allow students to be creative as they name a tool that is similar to the beak of each bird. (**Possible answers:** *sparrow:*

a nutcracker; *spoonbill*: a spoon; *heron*: a fork; *hummingbird*: a straw; *hawk*: a hook; *woodpecker*: a hammer; *mallard*: a slotted spoon) State that when a woodpecker drills holes, it has special characteristics that help keep it safe:

- Its skull has a special shock absorber so the impact of the pecking does not hurt its brain.
- Powerful legs allow the woodpecker to easily grip the tree.
- Stiff tail feathers help prop the bird up as it pecks the tree.

Direct student's attention to the picture of the mallard. Then have students look at you as you pour the BOWL of GREEN-COLORED WATER and the DRIED KIDNEY BEANS into the LARGE CLEAR BOWL. Use the STRAINER to scoop up some beans to illustrate how the mallard's beak acts as a tool when the mallard strains water for food, just as the strainer—a tool—strains the beans out of the water. Instruct students to explain to an adult at home that, like a strainer, some birds' beaks work to filter water for food.

4 Continue with the question about the sparrow. Encourage students to look back at the picture of the sparrow on their first page in order to fill in the blank.

5 Complete the review questions. Ask a different volunteer to read each question. Give students time to write their answers. Check accuracy and comment on each answer.

Extension

Materials
- Cooking utensils, food items, bowls, tubs

In a learning center, provide cooking utensils, such as strainers, spoons, and measuring cups. Also set out bowls and tubs of uncooked rice, dried beans, and noodles. Allow students to experiment with the utensils to discover their purpose.

Beaks and Food 3.3

What utensils help people eat food?

How do birds eat? They have no teeth. God designed birds with different beaks, or bills.

The sparrow's beak cracks seeds.

The spoonbill sweeps its bill from side to side to catch fish.

The blue heron uses its beak to stab fish.

The hummingbird sticks its bill in a flower to get nectar.

© Science Level 1   39

The hawk's hooked beak tears small mammals, shellfish, and insects.

The woodpecker's hard beak drills holes into trees to get insects.

The mallard strains water through its bill to get plants and animals.

Fill in the blank.
What is the sparrow designed to eat? _____ seeds _____

Write **yes** or **no**.
1. Do all beaks look the same? _____ no _____

2. Do all birds eat the same food? _____ no _____

3. Does a bird's beak help it stay alive? _____ yes _____

40   © Science Level 1

Objective

Students will distinguish between the different types and uses of birds' feet.

Materials

Directed Instruction
- Tracing paper
- Modeling clay

Preparation

Purchase enough TRACING PAPER from an office supply or a craft store to provide a sheet for each student. (*Directed Instruction*)

Obtain a small portion of MODELING CLAY for each student. (*Directed Instruction*)

Alternatives

Use chenille stems instead of modeling clay to make feet.

Content

The form of a bird's feet fits the function it serves, such as walking, climbing, swimming, perching, or grasping. The form also correlates with its diet and habitat. For example, eagles have strong, raptorial feet—one toe on the back of its foot and three toes on the front. This arrangement of toes and the presence of heavy claws allow the bird to catch and kill prey. The beak then tears the prey so the bird can eat.

Another example of form and function can be seen in water birds, like the grebe. Although easily mistaken for a duck, the grebe is actually a diving bird. The legs on this water bird are set farther back on its body. This structural design allows it to use its strong legs to swim efficiently. The toes do not have webbing connecting them; instead, they have lobes of skin. As the grebe brings a leg forward, the lobes of skin on the toes contract and the foot moves forward with much less effort. The skin then expands as the bird thrusts its leg backward through the water. This design makes walking on land awkward, so the grebe builds its nest on a platform in the water.

Introduction

Ask students to state their favorite sport and the gear needed for that sport. (**Possible answers: skiing with boots, skis, goggles, and poles; in-line skating with in-line skates, kneepads, elbow pads, and helmet; racing with running shoes**) Guide students to understand that the right gear helps people play each sport more effectively.

Directed Instruction

1 Direct the class' attention to the student pages. Read the first two sentences at the top of the first page. Give students time to observe the two photos. Ask how the clothing helps the children. (**Possible answers: A child who plays soccer wears soccer shoes to allow him or her to run well; shin guards protect the legs. A child walking in the rain can stay dry by wearing a raincoat and boots.**)

2 Emphasize that birds have special feet that are best suited for their way of life. Read the paragraph about feet. Direct students' attention to the three illustrations. Have students put a finger on each as it is being discussed. Allow student volunteers to describe each type of foot. (**Possible answers:** *grasping*: **sharp claws, strong toes;** *climbing*: **pointed claws, two toes in front, two in back;** *swimming*: **webbed**) Relate how each is designed to do something special—grasp, climb, swim.

3 Have students use TRACING PAPER to trace the bird feet on the page. For each foot, ask students which bird's foot it might be. (*grasping*: **eagle, hawk;** *climbing*: **woodpecker, parrot;** *swimming*: **goose, gull**)

4 Announce that now students will get to do what the children in the picture at the bottom of the page are doing. Direct students to use MODELING CLAY to make one of the bird's feet displayed on the page. Remind them of the function or job of each foot. Give students time to share in groups of two or three about the foot they made.

5 Direct students' attention to the second page. Have them place a finger on the bird's feet as you read each sentence. Then direct students to circle the

word in each of those three sentences that tells how each bird uses its feet. Read the sentence at the bottom of the page as well as the following related information:
- Climbing: The woodpecker's feet have two toes in the front of the foot and two in the back. The toes have claws, which help the woodpecker climb trees.
- Swimming: The webbed feet of the puffin help it swim. Its front three toes are webbed together, while a separate toe is in the back of the foot.
- Grasping: The bald eagle's feet have one toe in the back and three toes in the front of each foot. The arrangement of toes and heavy claws allows the bald eagle to grasp its prey.
- Perching: Many different kinds of birds can perch, including parrots and sunbirds. Most birds that perch have one toe in back and three in front.

6 Allow adequate time for students to complete the exercises. Provide as much reading support as needed. Discuss their answers.

Notes:

⊕ **Extension**

Materials
- Milk cartons, pencils or sticks, paint, birdseed, string

Guide students in creating a milk-carton bird feeder. Follow the steps below:
1. Cut 2 squares from the sides of a milk carton for windows.
2. Make a small hole under each window. Insert a pencil or stick through both holes for a perch.
3. Paint the outside a bright color.
4. Fill with birdseed.
5. Make a hole at the top and tie a string through the hole.
6. Hang the feeder from a tree. To prevent birds from colliding with windows, place the feeder within 3 ft of the window or up to 25 ft away.
7. Observe the birds that visit your feeder.

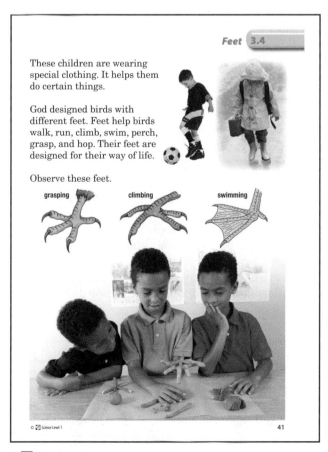

Objective

Students will match different types of birds to their habitat.

Materials

Directed Instruction
- Scissors, glue
- Crayons
- BLM 3.5A Bird Shapes

Preparation

Plan to take students outside for bird-watching. (*Introduction*)

Gather SCISSORS and GLUE for students. (*Directed Instruction*)

Obtain CRAYONS for student use. (*Directed Instruction*)

Print **BLM 3.5A Bird Shapes** for each student. (*Directed Instruction*)

Content

God made the sky, bodies of water, and land. He filled them with a great variety of living things. Birds live and move around in all of these places. Each habitat supplies all the needs of the birds that live in it. Each bird species is equipped to thrive in the habitat God designed for it.

Birds such as the ruffed grouse make their habitat in the woodlands. The woodlands include an area of deciduous trees with clearings and plant undergrowth; the birds in this habitat have feet capable of walking on the ground as well as standing in trees to feed. The mourning warbler perches in dense areas of plant growth.

Birds that live at the ocean's shore include species of gulls and some species of albatross. The feet of these birds have webbing, allowing them to swim in the water and to walk on land.

Many types of deserts—hot and dry, semiarid, coastal, cold—provide a habitat for birds. The cactus wren lives in the Sonoran Desert. This bird builds its nest in a saguaro cactus to protect its babies from predators.

Many field guides show silhouettes of birds in their habitats. This helps a bird-watcher identify a bird by its shape. It is easiest to identify a bird's group or family first and then proceed with more-specific identification.

Introduction

Escort the class outdoors for a bird-watching adventure. Before going, advise students to be very quiet as they go into the birds' habitat. Advise them to observe the whole environment because different kinds of birds live in specific locations within a habitat, such as in trees, in bushes, or on rooftops.

Directed Instruction

1 After students are back in the classroom, have them describe the birds they saw in the habitat outside. Elaborate on the fact that God made the sky, land, and waters and that there are many different kinds of habitats for birds. Share that God designed different types of birds to have bodies that function well in their habitat.

2 Refer to the first student page. Read aloud the verse at the bottom. Describe how God made the sparrow and gave it a habitat. In its habitat, it makes a nest and gets all the things that it needs in order to live. Ask students what birds need to live. (**food, water, air, shelter**)

Read the directions at the top of the page. As the class observes each of the different habitats, allow time for discovering which bird fits each habitat. Share the following information:
- Woodlands: Some trees here have green leaves in the spring and summer. Many kinds of birds here walk, climb, and perch.
- The ocean shore: At the shore, the water rushes in and out. Winds at the shore affect the birds' flight. Some birds walk on the beach. Not all gulls wait by the water; many are found inland.
- The desert: A desert does not receive much water. The tall saguaro cacti thrive in this hot desert. At some times of the year, the temperatures can be very hot during the day, yet the evenings can get quite cold.

3 Distribute SCISSORS and GLUE. Explain how to cut out the pictures of birds on the right side of the page and then to place each in the habitat where it belongs. Check for accuracy before instructing students to glue.

4 Direct students' attention to the next page to learn what the smallest and largest birds are. Help students compare the hummingbird's weight to that of the coin and the ostrich's size to that of the boy. Have students complete the exercises. There is no Word Bank provided; encourage students to find each answer word on the page and to check their spelling.

5 On a sheet of paper, have students design a bird. Encourage them to include details of its beak and feet, to use CRAYONS to color, and to share about its habitat and diet. Upon completion, have students share with a classmate the physical characteristics of the bird and the particular environment in which it lives.

6 Distribute a copy of **BLM 3.5A Bird Shapes** to each student. Clarify that sometimes when people bird-watch, they can begin to identify the kind of bird they see by the bird's shape. Instruct the class to observe the shape of each bird on the top half of the page. Then have them find the same bird on the bottom half of the page. Remind students to observe the general shape or outline of the body to find a match. Encourage them to focus on the shape of the head and any other distinguishing features.

Notes:

➕ **Extension**

Materials
• State bird information source
• CP-3.5 Animal Habitats: Birds and Insects, Part 1

Have students gather information about their state bird. Some points of interest may include the name, color, shape, nest, number and color of eggs, song, beak, feet, wingspan, and habitat. Depending on the reading level of the class, this may be done using books or a computer. After the research has been completed, allow students to share the information.

Present and discuss slides that relate to birds from **CP-3.5 Animal Habitats: Birds and Insects, Part 1**.

Habitats 3.5

The habitat gives a bird the things it needs to live. Cut on the dotted lines and glue the birds where they live.

I take care of my young.
3. grouse
5. warbler
I like to walk on the ground.
woodlands

I fly over the sea.
1. gull
4. albatross
I wait by the water.
ocean shore

I perch on a cactus.
2. wren
desert

Even the sparrow has found a home, and the swallow a nest for herself, where she may have her young.
Psalm 84:3a

© Science Level 1   43

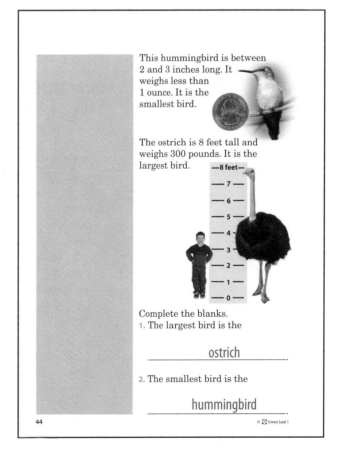

This hummingbird is between 2 and 3 inches long. It weighs less than 1 ounce. It is the smallest bird.

The ostrich is 8 feet tall and weighs 300 pounds. It is the largest bird.

—8 feet—
— 7 —
— 6 —
— 5 —
— 4 —
— 3 —
— 2 —
— 1 —
— 0 —

Complete the blanks.
1. The largest bird is the

ostrich

2. The smallest bird is the

hummingbird

44

© Science Level 1

3.6 Birds Grow

Objective

Students will sequence the life cycle of birds, explain the purpose of a bird nest, and describe why birds migrate.

Materials

Introduction
• Plastic eggs, balls

Directed Instruction
• Globe
• BLM 3.6A Robin, crayons, scissors, glue, construction paper

Preparation

Collect a PLASTIC EGG and a SMALL BALL such as a tennis ball, a softball, or a handball for every three to four students. (*Introduction*)

Write the definition of *migration* on the board. (*Directed Instruction*)

Have a GLOBE on hand. (*Directed Instruction*)

Print **BLM 3.6A Robin** for each student. Gather CRAYONS, SCISSORS, GLUE, and CONSTRUCTION PAPER for each student. (*Directed Instruction*)

Content

God designed features of birds such as shape, feet, beak, and diet. His plan also included a nest type and location to suit the bird's habitat, providing protection from predators.

Most birds build nests. Nests vary in location, size, shape, and material. Different bird species lay differently shaped eggs. An egg's shape complements the type and location of a bird's nest. Some birds produce round-shaped eggs that are strong and require less shell material. This shape suits a species that makes a cup-shaped nest. An oval-shaped egg is better suited for birds that build their nests on cliffs. These eggs roll in a tight circle and do not go far from the nest.

Some birds migrate, traveling a variety of distances; others do not migrate at all. The arctic tern's migration may be more than 20,000 miles, traveling from the Arctic to the Antarctic and back. The sandhill crane may travel up to 3,000 miles.

Introduction

Hold up a PLASTIC EGG and a SMALL BALL. Explain that birds have different egg shapes similar to the plastic egg and the ball. Ask the class which shape would be better for the eggs if the bird built its nest on a cliff by an ocean. (**Answers will vary.**) State that students will discover which shape is better. Divide the class into small groups. Distribute an egg and a ball to each group. Allow time for groups to gently roll the two objects. Have a volunteer describe the difference in the movement of the two objects. (**Possible answer: The plastic egg rolls, but not far; the small ball rolls straight and keeps going.**) Lead the class to conclude that if the egg on the cliff were designed like a ball, it might fall off the cliff. With a plastic-egg shape, an egg might roll but not very far. Convey that God designed the shapes of different bird eggs to help them stay safe.

Directed Instruction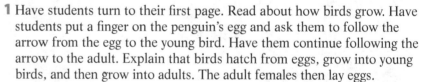

1 Have students turn to their first page. Read about how birds grow. Have students put a finger on the penguin's egg and ask them to follow the arrow from the egg to the young bird. Have them continue following the arrow to the adult. Explain that birds hatch from eggs, grow into young birds, and then grow into adults. The adult females then lay eggs.

2 Point out each picture of the birds at their nest. Ask students where each of these birds has its nest. (**The loon has its nest by the water; the woodpecker's nest is in a hole of a tree; the meadowlark has its nest in a grassy spot on the ground; the killdeer's nest is in the open on the ground.**) Do you think the loon would have round or more-pointed eggs? (**more-pointed**) How could this shape help the eggs? (**They could not roll far and fall into the water.**) Allow time for students to do the exercises at the bottom of the page.

3 Direct students' attention to the second page. Convey that some birds are able to stay in the same place all year. Then read the definition of **migration** from the board: *a move from one place to another*. Read the section about migration on the page, and emphasize that migration is important for some birds in order to stay warm and find food. Have

students read the questions at the bottom of the page. Lead a class discussion to determine the answers.

Have students put a finger on the tern's picture. Share that this amazing bird migrates many miles every year. Display a GLOBE. Point out the Arctic at the top of the globe. Explain that every year, the arctic tern flies from the Arctic to the Antarctic and returns. Show the distance on the globe. Mention that the arctic tern can fly over 20,000 miles! As students place a finger on the sandhill crane, report that this bird migrates about 3,000 miles. Discuss the questions at the bottom of the page.

4 Distribute **BLM 3.6A Robin**, CRAYONS, and SCISSORS to each student. Allow time for students to color the pictures and to cut out the six boxes. Read "Robin" below and direct students to place each picture in order across their desk. Have students GLUE the pictures to a piece of CONSTRUCTION PAPER.

Robin
Mother robin is at her nest, protecting her eggs and keeping them warm. After a few weeks, the eggs are ready to hatch. A small crack appears in each egg. The crack grows larger. A baby robin pokes out its head. Mother robin feeds insects and worms to her babies. Food helps them grow bigger. They grow feathers too. Father robin also cares for and trains the young robins. The robins that were once eggs are now young birds. They have left the nest and will soon become adults.

Permit students to take the pictures home and to share the robin story.

➕ Extension

Materials
• Jar, candy eggs
• Plastic eggs, empty egg carton
• BLM 3.6B Recipe: Bird Nest

Fill a jar with candy eggs. Have students estimate how many eggs are in the jar. Count the candy as a class and commend the student with the closest estimation.

In a learning center, have students create a color pattern of plastic eggs in an egg carton. Write patterns on strips of paper for students to follow. For a challenge, have students connect different egg halves to make a pattern.

Use **BLM 3.6B Recipe: Bird Nest** to make a class treat, or print copies for families to make the snack at home.

Students will compare the design of aircraft to the design of birds.

Introduction
• BLM 3.7A Airplane

Directed Instruction
• Balloon

Print **BLM 3.7A Airplane** for each student. (*Introduction*)

Have a BALLOON available. (*Directed Instruction*)

Content

People have learned about flight by observing birds. The history of aviation and space flight includes many different designs of aircraft. From hot-air balloons to space travel, God's gift of scientific creativity to individuals has allowed humans to soar.

In 1783, the Montgolfier brothers built the first hot-air balloon. The air in hot-air balloons is heated and is lighter than atmospheric gases, allowing the balloon to ascend. Airships like the *Hindenburg* used hydrogen to lift them into the air. In 1903, the Wright brothers accomplished the first powered and controlled flight in a heavier-than-air craft. Technology advanced quickly, and in 1969, people landed on the moon. The year 1981 brought the first space shuttle mission, in 1997 *Mars Pathfinder* landed on Mars, and by 2010 an experimental solar-powered plane had flown a 24-hour test flight.

Introduction 🖐

Ask the class if they have ever flown on an airplane. (**Answers will vary.**) Allow time for volunteers to share when and where they went. Explain that people have learned about flight by observing the design that God gave to birds. The design of birds has helped people build vehicles that fly.

Distribute copies of **BLM 3.7A Airplane**. Demonstrate how to make a paper airplane as you read the step-by-step directions below. Point out the numbers on BLM 3.7A that correlate with each step. Read the steps and assist students as needed:
1. Fold the paper in half along the center line. Crease and unfold.
2. Fold on Line 1 so that the paper edge lines up with the center line. Crease the fold. Repeat on the other side.
3. Fold on Line 2 so that the paper edge lines up with the center line. Crease the fold. Repeat on the other side.
4. Fold on Line 3 so that the paper edge lines up with the center line. Crease the fold. Repeat on the other side.
5. Fold the plane in half along the center line so that the wings fold out.
6. Flip the plane over and extend the wings.

Have students write their name on their plane. Line students up and give them each a turn to fly their plane across the room or down a hallway. Collect planes until an outdoor time or the end of the day.

Directed Instruction 🖐

1 Ask the class to describe how the flight of the paper airplane is similar to bird flight. (**Answers will vary, but should include that they both fly; they go from one place to another; they lift off and land.**)

2 Discuss how people have learned many things about flying by studying birds. Direct students' attention to the first student page. Read the caption of the hot-air balloon. Blow up a BALLOON, tie a knot, and let the balloon go. Ask students to describe what happened to it. (**It fell to the ground.**) Have them put a finger on the hot-air balloon picture. Ask them what direction this balloon goes. (**It goes up in the air.**) Inform the class that the hot-air balloon in the picture has heated air that makes it rise. This heated air is much hotter than the air a person blows into a balloon.

3 Discuss the flights of the Wright brothers. Advancement of flight technology has led to the development of special planes, rockets, and even spacecraft. Discuss the picture of the 747 Jumbo Jet. Today airplanes are used to transport people, carry freight, fight wars, spray crops, combat forest fires, and rescue people.

4 Discuss that in 1981 a space shuttle went into space for the first time. Explain how the space shuttle was launched like a rocket and returned to Earth much like an airplane. The last shuttle mission was flown in 2011. Discuss that NASA and some private companies are currently testing high-tech planes.

5 Direct students' attention to the second page and instruct them to observe the gull and the commercial airplane. Have them notice how the wings of the bird of prey and the fighter plan are similar. Ask students to compare the different parts of the bird to the plane. (**the long center of the bird and the long center of the airplane; the bird's two wings and the airplane's wing shape; the head of the bird and the cockpit**)

Direct students' attention to the bottom of the page. Compare the wing shape of the bird of prey and the fighter airplane; have them trace the shape of both with a finger. Convey that a bird of prey looks for other animals to eat. It performs a similar task to a fighter plane, which seeks out its enemy. Explain that the wings assist both in lifting off and staying up in the air. Let student pairs share answers.

⊕ Extension

Materials
• Completed BLM 3.6A Robin, bird and habitat pictures, sticks, newspaper, hay, grass, glue, plastic eggs, small balls, nest pictures, chenille stems, feathers, foam balls, paint

Assign topics to groups to give a presentation during Lesson 3.8:
• Life Cycle: Retell the story from the completed **BLM 3.6A Robin**.
• Habitat: Match pictures of birds to pictures of their habitat.
• Nest: Use sticks, newspaper, hay, grass, and glue to make a nest.
• Egg Shape: Use plastic eggs and small balls, and pictures of a cliff nest and a grassy area nest. Demonstrate the better habitat for each egg.
• Body: Make a bird with chenille stems, feathers, foam balls, and paint; label each body part.

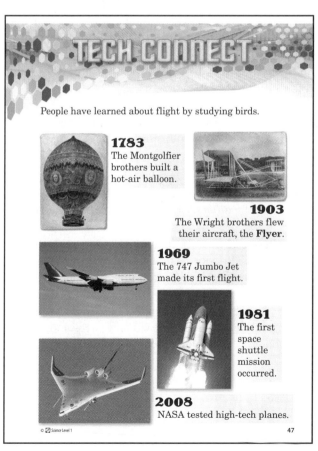

People have learned about flight by studying birds.

1783
The Montgolfier brothers built a hot-air balloon.

1903
The Wright brothers flew their aircraft, the **Flyer**.

1969
The 747 Jumbo Jet made its first flight.

1981
The first space shuttle mission occurred.

2008
NASA tested high-tech planes.

© Science Level 1   47

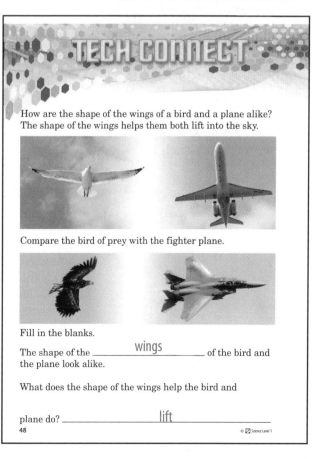

How are the shape of the wings of a bird and a plane alike? The shape of the wings helps them both lift into the sky.

Compare the bird of prey with the fighter plane.

Fill in the blanks.

The shape of the _____wings_____ of the bird and the plane look alike.

What does the shape of the wings help the bird and

plane do? _____lift_____

48   © Science Level 1

3.8 Chapter 3 Review

Materials

Introduction
• Scissors, BLM 3.8A Bird Names

Directed Instruction
• TM-3.2A Parts of a Bird
• BLM 3.8B Bird Facts
• BLM 3.8C Chapter 3 Test

Preparation

Obtain scissors and print **BLM 3.8A Bird Names** for each student. (*Introduction*)

Draw the following Creation web on the board. (*Directed Instruction*)

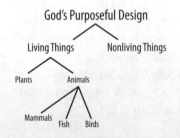

Select **TM-3.2A Parts of a Bird** for review. (*Directed Instruction*)

Print **BLM 3.8B Bird Facts** for each student. (*Directed Instruction*)

Print **BLM 3.8C Chapter 3 Test** for each student. (*Directed Instruction*)

Introduction

Relate to the class that the Bible mentions many birds. Distribute scissors and **BLM 3.8A Bird Names**. Direct students to cut on the dotted lines.

Have students spread out the slips of paper on their desk. Instruct them to listen carefully for a bird name as you read each of the following verses. When students hear the name of a bird, have them hold up their slip of paper with the name written on it. Read the verses: **Genesis 8:10–12** (**dove**), **Psalm 84:3** (**sparrow, swallow**), **Psalm 147:9** (**raven**), **Isaiah 40:31** (**eagle**), **Job 39:13–14** (**ostrich, stork**).

Directed Instruction

1 Remind the class that birds are important to God. He created them. People have learned many things by observing birds. Direct students' attention to the Creation web drawn on the board. Reiterate that this graphic shows how God purposefully designed living and nonliving things. Two groups of living things are plants and animals. Select a volunteer to read the three types of animals that are shown. (**mammals, fish, birds**) Ask students to name some animals that God purposefully designed. (**Answers will vary.**)

2 Review the definitions of *bird* and *migration*. (*bird*: **an animal that lays eggs and has feathers and wings**; *migration*: **a move from one place to another**) Refer to **TM-3.2A Parts of a Bird** to review the parts of a bird. Have volunteers point to the part being discussed. Review the following information and encourage student dialogue:
• Birds are the only animals with feathers. Feathers and wings help birds fly. Their hollow bones make birds lightweight, making it easier to fly.
• The shape of their beaks and feet allows them to get things they need from their habitat in order to live.
• The nest, care from their parents, and shape of the eggs allow the young to grow and mature.

3 Distribute **BLM 3.8B Bird Facts** to each student. Upon completion, have a volunteer read a fact and explain the fact in his or her own words.

4 Use student pages as a review or pretest. Complete these pages with the class. Brainstorm words for students to include in their journal, such as *bird-watching, nest, wings,* and *feathers*. List these words on the board.

5 You may use **BLM 3.8C Chapter 3 Test** for individual assessment. Read through this page with the class. Provide as much reading support as necessary. You may choose to use BLM 3.8C as an oral assessment or not to do it at all.

6 Chapter 3 Birds has been completed. Staple the student pages and send them as a booklet to be shared with a family member.

Notes:

Chapter 3 Review 3.8

Number the circles **1**, **2**, and **3** to tell how a bird grows.

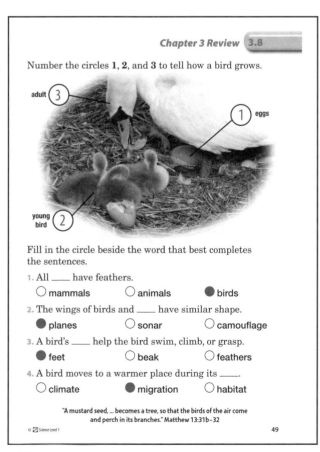

adult ③

① eggs

young bird ②

Fill in the circle beside the word that best completes the sentences.

1. All ___ have feathers.
   ○ mammals   ○ animals   ● birds

2. The wings of birds and ___ have similar shape.
   ● planes   ○ sonar   ○ camouflage

3. A bird's ___ help the bird swim, climb, or grasp.
   ● feet   ○ beak   ○ feathers

4. A bird moves to a warmer place during its ___.
   ○ climate   ● migration   ○ habitat

"A mustard seed, ... becomes a tree, so that the birds of the air come and perch in its branches." Matthew 13:31b–32

© Science Level 1   49

Read the Creation web.

God's Purposeful Design

Living Things   *Nonliving Things*

Plants   *Animals*

Mammals   Fish   Birds

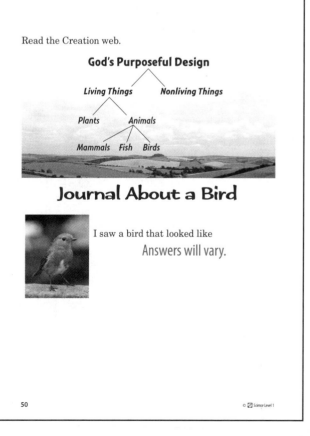

Journal About a Bird

I saw a bird that looked like
Answers will vary.

50   © Science Level 1

Key Ideas

- Insects are a class of the animal kingdom.
- Insects have three main body parts and six legs.
- Each species of insect is unique in body features that help it survive in its habitat and obtain food.

4.0 Chapter Preparation

Looking Ahead

- For an *Extension* activity in **Lesson 4.1** or sometime during the teaching of Chapter 4, invite a guest speaker from a local museum to speak to the class about insects.
- In **Lesson 4.3**, you will need to take the class outside to a place with many insects. Arrange for parent volunteers to assist. Or, obtain some insect specimens from your local area for students to observe with a hand lens.

Introduction

The class Insecta makes up the largest group of animals. By learning features common to all insects—three main body sections and six legs—first graders will be able to identify insects. They will study features such as mouthparts, legs, and wings, and will also distinguish differences in design for specific functions. Because they are aware of their own growth, students can relate to the growth and development of animals. They will have the opportunity to practice skills of observation and graphing through the study of insect metamorphosis. The amazing characteristics, variety, and roles of insects help students appreciate the infinite detail of God's creation.

About This Chapter

Lesson 4.1 – What Insects Are
Materials
- Pattern blocks

Lesson Content
There are over a million insect species in the world. An insect is identified as an animal that has three main body sections—head, thorax, and abdomen—and six legs. Spiders are not insects.

Lesson 4.2 – Parts of an Insect
Materials
- Insect book
- Pointer
- Marshmallows
- Cotton swabs
- Plates

Lesson Content
Insects have no backbone; they are covered by an outer layer—an exoskeleton—that sheds as insects grow. Other common insect body parts include eyes, mouth, and antennae.

Lesson 4.3 – Differences in Insects
Materials
- Hand lenses

Lesson Content
God designed insects with differences to allow them to survive in their specific habitat and to eat the food He provided for them. Insect mouths, antennae, and wings vary between species.

Lesson 4.4 – Insects Grow
Materials
- Balloon
- Crayons

Lesson Content
Many species of insects such as butterflies, flies, and moths undergo the four stages of complete metamorphosis—egg, larva, pupa, and adult. Because graphs are charts that show and compare information that has been collected, they can be used to chart stages of insect growth.

Lesson 4.5 – Amazing Insects

Materials
- Paper towels
- Cups
- Water
- Paper clips
- Toothpicks

Lesson Content
The variety of insect species is amazing, and each one is unique. Characteristics, including body shape, antennae, mouthparts, and behavior, may differ between orders of insects and even individual species.

Lesson 4.6 – Chapter 4 Review

Materials
- Scissors
- Plastic insects
- Crayons
- Number cubes
- Index cards
- Tape

Teacher Resources

Butterfly by Thomas Marent and Ben Morgan. DK, 2008.

Creation Proclaims: Climbers and Creepers, Volume 1 DVD by Dr. Jobe Martin and Dan Breeding. Biblical Discipleship Ministries, 2009.

National Wildlife Federation Field Guide to Insects and Spiders and Related Species of North America by Arthur V. Evans. Sterling, 2007.

Student Resources

Bugs, Bugs, Bugs: 21 Songs and Over 250 Activities for Young Children by Pam Schiller. Gryphon House, 2006.

Discover Science: Insects by Barbara Taylor. Kingfisher, 2011.

Explore Bugs by Maurice Pledger. Silver Dolphin Books, 2010.

Supplemental Materials

Blackline Masters
4.1A Pattern Block Insects, Part 1
4.1B Pattern Block Insects, Part 2
4.1C Pattern Block Insects, Part 3
4.1D Pattern Block Insects, Part 4
4.1E Insect, Part 1
4.3A Insect, Part 2
4.4A Metamorphosis Wheel, Part 1
4.4B Metamorphosis Wheel, Part 2

4.5A Float or Sink
4.5B Insect Facts
4.6A Insect Game, Part 1
4.6B Insect Game, Part 2
4.6C Insect Game Board
4.6D Chapter 4 Test

Transparency Masters
4.2A Parts of an Insect
4.4A Growing Up, Part 1
4.4B Growing Up, Part 2

4.5A Exoskeleton
4.6A Life at the Pond
4.6B Helpful Insects

Computer Presentation
3.5 Animal Habitats: Birds and Insects, Part 2

4.1 What Insects Are

Objective

Students will identify an insect as having three main body parts and six legs.

Materials

Introduction
• Pattern blocks; BLMs 4.1A–D Pattern Block Insects, Parts 1–4

✋ Preparation

Obtain PATTERN BLOCKS for small groups of students. Blocks can be found in the ACSI Math Manipulatives Kit. Print **BLMs 4.1A–D Pattern Block Insects, Parts 1–4** so that each group has a pattern. (*Introduction*)

Write the definition of *insect* on the board. (*Directed Instruction*)

Content

The roles, lives, behaviors, and structures can vary among insects. The current estimate of the number of insect species is between 1.5 million and 30 million, with insects making up approximately three-quarters of all animal species. Common features of insects include three body sections (head, thorax, and abdomen), an outer skeleton called *an exoskeleton*, and six legs attached to the thorax. When wings are present, they are attached to the thorax as well. Insects are cold-blooded, being dependent on external energy sources such as the sun to maintain their body temperature.

Insects are classified as being within the animal kingdom, and as such, they need food, water, air, and shelter as other animals do. Insects are further classified within the phylum called *Arthropods*, meaning *jointed feet*. They exhibit characteristics such as jointed appendages and the presence of an exoskeleton. A common misconception is that spiders and other arachnids are insects. When one observes spiders, scorpions, lobsters, and ticks, it is easy to see that their legs and antennae are jointed. But spiders are in the class Arachnida, while insects are in the class Insecta. Spiders have two body sections and eight legs—characteristics of the class Arachnida.

The term *bugs* is often used to refer to all insects; however, there is a small group of insects known as *true bugs*. This term is not accurately used when describing all insects.

Introduction

Arrange students into small groups. Distribute PATTERN BLOCKS and patterns from **BLMs 4.1A–D Pattern Block Insects, Parts 1–4**. State that students will work together in their group to make a special kind of animal. Allow groups time to fit the blocks onto the pattern to complete their animal. When groups finish, instruct each one to describe its animal. (**Possible answers:** *dragonfly*: **four pointed wings and two antennae that attach to its body;** *butterfly*: **two rounded wings and two antennae that attach to its body;** *bee*: **two wings, a head, and a pointed body;** *caterpillar*: **a head, antennae, and a long body with many legs**) State that the patterns form the shapes of insects, which are animals. Insects have special things about them that make them insects, even though each kind of insect looks different and performs different functions.

Directed Instruction ✋ ➕

1 Read the definition of **insect**: *an animal that has three main body parts and six legs*. Direct the students to turn to their first student page. Invite a volunteer to read the definition of *insect* aloud; then have the class read it orally. Discuss the pictures and point out the beauty that many insects add to the earth. Ask students if they have seen any of the insects pictured on the page. (**Answers will vary.**) Encourage students to share an experience. Ask what it might feel like to have six legs. (**Answers will vary.**)

2 Convey that in God's design of creation, insects play important roles. They are food for other animals. They help plants grow by pollination, or bringing pollen from one plant to another. Studying insects is a way for people to understand what God desires to teach them. Read **Proverbs 30:25**. Explain that God designed ants to be able to store up their food despite their size. From the ant, people can learn a life lesson of planning and saving for the future.

3 Go over the information about the insect's three main body sections. As you pronounce the name of each section, have students place a finger on the part being identified. Direct students to repeat the name of the body part. Write on the board *thorax* and *abdomen* divided into syllables (*tho·rax* and *ab·do·men*). Allow students time to count and write in the number of legs on the insect.

4 Direct the class' attention to the second page. Allow time for students to complete the exercise on the top of this page, identifying and labeling the three main sections of the damselfly's body. If a student mentions other parts of the insect's body like the eyes, wings, or antennae, relate where those parts are and that they will be discussed in the next lesson.

5 Lead students to apply the information learned about insects to determine if a spider is an insect. (**Spiders are not insects.**) The picture shows that the spider has eight legs; this fact should lead students to conclude that the spider is not an insect. An observant student may point out that the spider has only two main body parts, not three like the insect.

6 Complete the questions with the class. Assess the amount of reading support needed. Direct students to use the Word Bank to answer Exercises 1 and 2.

7 Allow time for students to share with a partner the names of the three main body sections of an insect. Encourage discussion of the differences between insects and spiders.

➕ Extension

Materials
• Egg cartons, chenille stems, paint; or BLM 4.1E Insect, Part 1; construction paper, scissors, glue
• Guest speaker

Assist students in making an insect by cutting an empty upside-down egg carton into sections of three for the body parts. Supply chenille stems for the legs. Allow students to paint their insect. Or, have students cut and glue the insect sections together from **BLM 4.1E Insect, Part 1** printed on construction paper. Students will add more body parts in Lesson 4.3.

Present your guest speaker from the local museum to speak to the class about insects today or another day during Chapter 4.

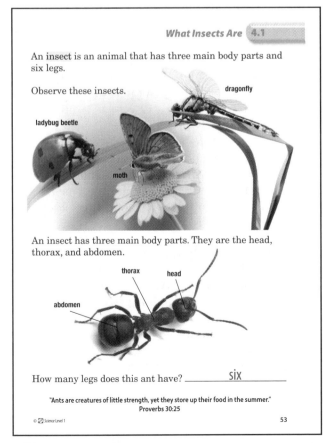

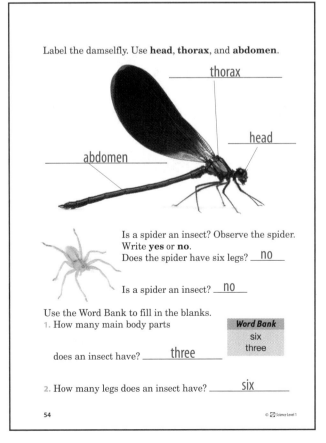

4.2 Parts of an Insect

Objective

Students will make a model of an insect to exemplify the three body parts and six legs.

Materials

Introduction
• Insect book

Directed Instruction
• TM-4.2A Parts of an Insect, pointer
• Marshmallows, cotton swabs, paper plates

Preparation

Obtain a copy of an interesting INSECT BOOK, such as *Bugs Galore* by Peter Stein (Candlewick, 2012) or *Step Gently Out* by Helen Frost (Candlewick, 2012), to read to the class. (*Introduction*)

Select **TM-4.2A Parts of an Insect** for display. Obtain a POINTER for students to use. (*Directed Instruction*)

For each student, arrange 3 LARGE MARSHMALLOWS and 9 COTTON SWABS on a PAPER PLATE to create a model insect. (*Directed Instruction*)

Content

Insects have unique features that set them apart from other animals and allow them to acquire the things they need to keep themselves alive. Some important features are described below.

• Head: The head is the location of the eyes, antennae, and mouthparts. There are two types of insect eyes—compound and simple. The compound eye has many lenses, while the simple eye has one lens. Each type senses light in a different way. Antennae are segmented sense organs that are important for taste, smell, and touch. There are many types of antennae. The design of the mouthparts fits the way in which an insect obtains food.

• Thorax: The legs and, when present, wings of an insect are attached to the thorax. An insect's legs are designed to match the insect's needs for survival. Wings are designed to allow the adult to flex and move for flight. Wings are a feature by which insects are classified.

• Abdomen: The abdomen is the third body section of an insect; it is posterior to the head and thorax.

• Exoskeleton: This is the hard outer skeleton or covering that protects the animal and keeps it watertight. The exoskeleton does not grow as the insect grows. It must be shed, or molted, and the insect makes a new one to take its place. The exoskeleton allows for necessary movement. Insects are invertebrates; they have no backbone.

Introduction

Select and read an INSECT BOOK. After the story, point out the wide variety of insects mentioned. Remind students that even though all insects have six legs and three main body sections, God made different types of insects unique. Some insects have wings. Ask students to recall different types of insects from the book. (**Answers will vary but should include a type of insect mentioned in the book.**)

Directed Instruction

1 Display **TM-4.2A Parts of an Insect**. Point to the parts noted on TM-4.2A. Then have student volunteers use a POINTER to point to each part. Allow a student volunteer to quiz the class.

2 Direct the class' attention to the top of the student page. Have students place a finger on the three main body sections of the beetle: head, thorax, and abdomen. Have students find the eyes, mouth, and antennae. Convey that God designed the antennae as a tool to help insects taste, smell, and touch. Remind students that six legs connect to the thorax, the middle part of an insect. The abdomen is the third part.

Relate that the insect's skeleton is different from some other animal skeletons. God designed mammals, fish, and birds with a skeleton inside their body. Ask the class where they think the skeleton of an insect is. (**Answers will vary.**) Explain that the insect's skeleton covers the body like a hard coat. The skeleton protects the insect. Ask students what happens when their feet outgrow their shoes. (**They need to get larger shoes.**) Share that this is similar to what happens to an insect as it grows. The insect's body grows, just as students' feet grow. The insect's skeleton does not grow with its body. God designed insects to shed their old skeleton and make a new one, just like students need to get new shoes. Share that the insect's outer skeleton is called *an exoskeleton.*

3 Check for understanding by asking several review questions: What is the first or front section of an insect's body? (**head**) What is the middle body section that is connected to the head? (**thorax**) What main body sections connect to the thorax? (**head and abdomen**) Where are an insect's eyes, mouth, and antennae? (**on its head**) To which main body section are an insect's legs connected? (**thorax**) What part of the insect is most interesting, and why? (**Answers will vary.**) Where is an insect's skeleton? (**covering the outside of its body**)

4 Continue down the page. Read the directions and state the insects shown: a beetle and a praying mantis. Check that students have drawn lines from each word to the appropriate part of the insect.

5 Direct students' attention to the second page. Read the directions for the activity. Distribute MARSHMALLOWS and COTTON SWABS on PAPER PLATES to each student, and reiterate that these supplies are to be used for the insect model only. Instruct the class to follow the pattern for making an insect model. Take them through each step and encourage them to use the picture for understanding. Demonstrate Step 2 in front of the class. Push a cotton swab completely through the middle marshmallow so the swab extends equally on both sides. Push the remaining marshmallows on the extended ends of the cotton swab. Pair students to discuss the parts of an insect. Complete the exercise at the bottom with the class.

Notes:

⊕ Extension

Materials
• Insect field guide
• Black beans, glitter, cups

Share with students an insect field guide like *National Wildlife Federation Field Guide to Insects and Spiders of North America* by Arthur V. Evans (Sterling, 2007).

Glue gold glitter to an end of each dried black bean. Place the beans in small cups. Create math story problems about catching and releasing fireflies. (Example: I caught 10 fireflies in a jar but let 3 go. How many do I have left?) Have students use the beans and cups to work the problems.

Search the Internet for a virtual insect field trip. Engage students in exploring nature without leaving the classroom.

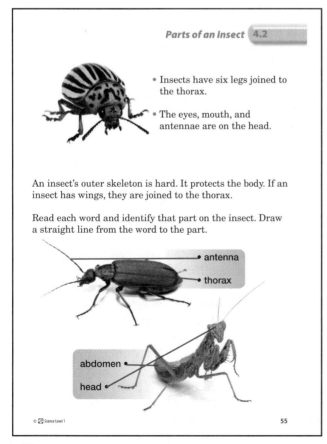

Parts of an Insect 4.2

• Insects have six legs joined to the thorax.

• The eyes, mouth, and antennae are on the head.

An insect's outer skeleton is hard. It protects the body. If an insect has wings, they are joined to the thorax.

Read each word and identify that part on the insect. Draw a straight line from the word to the part.

• antenna
• thorax
abdomen •
head •

© Science Level 1   55

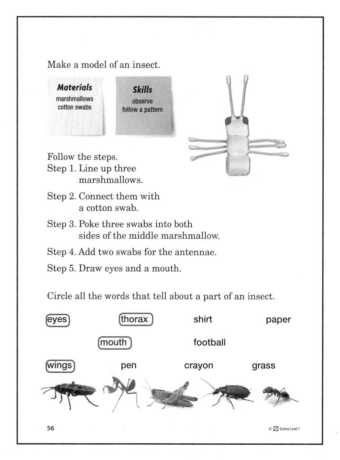

Make a model of an insect.

Materials	Skills
marshmallows cotton swabs	observe follow a pattern

Follow the steps.
Step 1. Line up three marshmallows.

Step 2. Connect them with a cotton swab.

Step 3. Poke three swabs into both sides of the middle marshmallow.

Step 4. Add two swabs for the antennae.

Step 5. Draw eyes and a mouth.

Circle all the words that tell about a part of an insect.

(eyes)   (thorax)   shirt   paper

(mouth)   football

(wings)   pen   crayon   grass

56   © Science Level 1

4.3 Differences in Insects

Content

A close-up view of an insect reveals incredible detail and variety. Some characteristics that exhibit variety among species of insects include mouthparts, antennae, legs, and wings. The design of insect mouthparts shows form—God's design for the body. It also shows function—God's design for what the insect does. Insect mouthparts vary greatly in detail and are designed to fit the type of food the insect eats. There is a great variety of antennae. The butterfly has antennae with a little club at the tip, while the moth has antennae that resemble feathers. Butterfly antennae help it find nectar. Moth antennae, especially those found on male moths, help in locating a mate; the female produces chemicals called *pheromones*. The design or form of insect legs allows the insect to function in its unique way. For example, a grasshopper's hind legs are large, making it possible for the grasshopper to hop away from danger. Scientists classify insects by the type of wings. Some kinds of insects, such as beetles (order Coleoptera), have a shielded-wing design. Some have two wings, or one pair of wings, and are in the order *Diptera* (*di* means *two*).

Introduction

Take the class outdoors for an insect search. Caution students not to harm any insects and not to touch any, as they may bite or sting. Have HAND LENSES available for students to use in observation. Monitor students closely.

Directed Instruction ⊕

1 When students return to the classroom, have them describe or draw an insect they saw outdoors. Ask if they were able to see any insects eating. If so, ask what the insects were eating. (**Answers will vary.**)

2 Direct students to turn to their first page. Discuss the picture of the children. Inform students that today they will find out if the body sections of all insects are alike or different. Begin by studying the insect mouths shown. Explain that God designed insects to have the kind of mouth they need in order to get the food they eat. Discuss how the beetle has a special mouth that allows it to catch its prey. The beetle's mouth is somewhat like pliers. Explain how the butterfly can get nectar from a flower because God designed it with a mouth that is like a straw. Another common insect is the housefly. It is not pictured, but continue with an explanation of a fly's mouth, which soaks up food. A fly's mouth is somewhat like a sponge. Check for understanding by asking why a butterfly is unable to eat grass. (**Butterfly mouths are made for sucking nectar.**) Why can a beetle chew a leaf? (**because God designed its mouth for chewing**)

Allow the class time to circle the mouth of the beetle and the butterfly. Discuss the sentences about insect mouths, and explain that God designed the mouth of insects so they can eat the food He provides. Point out that God designed people with a mouth different from any insect's mouth; people eat more kinds of foods than insects do. Have the class name some ways that people can use their mouths to eat and drink. (**Possible answers: biting, chewing, sipping, drinking from a straw**)

3 Share that the mouth is not the only part of insects that varies. Read the antennae section at the bottom of the page and direct students to place a finger on the picture of the antennae of the butterfly. Ask a volunteer to describe the shape of this insect's antennae. (**Possible answers: long, with a tip at the end**) Ask another volunteer to describe and compare the antennae of the moth. (**Possible answer: feathery, not skinny like the butterfly antennae**)

Direct students' attention to the second page and continue with the pictures of different insect legs. Discuss how God's design of each leg is the best design for what it does. Have students place a finger on the front leg of the praying mantis and ask how this shape helps the praying mantis survive. (**The big front legs of the praying mantis help it catch food.**) How is the design of the grasshopper's legs different from the praying mantis' legs? (**The grasshopper has big hind legs.**) How is this the best design for the grasshopper? (**The grasshopper jumps, so having big hind legs that are strong is the best design for it.**)

Direct students' attention to the pictures of the insect wings. Explain that God designed special wings for each kind of winged insect. Have students place a finger on the fly. Ask volunteers to describe experiences they may have had with flies. (**Answers will vary.**) Point out that a fly has one pair of wings while a dragonfly has two pairs.

4 Complete the exercise at the bottom of the page together. Guide students to understand that God designed all insects differently to survive in their habitat.

Notes:

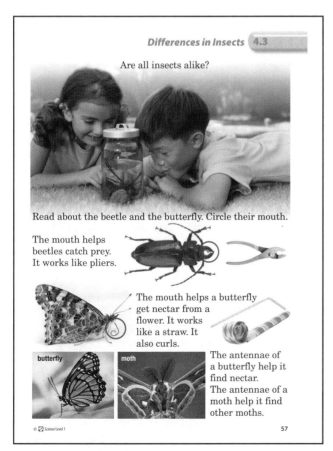

Differences in Insects 4.3

Are all insects alike?

Read about the beetle and the butterfly. Circle their mouth.

The mouth helps beetles catch prey. It works like pliers.

The mouth helps a butterfly get nectar from a flower. It works like a straw. It also curls.

butterfly moth

The antennae of a butterfly help it find nectar. The antennae of a moth help it find other moths.

© Science Level 1   57

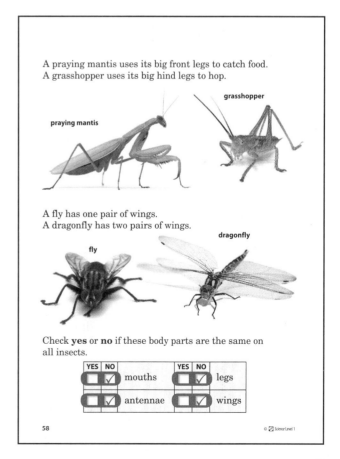

A praying mantis uses its big front legs to catch food. A grasshopper uses its big hind legs to hop.

grasshopper

praying mantis

A fly has one pair of wings. A dragonfly has two pairs of wings.

dragonfly

fly

Check **yes** or **no** if these body parts are the same on all insects.

YES	NO		YES	NO	
	✓	mouths		✓	legs
	✓	antennae		✓	wings

58   © Science Level 1

4.4 Insects Grow

Objective

Students will order and graph the stages of insect growth.

Materials

Introduction
• Balloon
• TMs-4.4A–B Growing Up, Parts 1–2

Directed Instruction
• Crayons

Preparation

Obtain a BALLOON for a demonstration. (*Introduction*)

Select **TMs-4.4A–B Growing Up, Parts 1–2** for display. (*Introduction*)

Write the definitions of *metamorphosis* and *graph* on the board. (*Directed Instruction*)

Have CRAYONS available for students. (*Directed Instruction*)

Content

Metamorphosis is essentially a developmental change of shape, form, or structure. Metamorphic change does not cause one insect to become another kind of animal; it is the process by which an insect grows into an adult. Many species of insects, such as butterflies, flies, and moths, undergo the four stages of complete metamorphosis—egg, larva, pupa, and adult. Insects such as the grasshopper and termite undergo incomplete metamorphosis—egg, nymph, and adult. Some species, like butterflies, exhibit the head, thorax, and abdomen only as an adult. Although the larva, or caterpillar, of a butterfly lacks the three main body sections, it has them when the process of metamorphosis is complete.

A common misconception is that larvae are worms. Worms are in a different phylum from insects. Instead, larvae represent the second, or larval, stage in an insect with complete metamorphosis. A common name for a butterfly larva is *caterpillar*; a housefly larva is *a maggot*. The third stage of complete metamorphosis is the pupa. In insects like the butterfly, the pupa is encased in a chrysalis, while the pupa of a moth is encased in a cocoon.

Introduction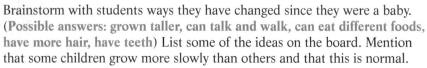

Brainstorm with students ways they have changed since they were a baby. (**Possible answers: grown taller, can talk and walk, can eat different foods, have more hair, have teeth**) List some of the ideas on the board. Mention that some children grow more slowly than others and that this is normal.

Demonstrate blowing up a BALLOON. Show the first stage when the balloon is void of air. Blow it up slightly and make the point that the balloon has changed shape. Blow up the balloon a little more and again state that the balloon is yet a different shape. Lastly, blow the balloon until it appears full. Ask a volunteer to describe the different stages from the balloon being void of air to being filled with air.

Display **TM-4.4A Growing Up, Part 1** to help students understand that living things change as they grow. Discuss the growth order from bulb to plant sprout, young plant, and mature plant. Display **TM-4.4B Growing Up, Part 2** and have student volunteers number the pictures 1–4 to show growth order.

Directed Instruction

1 Convey that, just like people and plants, God designed different kinds of insects to grow up in different ways. Some grow from an egg and look like a small adult right away; others grow from an egg and look very different from the adult they will become.

2 Direct students to turn to their first page. Read the information at the top about the butterfly and state that this process shows a way that some insects grow up. Have students place a finger on each stage as it is discussed. Ask which picture shows the way it looks first, after its mother lays it. (**egg, its first stage of growing up**) Which picture shows the way it looks next? (**caterpillar, its second stage of growing up**) Convey that the next thing that happens to this butterfly is that it grows a coat, or a chrysalis, around itself. When the butterfly is in the chrysalis, it waits and grows. (If students call the chrysalis a cocoon, clarify that the butterfly makes a chrysalis and the moth makes a cocoon.) The insect in this third stage is changing again. Ask students what the next stage is. (**adult**

butterfly, its fourth stage of growing up). Now it is all grown up. Have students carefully move their arms to represent an adult butterfly moving its wings. Emphasize that the caterpillar is not one type of insect that changes into another; rather it is a young age of the adult butterfly.

3 Read the definition of **metamorphosis** from the board: *the change of shape of an insect as it goes through stages of growth.* Teach the class that insects and some other animals go through metamorphosis. Divide *metamorphosis* on the board into syllables (*me·ta·mor·pho·sis*). Repeat the term with the class. Have volunteers describe the shape of the insect in each of its four stages. (**Answers will vary.**) Allow time for students to number the pictures to show the order in which this butterfly grows. To reinforce the new vocabulary word, lead students in the following song to the tune of "Bingo."

Metamorphosis
An insect's body changes shape
In each stage of growth.
Me-ta-mor-pho-sis, me-ta-mor-pho-sis, me-ta-mor-pho-sis,
That's how an insect grows.

4 Read the definition of **graph** from the board: *a chart that shows and compares information.* Direct students to turn to the second page. Read about Diego's photos. Then explain that every picture is an insect in one of the four stages of a butterfly's metamorphosis. Distribute CRAYONS. For each picture, have students color one space on the graph. Then count how many insects there are in each stage in Diego's photo collection.

Insects Grow 4.4

Insects change as they grow up. See how this insect changes.

1 2 3 4

Metamorphosis is the change of shape of an insect as it goes through stages of growth.

Number the pictures above **1** through **4** to show how the butterfly grows. Start with the egg.

59

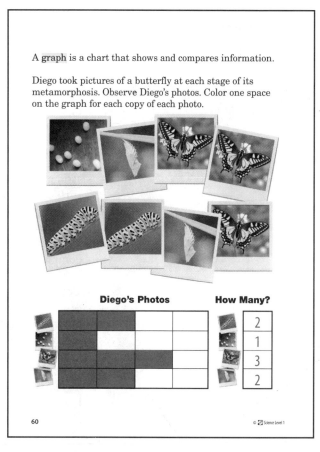

A graph is a chart that shows and compares information.

Diego took pictures of a butterfly at each stage of its metamorphosis. Observe Diego's photos. Color one space on the graph for each copy of each photo.

Diego's Photos   **How Many?**

2
1
3
2

60

4.5 Amazing Insects

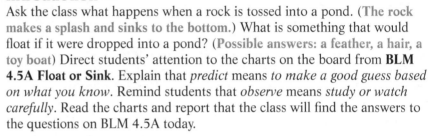

Objective

Students will analyze features in a variety of insect species.

Materials

Introduction
• BLM 4.5A Float or Sink

Directed Instruction
• BLM 4.5A Float or Sink, paper towels, cups, water, paper clips, toothpicks
• BLM 4.5B Insect Facts

Preparation

Select **BLM 4.5A Float or Sink** for display or draw the charts on the board. (*Introduction*)

Prepare for each group of students: **BLM 4.5A Float or Sink**, a PAPER TOWEL, a CUP of WATER, a PAPER CLIP, and a TOOTHPICK. (*Directed Instruction*)

Select **TM-4.5A Exoskeleton** for display. (*Directed Instruction*)

Print **BLM 4.5B Insect Facts** for each student. (*Directed Instruction*)

Content

Considering the enormous number of insect species, it is amazing to think that each is unique in some way. Body shape, antennae, mouthparts, and behaviors may differ from species to species of insects and even within individual species.

A water strider stays on top of the water, or floats, because it does not break the surface tension of the water. In this lesson, the term *float* will be used to describe the means by which things rest on the water's surface or stay at the top of the water.

Insects have the same body temperature as the air around them. Insects breathe air through tiny holes called *spiracles*.

Introduction

Ask the class what happens when a rock is tossed into a pond. (**The rock makes a splash and sinks to the bottom.**) What is something that would float if it were dropped into a pond? (**Possible answers: a feather, a hair, a toy boat**) Direct students' attention to the charts on the board from **BLM 4.5A Float or Sink**. Explain that *predict* means *to make a good guess based on what you know*. Remind students that *observe* means *study or watch carefully*. Read the charts and report that the class will find the answers to the questions on BLM 4.5A today.

Directed Instruction

1 Arrange the class into small groups. Have a member from each group pick up a PAPER TOWEL and a CUP of WATER. Have another group member gather a PAPER CLIP, a TOOTHPICK, and **BLM 4.5A Float or Sink** to record their group's observations.

2 Give students time to make their prediction, to experiment, and to record their observations. Discuss groups' findings and write them on the board. (**The paper clip sank; the toothpick floated.**) Share with the class that God designed an amazing insect to be light enough to float on the water and not sink.

3 Direct students' attention to the first student page and point out the water strider. Convey that God designed this insect to glide and walk on the surface of the water. It has short front legs for catching prey and long clawed middle and hind legs for propelling and steering. Ask if anyone has seen a water strider. (**Answers will vary.**) If so, have him or her share the experience. Read the words in the Word Bank to prepare students to complete each blank. Provide reading support as needed.

Convey that the next photo is of a fossilized insect. It shows the remains of a wasp that lived many years ago. Scientists believe that this wasp was covered by ash from a volcano. After it died, the carbon from its body was left on the ash. Today the ash is hard, and the remains from this insect stay like a fingerprint in time. Ask students what the next picture reminds them of. (**a leaf**) Discuss how God designed this butterfly to look like a dead leaf. Direct students to look at the fourth picture. Share that beetles have two pairs of wings that are unique. The first pair is hard, forming a sheath, or shield, that lifts so the delicate inner wings can function in flight.

4 Direct the class' attention to the second page. Read each question aloud and provide enough time for students to circle the better answer. Share the following facts for more information about each insect:

- Some insects look like other animals. God designed the big spots on these butterfly wings to look like an owl's eyes. They may scare off an animal that wants to eat this butterfly.
- Other insects exhibit camouflage—the ability an animal has to blend in with its surroundings. The lines on the thorax and abdomen of the grasshopper blend in with its surroundings.
- The name suits the stink bug because it produces a foul odor when it is bothered.
- Female mosquitoes lay eggs in watery habitats. The larvae are called *wrigglers*. In the third stage of metamorphosis, they look like a question mark and are called *tumblers*.
- Fireflies are beetles that God designed to have chemicals that can make light. Each kind of firefly uses a special pattern of flashes to communicate with its species.
- Insects breathe air through tiny holes. Insects also keep the same body temperature as the air around them.

Display **TM-4.5A Exoskeleton**. Remind students that insects have an outer skeleton. This skeleton is shed and a new one grows. This process allows the insect to grow. Divide the class into groups. Assign each group an insect to imitate, and let the other groups guess the insect.

5 Distribute **BLM 4.5B Insect Facts**. Review by reading each of the facts and completing the blanks.

Extension

Materials
- Newspaper, eyedroppers, water, food coloring, coffee filters, clothespins, chenille stems

Create coffee-filter butterflies. Cover a table with newspaper. Fill eyedroppers with water and food coloring, one color per dropper. Instruct students to fold a coffee filter in half and to squeeze a few drops of each color onto the folded filter. Unfold and let dry. Point out the symmetry and the way the colors mixed together to make new colors. Then pinch the center and clasp with a clothespin. Draw on eyes and add a chenille-stem mouth and antennae.

Create a class graph of students' favorite insects. Assist students in reading the graph.

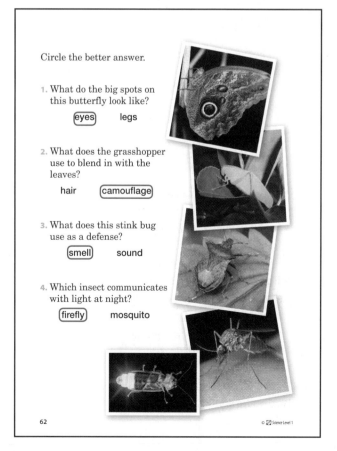

Introduction

- Scissors; BLMs 4.6A–B Insect Game, Parts 1–2; BLM 4.6C Insect Game Board; plastic insects (optional); crayons (optional); number cubes

Directed Instruction

- TM-4.2A Parts of an Insect
- BLM 4.6D Chapter 4 Test
- Index cards, tape
- TM-4.6A Life at the Pond

🖐 Preparation

Cut out the markers and game cards from **BLMs 4.6A–B Insect Game, Parts 1–2**; or replace markers with a SMALL PLASTIC INSECT for each student. Print **BLM 4.6C Insect Game Board** for small groups. Obtain CRAYONS. Get NUMBER CUBES, which can be found in the ACSI Math Manipulatives Kit. (*Introduction*)

Draw the Creation web on the board. (*Directed Instruction*)

Select **TM-4.2A Parts of an Insect.** for display. Print **BLM 4.6D Chapter 4 Test** for each student. (*Directed Instruction*)

Write an animal species on an INDEX CARD for each student. Be sure the cards well represent each animal class. Make 4 paper signs that read *mammal, fish, bird,* and *insect*. Adhere the signs in the room's corners with TAPE. (*Directed Instruction*)

Select **TM-4.6A Life at the Pond** for display. (*Directed Instruction*)

Introduction

Distribute insect game components from **BLMs 4.6A–B Insect Game, Parts 1–2**, and **BLM 4.6C Insect Game Board**, NUMBER CUBE, and PLASTIC INSECTS (optional) to small groups. Read through the directions and the cards with students. Ask them what type of animal the butterfly on the game board is. (**insect**) Inquire what the stages of growth shown on the board are called. (**metamorphosis**) If time allows, give students the opportunity to use their CRAYONS to color the game board. Direct each student to roll the cube to see who goes first in their group. The highest number goes first. Allow students time to play, and monitor that they are correctly pronouncing the vocabulary and following the rules. Encourage students to maintain good sportsmanship during the game and to congratulate each other. When groups finish, give instructions for cleaning up the game.

Directed Instruction

1 Use **TM-4.2A Parts of an Insect** to review the features of an insect. Review the definitions of *insect*, *metamorphosis*, and *graph*. (***insect***: **an animal that has three main body parts and six legs; *metamorphosis*: the change of shape of an insect as it goes through stages of growth; *graph*: a chart that shows and compares information**)

2 Direct students' attention to the Creation web drawn on the board. Explain that this graphic shows that God purposefully designed living and nonliving things. Two groups of living things are plants and animals. Select a volunteer to read the four types of animals that are shown. Ask students to name animals that God purposefully designed. (**Answers will vary.**)

3 Complete the student pages together as a review or pretest. To help students brainstorm ideas for their journal, consider creating a class graphic organizer. Write the heading *Insects* on the board and draw three columns labeled *can*, *have*, and *are*. Have students supply answers for the organizer with facts they have learned about insects. (**Possible answers: Insects can eat other insects; insects have six legs; insects are animals.**)

4 You may use **BLM 4.6D Chapter 4 Test** as individual assessment. Read through this page with the class. Provide as much reading support as necessary. Collect the test and review the answers with the class.

5 As a review of Unit 1, ask students to name the group of animals they studied that produces milk for its young. (**mammals**) What group of animals has scales and fins? (**fish**) Which animals have feathers? (**birds**) Point out the signs in the corners of the room. Hand each student a prepared INDEX CARD and read the animal on the card aloud. Instruct students to walk to the corner that shows which animal category the animal on their card belongs to. Once all students have found their corner, have each animal group read their cards. Redirect any misplaced students to their correct corner. Collect and shuffle cards; play again as time allows.

6 Display **TM-4.6A Life at the Pond**. Discuss the interaction between insects and the other three animal groups they have studied—mammals, fish, and birds. Allow time for students to observe and discuss the variety of life and form of the living things. Reiterate that God's design of all these animals is suited for where they live and what they do. If desired, share the following questions and answers with students:

- Do fish breathe the water? (No.) God made fish to breathe oxygen like people. He put oxygen in water. Fish get oxygen from the water.
- Are turtles really slow? (Yes and no.) God designed turtles to walk slow on land. But He made them to swim fast in water.
- Are frogs a kind of fish? (No.) Baby frogs—tadpoles—do look like fish. Then they grow legs. Grown-up frogs can crawl out of the water.
- Can all birds swim like ducks? (No.) God made webbed feet for ducks. Their feet push them through the water. Most other birds do not have webbed feet. They need other kinds of feet. God designed each bird with the right feet for its habitat.
- Why can I not see raccoons during the day? (Answers will vary.) God gave raccoons the daytime for sleeping. They hide during the day so they will be safe for sleeping. At night, raccoons wake up. Then they go out and search for food. God designed them for night hunting. Their eyes work well in the dark.

7 Chapter 4 Insects has been completed. Its pages can be stapled and sent home as a booklet to be shared with a parent.

Notes:

✚ Extension

Materials
- CP-3.5 Animal Habitats: Birds and Insects, Part 2
- TM-4.6B Helpful Insects
- *A Bug Collection: Four Stories from the Garden*

Present slides from **CP-3.5 Animal Habitats: Birds and Insects, Part 2** about insects.

Display **TM-4.6B Helpful Insects** and discuss how insects help plants and people. Bees carry pollen to flowers that make more flowers, and make honey for people to enjoy. Crickets and flies provide a meal for other animals and some plants.

Read and discuss stories from *A Bug Collection: Four Stories from the Garden* by Max Lucado (Thomas Nelson, 2007).

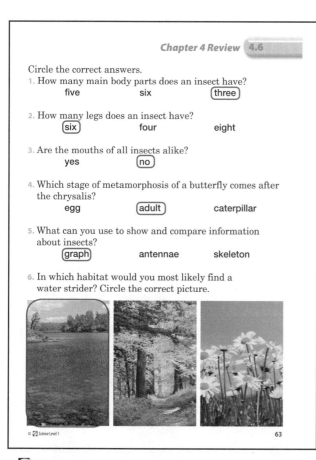

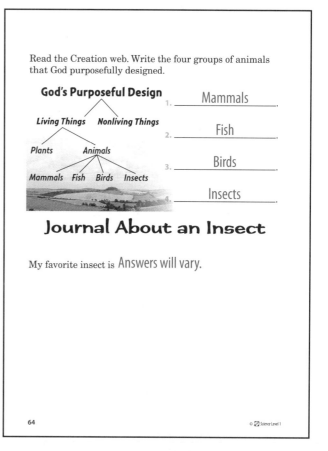

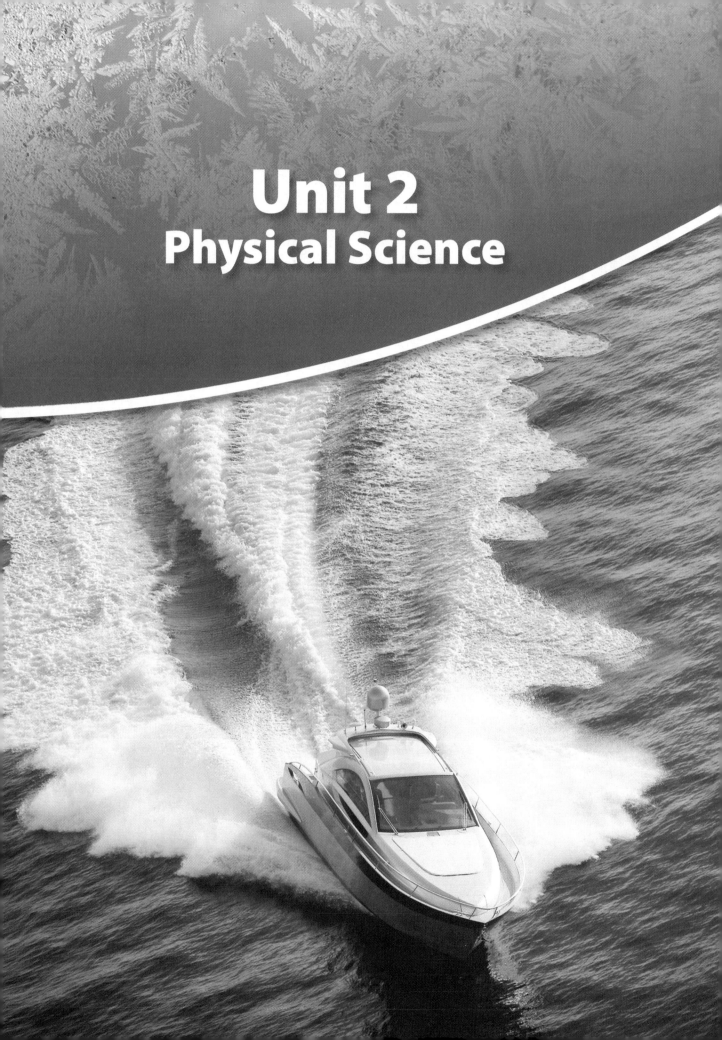

Unit 2
Physical Science

Movement
Chapter 5

Key Ideas
- God designed some living things with the ability to move on their own.
- Nonliving things are moved by forces, vibration, and magnets.
- Movements differ in type and in speed, serving different purposes.

5.0 Chapter Preparation

Introduction

Movement is a topic of study that offers students an opportunity to reinforce skills of observation and classification. By moving in different ways—straight, zigzag, back and forth, and round and round—students will learn to identify movements. They will understand how movement connects with the science of sound and human hearing. Students will be able to experience and study viscosity of several liquids that move at different speeds. They will discover properties of magnets and the attraction or repulsion of magnetic and nonmagnetic materials. Studying movement also assists in analyzing other aspects of the created world.

About This Chapter

Lesson 5.1 – What Movement Is
Materials
• No additional materials are needed.
Lesson Content
Movement is a change in place or position. Movement occurs everywhere. Some living things, such as animals and people, are able to move on their own.

Lesson 5.2 – Ways Things Move
Materials
• Eraser   • Scissors
• Tape   • Hole punch
• Colored paper   • Push pins
Lesson Content
God designed some things to move on their own; other things move in response to a push or a pull. Some simple movements include straight, zigzag, back and forth, and round and round.

Lesson 5.3 – Movement and Sound
Materials
• Jelly beans   • Paper clips   • Container
• Rice   • Canisters   • Water
• Seeds   • Tuning fork
Lesson Content
Movement is essential to hearing. Vibration produces sound waves, which enter the ear and vibrate the eardrum. Nerves send a message to the brain, which identifies the sound. Items that vibrate to produce sound include a tuning fork, a doorstop, a triangle, and a guitar.

Lesson 5.4 – Observing Movement
Materials
• Syrup   • Lids   • Cylinders   • Jar
• Molasses • Index cards   • Funnels
• Oil   • Paper towels • Timer
Lesson Content
Some substances are thicker than others. Molasses moves very slowly compared to water; it is thicker than water. The design of certain substances such as syrup, molasses, and oil lets them be used for different purposes.

Lesson 5.5 – Magnets

Materials
- Cups
- Water
- Magnets
- Paper clips
- Corks
- Compasses
- Plastic bags
- Coins
- Nails
- Rubber bands
- Foil
- Washers
- Wood
- Spoons

Lesson Content
Magnets move objects by using magnetic force. The north and south poles of a magnet attract or repel objects made of different materials.

Lesson 5.6 – Chapter 5 Review

Materials
- Magnet
- Scissors
- Glue

Teacher Resources

The Handy Physics Answer Book by Paul W. Zitzewitz. Visible Ink Press, 2011.
Science Lessons for the SMART Board: Grades 1–3 by Sarah Carpenter, Karen Mawer, and Jon Audain. Scholastic Teaching Resources, 2011.

Student Resources

Force and Motion by Clint Twist. Bearport, 2006.
Fun with Magnets. Game by Lauri.
Gravity Is a Mystery by Franklyn M. Branley. HarperCollins, 2007.

Supplemental Materials

Blackline Masters

5.2A Pinwheel
5.5A Magnets
5.6A Movement Facts
5.6B Chapter 5 Test

Content

Most first graders are familiar with the concept of movement since they experience movement all around them. At this age students can be encouraged to recognize different kinds of movement, such as straight, zigzag, back and forth, and round and round. They can determine how the movement is accomplished—by a push, a pull, or another force. In this lesson, students will identify movement and describe how different movements serve a purpose.

Introduction

Introduce this lesson by having individual students pantomime movements, and after an adequate amount of time, encourage the remaining students to guess what their classmate is imitating. Have the students do movements from one or more of the following activities:
- Playing basketball, sewing, playing hopscotch, playing softball, jumping rope, drawing pictures, fishing, painting, singing, playing the piano
- Swimming like a fish, walking like a giraffe, swinging like a monkey, nibbling like a mouse

Point out that movement is mentioned in the first chapter of the Bible. Read **Genesis 1:21a**. State that movement is seen in Creation.

Directed Instruction

1 Inform the class that they have just made movements. Read the definition of **movement**: *a change of position or place*. Ask volunteers to name movements they see in the classroom. (**Possible answers: teacher walking, something moving because of circulating air, students moving in their seat**) Mention that some living things—people and animals—have the ability to move on their own; while nonliving things need to be pushed by a force, such as wind. (This concept will be expanded upon in Lesson 5.2.)

2 Direct the class' attention to the first student page. Read the first two sentences about movement. Then have a student name and describe the kind of movement the horses are exhibiting in the picture. (**They are running from one place to another.**) Reiterate that God designed horses to be able to run.

Read the directions for the activity on this page. Complete the first one as an example. Ask what kind of movement the child is making in the first picture. (**a kick**) Allow time for students to study each of the remaining pictures and to select the appropriate word from the Word Bank.

3 Check for understanding of the concept of movement. Invite a student volunteer to choose a simple movement, such as raising a hand, standing up, clapping, or waving. Allow the class a minute to practice that simple movement. Inform them that you are going to say several phrases. If the phrase includes movement, students should act out the movement that the child, animal, or object in the phrase demonstrated. If it does not include movement, they are to stay very still. Read the following phrases:
a boy jumping (**move**), a girl running (**move**), a tiger chasing (**move**), a rock on the ground (**stay still**), a rock rolling down a hill (**move**), a feather floating across a room (**move**), someone lifting a cup from a table (**move**), a cup on a table (**stay still**), an ant carrying food (**move**), a leaf falling from a tree (**move**), a teacher picking up a pencil (**move**).

Mention that God designed human bodies to be able to move in important ways. Direct students to hold their head perfectly still as they move just their eyes back and forth by following their finger moving in front of them. Have students put their hand over their heart to feel the movement of the heart as it pumps. Point out to students that even though they do not see the movement, they know that it is happening.

4 Reiterate that observation is an important part of science and that to observe is to study or watch carefully. Direct students' attention to the second page. Explain that students need to look carefully at the picture at the top of the page and to observe how the children and teacher are moving. Direct the class to list the movements they observe.

5 Complete the exercise at the bottom of the page together. Have students circle the word that names a movement in each picture. Then ask volunteers to name the movement and describe it. (**Possible answers:** *run*: **I would move straight, and the wind would be cool on my face;** *jump*: **I would move up and down; I would stretch and reach, and my feet would come up off the ground.**)

6 To conclude, have students work in pairs to describe their favorite activity and any movements associated with that activity. (**Possible answers:** *play the piano*: **I would move my fingers, feet, and eyes;** *eat a slice of pizza*: **I would lift the slice to my mouth, bite, chew, and swallow.**) If time permits, have the pairs pantomime several activities for their partner and allow the partner to guess the activity.

➕ **Extension**

Materials
• Clipboard, stopwatch

Create a chart with several types of movements, such as running, walking, galloping, crab-walking, and hopping. Add several blank boxes next to each movement to record the fastest times. Attach the chart to a clipboard. Escort students to a large outdoor space or a gymnasium. Designate a start and a finish line. Have students race each movement in several heats. Allow them to take turns recording the fastest time for each heat. Create a graph of the races when students return to the classroom. Discuss which movements were the fastest and which were the slowest.

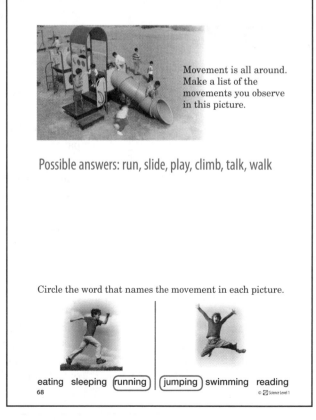

5.2 Ways Things Move

Students will distinguish differences in the ways things move.

Materials

Directed Instruction
• Board eraser
• Masking tape
• BLM 5.2A Pinwheel, colored paper, hole punch, scissors, push pins

Preparation

Obtain a BOARD ERASER for a demonstration. (*Directed Instruction*)

Make 2 LINES OF MASKING TAPE on the floor—one straight line and one line that zigzags. (*Directed Instruction*)

Print **BLM 5.2A Pinwheel** on COLORED PAPER. Obtain a HOLE PUNCH for you to use while assisting students. Have SCISSORS and a PUSH PIN available for each student. (*Directed Instruction*)

Safety

Advise caution as students work with push pins.

Content

Movement occurs at many levels—even in the atomic matter of the chair a person is sitting in or in Earth's gravitational pull, the force that keeps objects from floating into the atmosphere. In this lesson, much more obvious kinds of movement will be addressed, such as straight, zigzag, back and forth, and round and round. God designed animals and some other organisms to have the ability of locomotion—the power to move from place to place. Plants move in response to light (phototropism), but do not have the ability of locomotion.

Introduction

Play a game of Follow the Leader with the class. Lead students to do several types of straight, zigzag, back and forth, and round and round movements. Examples include bringing hands to shoulders, bending at the elbow; placing hands at their sides, moving them upward to above their head in a zigzag motion; tapping a foot slowly; tapping a foot quickly; making circles with their arms. Instruct students to take one step forward and one step back. Then have them squat and rise up slowly until they are standing. Finally, direct them to reverse the movement until they are squatting again.

Directed Instruction

1 Ask what kinds of movements students observed in the game. (**Answers will vary but should include several movements from the game.**) Reinforce the kinds of movements—straight, zigzag, back and forth, round and round.

Share with the class that things can go straight up, straight down, and straight across. Gently slide a BOARD ERASER in a straight line somewhere in the classroom. Ask how the eraser moved. (**straight across**) How does an eraser move when it falls off a desk? (**straight down**)

Discuss other ways that things move—zigzag, back and forth, and round and round. Ask students how a car travels on a curvy road. (**zigzag**) How do most doors move? (**back and forth or swing outward and inward**) In what direction does a merry-go-round move? (**round and round**)

2 Direct students' attention to the picture of the rocket on the first student page. Ask in what direction it goes. (**straight up**) Have students draw a straight arrow in the box provided to imitate the movement of the rocket. Guide students to draw the movements of a car on a curvy road—zigzag; the swing—back and forth; the train—round and round.

3 To foster better understanding of these movements, allow students to walk along the lines of MASKING TAPE on the floor. Permit a student to demonstrate back and forth movement by walking forward and backward on the straight line. Invite others to participate. Then have students hold hands and walk round and round in a circle.

4 Direct students to turn to the next page. Explain that a force is a push or a pull that can move things. Read the sentences and discuss the pictures. Share how nonliving things cannot move on their own—they must be pushed or pulled by a force. People, the wind, and gravity can force things to move.

Engage students in pretending to push a swing. Next, ask them how difficult it is to push a swing with their friend on it. (**It is harder to push.**) Explain that they must force the swing to move by pushing it. Ask how they can move a wagon. (**pull or push it**) State that they must force the wagon to move by pushing or pulling it. Push and pull are forces that people can do to an object to make it move. Brainstorm ways in which students push or pull things; write the suggestions in two columns on the board. Some answers may go in both columns. (**Possible answers:** *push*: **computer keys, piano keys;** *pull*: **a garbage bag out of a garbage can, shoestrings to tighten a bow, a tug-of-war game;** *both push and pull*: **a car door, a person in a wheelchair**)

5 Discuss that plants cannot get up and move from place to place, but they move in response to light. Point out that the wind moves things such as parts of plants, people's hair, and flags. Gravity moves objects to the ground when they are not supported by something. Share the following verses that tell how God is the one who causes the wind to blow: **Job 28:25a**, **Amos 4:13a**.

6 Guide students through the directions and exercise at the bottom of the page. Direct student pairs to tell each other things they saw move today and what caused that movement.

7 Distribute **BLM 5.2A Pinwheel**, scissors, and push pins for students to make a pinwheel. Allow students to take their pinwheel home to share with an adult.

➕ Extension

Materials
• Audio recordings of different types of music
• Items for an obstacle course

Play a game of Music Freeze. Play music as students move slowly around the room. Direct the class to freeze when the music stops.

Have students in groups create an obstacle course in an open area. Instruct groups to make sure their course involves the following movements: straight, zigzag, and round and round. Provide supplies such as cones, toy hoops, jump ropes, and flags. Have one student demonstrate the course for the class. Allow students to try each course and to notice the different types of movements in each.

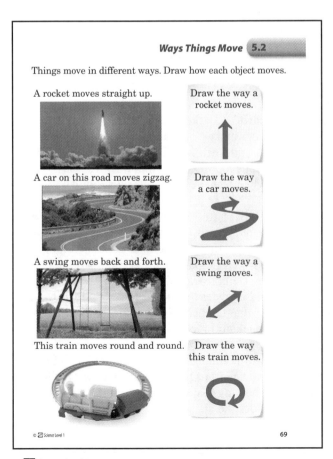

5.3 Movement and Sound

Objective

Students will apply knowledge of movement to vibration and sound waves.

Materials

Introduction
• Jelly beans, rice, seeds, paper clips, opaque canisters

Directed Instruction
• Tuning fork, clear container, water

✋ Preparation

Place small items such as JELLY BEANS, RICE, SEEDS, and PAPER CLIPS inside 4 EMPTY OPAQUE CANISTERS, one type of item inside each canister. Number each canister 1–4. (*Introduction*)

Write the definition of *vibrate* on the board. (*Directed Instruction*)

Obtain a TUNING FORK and a CLEAR CONTAINER of WATER for a demonstration. Select a tuning fork from the ACSI Science Equipment Kit, or borrow one from a local high school or college. You may also purchase one online or from a science supply catalog. (*Directed Instruction*)

↻ Alternatives

If a tuning fork is not available, pluck the string of a musical instrument. Plucking a taut rubber band or a string will also make a sound.

Content

Movement is essential to hearing. In order to hear the sounds of an orchestra or a clap of thunder, movement is the first part of the process. A series of events happening extremely quickly involve a sound source, air, and God's design of the ear and brain. A sound source moves or vibrates, causing the molecules of air surrounding the object to move. This movement starts a sound wave that travels through the air. This is a compression wave, moving more like a line of dominoes than like an ocean wave. This sound wave reaches a person's ear canal and vibrates the eardrum. The next steps involve a series of movements of different parts of the ear, including the middle and inner ear. Eventually, the movements of tiny hair cells send electrical impulses along the auditory nerve that is connected to the brain. The job of the brain in hearing is to interpret the sound.

When a tuning fork is struck on a surface such as a table top, it vibrates. This movement causes the air around it to move and the resulting sound waves to move away from the tuning fork. The sound waves continue, reaching the ear. A way to prove that the tuning fork is vibrating is to dip the tip of it into a container of water; the vibration causes the water to splash. The water moves, as does the air. The sound that paper makes as it rustles is another example of how vibration causes sound.

Introduction ✋

Display the 4 CANISTERS with small items inside. Have students pass around each canister, shake it, and listen to the sounds made by the contents. Direct volunteers to describe the sound they hear and to guess the contents. Have students write down their guesses. Reveal the contents of the canisters.

Directed Instruction ✋ ➕ ↻

1 Hold up a sheet of paper. Hold it still and instruct students to listen carefully. Ask them what sound you are making with the sheet of paper. (**No sound is heard.**) Move the paper very slowly and ask the question again. (**A soft sound is heard.**) Move the paper yet again, this time more quickly. (**A louder sound is heard.**) Ask the class what had to be done in order to hear the sound the paper makes. (**It had to be moved.**) Share that when you move the paper back and forth, you are making it vibrate. Read from the board that **vibrate** means *to move back and forth very fast*. Ask students what might happen when something vibrates. (**a sound**)

Display a TUNING FORK. Explain that a tuning fork is designed to make a certain sound; it is helpful in tuning a musical instrument, even though many musicians today use electronic tuners. Scientists can use tuning forks to experiment with sound waves. Share that when tapped on a hard object, the tuning fork vibrates. Demonstrate this for the class. Tap a tine of the tuning fork on a desk and allow each student to see that the tuning fork is vibrating. Ask students what happens to the tuning fork when it is tapped. (**It vibrates; it moves back and forth; it makes a sound.**)

Share another way to show that the tuning fork is vibrating. Tap a tine of the tuning fork to make it vibrate and put the tine in a CONTAINER of WATER. The water will briefly splash, showing that the vibrating tuning fork moves the water around it, just as it does the air.

2 Have students turn to the first student page. Read the first sentence. Explain that vibration is sometimes visible, as with the guitar strings or the doorstop. Have students fill in the blanks from the Word Bank. Direct students' attention to each picture and ask what sound is made when each of these things is vibrating. (**Answers will vary.**) What makes each of these things begin to vibrate? (*guitar string*: **a person plucking the string;** *doorstop*: **a door bumping into it;** *triangle*: **a person tapping it;** *tuning fork*: **a person striking it against a table**) What happens when they vibrate? (**They move and make sound.**) What can make each of these things stop vibrating? (**holding them to make them stop moving**) What happens when they stop vibrating? (**The sound stops.**) Strike the tuning fork and mention the vibration and the sound. Then hold the tine of the tuning fork with your hand and the sound and vibration will stop immediately.

3 Direct the class' attention to the second page. Read the question at the top of the page and instruct students that an object's vibration sends a sound wave which touches a person's ear. Share that sound waves cannot be seen.

4 Explain to the class that God designed an amazing way for people to hear. Direct students to place a finger on each picture as you read the explanation. Stress how important it is that they not put objects into their ears!

5 Complete the page with the class. Allow time for students to share with a partner the meaning of the word *vibrate* and their favorite music.

⊕ Extension

Materials
• Items to create instruments, such as tissue boxes, rubber bands, toilet-paper tubes, waxed paper, rubber bands, beans, rice, bottles, paper plates, spoons, forks, oatmeal boxes, sticks

Research the Internet for ideas on making different types of musical instruments. Have students work with a parent at home to create their own instrument. Have groups of students practice a song and perform for the class. Examples of homemade instruments include a guitar (tissue box and rubber bands); kazoo (toilet paper roll, waxed paper, rubber bands); percussion instruments (beans or rice inside bottles or paper plates); chimes (spoons and forks on strings); and drums (cylinder oatmeal boxes and sticks).

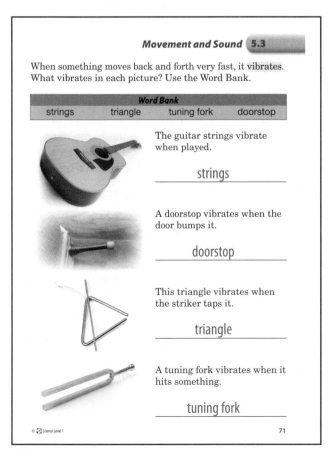

Movement and Sound **5.3**

When something moves back and forth very fast, it **vibrates.** What vibrates in each picture? Use the Word Bank.

Word Bank			
strings	triangle	tuning fork	doorstop

The guitar strings vibrate when played.

__strings__

A doorstop vibrates when the door bumps it.

__doorstop__

This triangle vibrates when the striker taps it.

__triangle__

A tuning fork vibrates when it hits something.

__tuning fork__

© Science Level 1   71

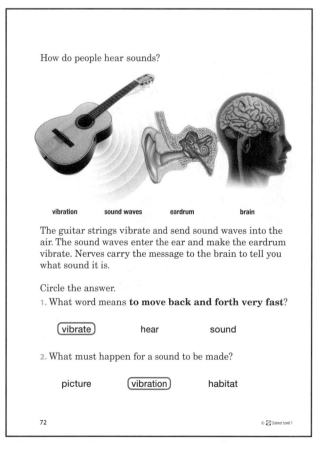

How do people hear sounds?

vibration   sound waves   eardrum   brain

The guitar strings vibrate and send sound waves into the air. The sound waves enter the ear and make the eardrum vibrate. Nerves carry the message to the brain to tell you what sound it is.

Circle the answer.
1. What word means **to move back and forth very fast**?

(vibrate)   hear   sound

2. What must happen for a sound to be made?

picture   (vibration)   habitat

72   © Science Level 1

5.4 Observing Movement

Content

Some substances are thicker than others. A term used to describe this quality in liquids and gases is *viscosity*.

One can compare the viscosity of different liquid substances, such as molasses and water. Molasses moves very slowly compared to water; it is thicker and has a higher viscosity than water. This may bring to mind the phrase *slower than molasses in January*, which emphasizes that temperature affects the viscosity of substances.

Introduction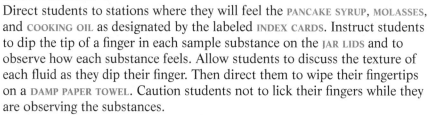

Direct students to stations where they will feel the PANCAKE SYRUP, MOLASSES, and COOKING OIL as designated by the labeled INDEX CARDS. Instruct students to dip the tip of a finger in each sample substance on the JAR LIDS and to observe how each substance feels. Allow students to discuss the texture of each fluid as they dip their finger. Then direct them to wipe their fingertips on a DAMP PAPER TOWEL. Caution students not to lick their fingers while they are observing the substances.

Directed Instruction

1 Direct students to turn to their student pages. Convey that they will be answering the question, how does each feel? Ask volunteers to provide some words to describe each substance and assist students with spelling if necessary. (**Possible answers: greasy, watery, oily, gooey, sticky, tacky, slippery, glue-like, gummy**)

2 Convey that in today's experiment students will study how these three substances move when poured. Proceed through each step. Use the *Scientific Inquiry* section at the beginning of this book as a reference for conducting an experiment.
1. Ask a question: Read the question that students will try to answer through the experiment.
2. Make a hypothesis: Ask students which substances they think will move fastest and slowest. Have them write their guesses.
3. Plan and do a test: Explain that the class will plan and do an experiment. It is a way to test their hypothesis. Use the FUNNELS and carefully pour each substance from the *Introduction* activity, one at a time, into a GRADUATED CYLINDER. Use a TIMER to time how long it takes to fill each cylinder. Watch the levels rise.
4. Record and analyze your results: Have students record the actual time each substance took to fill the cylinder. Discuss how each substance looked as it came through the funnel.
5. Make a conclusion: Have students compare the results with their hypothesis. Reassure students that scientific inquiry is not about being right or wrong; it is about discovering something they did not know before or confirming something they do know. Guide students to understand that the molasses is the thickest and moves the slowest. The syrup moves faster than the molasses because it is not as thick as the molasses. The oil is thinnest and moves the fastest.
6. Share your results: Have students share with a classmate about the phrase *slow as molasses*.

If time permits, draw a chart on the board to show the data and conclusions. When the experiment concludes, pour the syrup, molasses, and oil into a CLEAR JAR and observe throughout the day what happens—it separates into layers. Ask which layer is on the bottom. (**molasses**) Which layer is in the middle? (**syrup**) Which layer is on top? (**oil**) Why did the substances layer in this way? (**The heaviest is on the bottom.**)

3 Elaborate on the idea that the design of certain substances like syrup, molasses, and oil allows them be used for different purposes.

4 Group students into pairs to discuss the results of the experiment. They should discuss their work on their pages, including the data collected.

Notes:

Observing Movement 5.4

EXPERIMENT

Materials	Skills
syrup, molasses, oil	predict
3 labeled cylinders	observe
3 funnels	
timer	

How does each feel?   Answers will vary.

syrup _____

molasses _____

oil _____

1. **Ask a question.**   Which substance will move the fastest to fill the cylinder?

2. **Make a hypothesis.**   I think _____ will move the fastest to fill the cylinder.

   I think _____ will move the slowest to fill the cylinder.

3. **Plan and do a test.**   Use a clear funnel to pour each substance into a cylinder. Start the timer when each substance reaches the bottom of the cylinder. Watch it rise. Stop the timer when each substance fills the cylinder.

© Science Level 1   73

---

4. **Record and analyze your results.**

substance	time
syrup	Times will vary.
molasses	Times will vary.
oil	Times will vary.

5. **Make a conclusion.**

   ____Oil____ moved the fastest to fill up the cylinder.

   ____Molasses____ moved the slowest to fill up the cylinder.

   Was your hypothesis right?

   Answers will vary.

6. **Share your results.**   Share with a classmate what **slow as molasses** means.

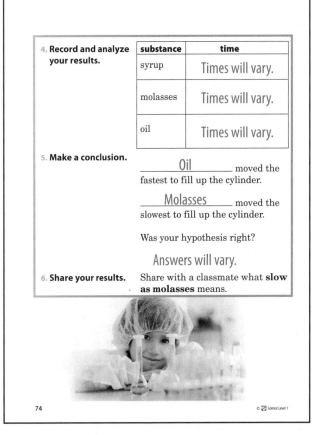

74   © Science Level 1

5.5 Magnets

Objective

Students will examine properties of magnets and how magnets generate movement.

Materials

Introduction
• Cups, water, magnets, paper clips, small corks, compasses

Directed Instruction
• Magnets, BLM 5.5A Magnets, plastic bags, coins, nails, rubber bands, foil, washers, wood, spoons, paper clips

 Preparation

Obtain 4 CUPS of WATER, 4 MAGNETS, 4 PAPER CLIPS, 4 SMALL CORKS, and 4 COMPASSES. Select the magnets, corks, and compasses from the ACSI Science Equipment Kit, or borrow them from a local college or high school. Straighten one end of each paper clip and stick it all the way through the center of a cork.

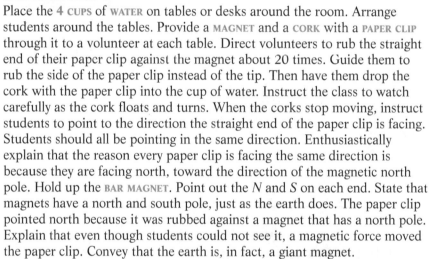

Obtain a BAR MAGNET for a demonstration. Make sure the magnet's poles are labeled *N* and *S*. (*Introduction*)

Divide the class into small groups. For each group, collect 2 MAGNETS, a PLASTIC BAG containing a COIN, a NAIL, a RUBBER BAND, ALUMINUM FOIL, a WASHER, a piece of WOOD, a PLASTIC SPOON, a METAL SPOON, and a PAPER CLIP. Magnets and washers can be found in the ACSI Science Equipment Kit. Print **BLM 5.5A Magnets** for each student. (*Directed Instruction*)

Content

Magnetism is a natural force that God created. The earth itself is a magnet! Over time, people have learned more about magnetism and have used its force in many inventions, such as refrigerators, computers, security devices, audio speakers, and magnetic resonance imagers (MRIs).

Every magnet has a north and south pole. The north pole of a magnet is attracted to the south pole of another magnet. Unlike poles attract; like poles repel each other. Magnets are strongest at their magnetic poles, where the magnetic field is most concentrated. A magnetic field is the space surrounding the magnet in which the magnet's force is active. Magnetic fields differ depending upon the magnet's size and shape. Not all metals are attracted to magnets.

Introduction

Place the 4 CUPS of WATER on tables or desks around the room. Arrange students around the tables. Provide a MAGNET and a CORK with a PAPER CLIP through it to a volunteer at each table. Direct volunteers to rub the straight end of their paper clip against the magnet about 20 times. Guide them to rub the side of the paper clip instead of the tip. Then have them drop the cork with the paper clip into the cup of water. Instruct the class to watch carefully as the cork floats and turns. When the corks stop moving, instruct students to point to the direction the straight end of the paper clip is facing. Students should all be pointing in the same direction. Enthusiastically explain that the reason every paper clip is facing the same direction is because they are facing north, toward the direction of the magnetic north pole. Hold up the BAR MAGNET. Point out the *N* and *S* on each end. State that magnets have a north and south pole, just as the earth does. The paper clip pointed north because it was rubbed against a magnet that has a north pole. Explain that even though students could not see it, a magnetic force moved the paper clip. Convey that the earth is, in fact, a giant magnet.

Distribute 4 COMPASSES for students to double check the direction of their paper clip. Advise students to keep the compass away from the magnet, as the magnet may interfere with the compass' direction. Point out that the *N* on the compass stands for *north*. Explain that a compass has a magnet inside that always faces the earth's magnetic north. Ask students when a person would need to use a compass. (**Possible answers: when hiking, when following a map**) Challenge students to think about what the *S* on the compass might stand for. (**south**) State that today students will learn other objects that are pulled by a magnet's force.

Directed Instruction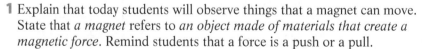

1 Explain that today students will observe things that a magnet can move. State that *a magnet* refers to *an object made of materials that create a magnetic force*. Remind students that a force is a push or a pull.

2 Announce that students will observe how objects respond to magnets. Divide the class into small groups, and distribute MAGNETS and **BLM 5.5A Magnets**. Direct students' attention to BLM 5.5A and read the directions. Distribute the PLASTIC BAGS OF ITEMS and give students time to predict and test each item to see if the magnet's force pulls it. If students are using bar magnets, demonstrate how to test the items by using the polar ends of the magnet. Instruct students to record their answers. When they complete

their testing, encourage them to find one more item in the classroom that is magnetic and one more that is not. Have them test both items. Discuss students' findings.

3 Collect the bags of items, and lead students in a discussion about magnets. Ask students to consider why some items were pulled to the magnets and some were not. (**Answers will vary.**) Inquire if the color or shape of the item was a factor. (**No.**) Point out that the washer and the foil are the same color; however, the washer was pulled by the magnet but the foil was not. Explain that the force depends on the type of material that makes up each item. Objects that are metal and made of iron are pulled to a magnet, but many other materials are not.

State that magnets not only pull as a force, but they also push. Redirect small groups to their two magnets and have them observe what happens when they try to connect the ends. Point out that they should pay close attention to which two poles they are trying to connect. Record student observations on the board. The class should come to the conclusion that opposite poles will pull toward each other, but poles that are the same will push each other away.

4 Direct students' attention to the first student first page. Have them write *N* and *S* on the magnet. Discuss which items should be circled. On the second page, give students time to draw the arrow on the compass. Read the sentences to students. Discuss the question at the bottom of the page. Have students share with a partner a way they have used a magnet at school or at home.

➕ Extension

Materials
• Magnets, magnetic objects
• Tub, water, magnetic and nonmagnetic objects, fishing pole, magnet

In a learning center, provide several types of magnets and items that are attracted to magnets. Allow students to explore magnetism and to draw conclusions based on their observation.

Fill a tub with water and add magnetic and nonmagnetic objects, like paper clips, nuts, bolts, and plastic toys. Tie a magnet to a fishing pole or a stick and thread. Direct students, one at a time, to call out something they think is magnetic and then to go fishing for that item.

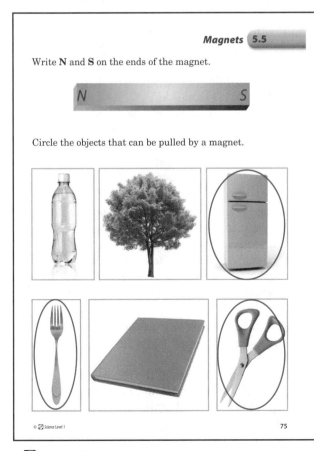

Magnets **5.5**

Write **N** and **S** on the ends of the magnet.

N   *S*

Circle the objects that can be pulled by a magnet.

Draw an arrow on the compass to point north.

How are magnets used every day?

Magnets hold your paper on the refrigerator. Magnets also help keep the refrigerator door closed.

An MRI is a magnetic machine that takes pictures of the inside of a person. Doctors use MRIs to help patients get better.

Maglev trains glide over magnets on the track. This train can travel at 268 miles per hour.

Some computers, phones, and televisions use magnets.

What are some ways people use magnets?
in a compass, on the refrigerator, in machines, and in trains

Materials

Directed Instruction
• Magnet
• BLM 5.6A Movement Facts, scissors, glue
• BLM 5.6B Chapter 5 Test

Preparation

Have a MAGNET available. (*Directed Instruction*)

Print **BLM 5.6A Movement Facts** for each student. Obtain SCISSORS and GLUE. (*Directed Instruction*)

Print **BLM 5.6B Chapter 5 Test** for each student. (*Directed Instruction*)

Introduction

Play the game Good Morning, Mr. Judge. One student acts as the judge and sits in a chair with his or her back facing the class. Other students take turns approaching the judge and saying, "Good morning, Mr. Judge." Without looking, the judge must listen carefully to distinguish which classmate is speaking. If the judge guesses correctly, the classmate must return to his or her own seat. If the judge cannot identify the classmate within three guesses, the classmate becomes the new judge. Play until all students have had a chance to approach the judge. For an added challenge, allow students to try to disguise their voice when speaking to the judge.

Directed Instruction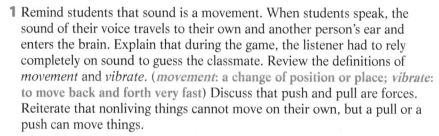

1 Remind students that sound is a movement. When students speak, the sound of their voice travels to their own and another person's ear and enters the brain. Explain that during the game, the listener had to rely completely on sound to guess the classmate. Review the definitions of *movement* and *vibrate*. (*movement*: **a change of position or place;** *vibrate*: **to move back and forth very fast**) Discuss that push and pull are forces. Reiterate that nonliving things cannot move on their own, but a pull or a push can move things.

Review that a magnet is an object made of materials that create a magnetic force. A magnet's force can pull items made of certain metals, including iron. Have students identify items in the classroom that are pulled to a magnet. Have volunteers test a MAGNET on each item mentioned.

2 Distribute **BLM 5.6A Movement Facts**, SCISSORS, and GLUE. Have a volunteer read a fact. Select another volunteer to explain the fact in his or her own words. Do this with all the facts. Instruct students to cut out the pictures on this page and to arrange them on a blank sheet of paper according to how fast they think the animals move. Share the correct placement and the miles per hour (mph) of each animal. Have students glue the pictures horizontally in the correct order:
1. Giant tortoise—less than 1 mph (a slow walking pace)
2. Domestic pig—11 mph (about as fast as a long-distance runner)
3. Domestic rabbit—35 mph (as fast as a car driving through town)
4. Cheetah—70 mph (as fast as a car on a highway)
5. Peregrine falcon—200 mph (faster than a race car)

3 Use student pages as a review or pretest. Complete these pages with the class. Assist with numbering the pictures in order and brainstorming words to include in the journal. List these words on the board. You may use **BLM 5.6B Chapter 5 Test** for individual assessment. Read through this page with the class. Provide as much reading support as necessary. You may choose to use this blackline as an oral assessment or to not do it at all.

4 Read the following scenarios and questions as a review. Read a second time and have students act them out. If desired, substitute student names for the names mentioned in the scenarios.
• Isabella loves to play with her cousin Mason at the playground. Today, Mason climbed up the slide and slid down. He went down the slide five times in a row. In what type of movement did Mason move on the slide? **(Possible answers: straight, curvy)**

- Nina and Sierra looked out the windows of the car as Dad drove carefully up the mountain road. The girls noticed how Dad had to drive slowly and turn the steering wheel to the left and right a lot to make the car turn on the zigzag road that led to the top. As the car turned one way on the road, Nina leaned on Sierra; as the car turned the other way, Sierra leaned on Nina. When they got to the top, Mom pointed down at the road they just drove up. It looked very curvy, or zigzag, as it came up the mountainside. What movement did the girls notice? (**the zigzag movement of the car, the girls leaning on each other**) What did the road look like from the top of the mountain? (**curvy, or zigzag**)
- William and Davion enjoyed Mrs. Robbins' violin class. They learned how to hold their instrument between their shoulder and chin. At home, the children practiced putting their fingers on the strings to make the right note. When it was time for the Christmas concert, the school's orchestra performed. Teachers and students heard the music as the children moved their bows back and forth across the strings, causing the strings to vibrate. What movements did the children make with their violins? (**back and forth movements of their fingers on the strings, back and forth movements of the bow**)
- Omar and Li's family went to the park together. The children rode the merry-go-round two times. Each time the merry-go-round went past their family, their mom and dad smiled and their grandparents waved. Omar and Li had the best day ever! How did the children move on the merry-go-round? (**round and round**)

5 Chapter 5 Movement has been completed. Staple its pages together and send it home as a booklet to share with a family member.

Extension

Materials
- Cup, rubber band, plastic wrap, colored sugar crystals

Stretch plastic wrap over the top of a cup and secure it tightly with a rubber band. Sprinkle sugar crystals on top. Have a student get close to the cup and talk loudly. The vibration from the student's voice will make the crystals bounce on the plastic. Reiterate that vibration causes movement of sound waves, which vibrate the plastic wrap and cause the crystals to move.

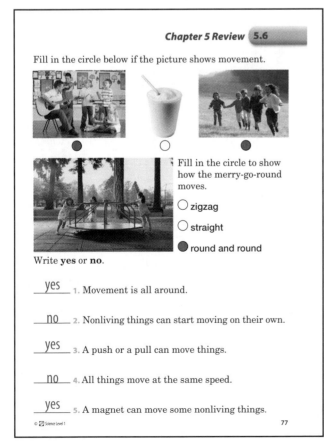

Chapter 5 Review 5.6

Fill in the circle below if the picture shows movement.

● ○ ●

Fill in the circle to show how the merry-go-round moves.

○ zigzag
○ straight
● round and round

Write **yes** or **no**.

___yes___ 1. Movement is all around.

___no___ 2. Nonliving things can start moving on their own.

___yes___ 3. A push or a pull can move things.

___no___ 4. All things move at the same speed.

___yes___ 5. A magnet can move some nonliving things.

© Science Level 1   77

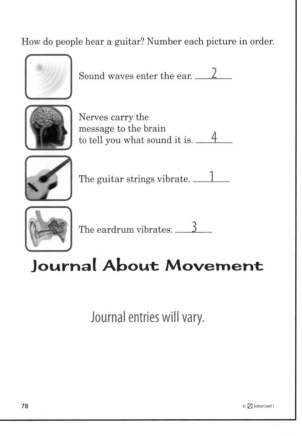

How do people hear a guitar? Number each picture in order.

Sound waves enter the ear. ___2___

Nerves carry the message to the brain to tell you what sound it is. ___4___

The guitar strings vibrate. ___1___

The eardrum vibrates. ___3___

Journal About Movement

Journal entries will vary.

78   © Science Level 1

Machines

Key Ideas

- Work is an activity involving force and movement.
- Machines help people do tasks more easily by performing work.
- Wheels and axles as well as inclined planes make moving things easier to do.
- Levers and pulleys help lift things.

6.0 Chapter Preparation

Vocabulary

force
work
energy

Looking Ahead

- You will consistently use the following items throughout the chapter: a cart, a large box, a small box, and a long board. Plan to fill a box with treats for **Lesson 6.1** that you will distribute to students in **Lesson 6.7**.
- For **Lesson 6.5**, you will need to create a pulley system, using the materials listed in the *Preparation* sidebar.

Introduction

Students are about to embark upon an exciting mystery-box adventure. This practical activity will assist students in becoming aware of how machines can help people. Starting with the wheel and axle, the chapter progresses to the inclined plane, the lever, and the pulley. Hands-on experiences afford students the opportunity to make machines. It is important for students to know that people and machines can push and pull objects, and that not all machines have an engine or a motor. They will also learn that, in science, movement must be made in order for work to be done. Students will understand that through God's provision of creativity and intelligence, people are able to design machines that make tasks easier to do.

About This Chapter

Lesson 6.1 – How Machines Help

Materials

- Cart
- Boxes
- Treats
- Tape

Lesson Content

A force is a push or a pull. Work is an activity involving force and movement. Work requires energy. Machines make work easier to do by applying force or effort, resulting in movement.

Lesson 6.2 – Wheel and Axle

Materials

- Cart
- Mystery box
- Crayons
- Scissors
- Tape
- Straws
- Candy

Lesson Content

A wheel and axle is a simple machine that operates by the wheel rotating on the axle. This machine helps move things easily. Wheels and axles can be found on bicycles and most vehicles and in doorknobs and some handles.

Lesson 6.3 – Inclined Plane

Materials

- Mystery box
- Cart
- Board
- Sciencemobiles
- Cardboard
- Tape

Lesson Content

An inclined plane is a simple machine. It is a slanted surface connecting a lower level to a higher level. The inclined plane makes moving things up easier. A ramp is an example of an inclined plane.

Lesson 6.4 – Lever

Materials

- Mystery box
- Cart
- Pry bar
- Rulers
- Tape
- Cups
- Rocks
- Coins

Lesson Content

A lever is a simple machine made from a stiff bar that pivots on a support or fulcrum. A lever helps lift, lower, or move things. Levers, such as light switches, hammers, and soda pop tabs, are used every day to make tasks easier to do because of the work the levers perform.

Lesson 6.5 – Pulley

Materials
- Mystery box
- Cart
- Board
- Rope
- Tape
- PVC pipe
- Broomstick
- Goggles
- Pulley materials
- Crayons

Lesson Content

A pulley is a simple machine that is the combination of a grooved wheel used with a rope or cable around it. A pulley is used to lift, lower, or move things. Two examples of a pulley in use are a flag being moved up a flagpole or a bucket being lowered to the ground.

Lesson 6.6 – Tech Connect

Materials
- Boxes
- Balls
- Assorted items

Lesson Content

Robots are machines that help people in many ways. They can explore space, assist in prosthetic limbs, and enable people to complete difficult or repetitive tasks. Even first-grade students can participate in designing and testing robots.

Lesson 6.7 – Chapter 6 Review

Materials
- Mystery box
- Lever
- Tubs
- Assorted materials

Teacher Resources

Exploring the World of Physics: From Simple Machines to Nuclear Energy by John Hudson Tiner. Master Books, 2006.

The LEGO Technic Idea Book: Simple Machines by Yoshihito Isogawa. William Pollock, 2011.

Student Resources

Cool Cars and Trucks by Sean Kenney. Henry Holt and Company, 2009.

I Use Simple Machines by Buffy Silverman. Rourke, 2011.

Simple Machines by Dana Meachen Rau. Scholastic Library, 2011.

Supplemental Materials

Blackline Masters	Transparency Masters	Computer Presentation
6.2A Sciencemobile	6.2A Wheel and Axle	6.2 Simple Machines Theme
6.7A Machine Facts	6.3A Inclined Plane	Park
6.7B Chapter 6 Test	6.4A Lever	
	6.5A Pulley	

6.1 How Machines Help

Machines

Objective

Students will identify how machines make tasks easier to accomplish because of the work the machines perform.

Materials

Introduction
• Cart, small box, treats, tape, large box

✋ Preparation

Obtain a CART. Prepare a mystery box by filling a SMALL BOX with TREATS (for example, fruit snacks, erasers, boxes of crayons, bookmarks, little notebooks) for the class. Use TAPE to lightly seal the box. You will open the small box in Lesson 6.7. Place the small box inside the LARGE BOX and lightly seal the large box. Place the mystery box on the cart. (*Introduction*)

Write the definitions of *force, work,* and *energy* on the board. (*Directed Instruction*)

⚠ Safety

After class, wheel the cart to the back of the room. Place the box on the floor.

Content

Machines help people do tasks more easily. In science, a task or a job is not necessarily the same thing as work. Scientifically, work is accomplished when a force causes something to move in the direction of the force. The effort or force comes from a source. For example, a person pushes a lawn mower, and a car tows a trailer. In these examples of work, the person and the car provide the force that causes the movement. Work requires energy. In the examples, the person's energy comes from food, and the car's energy comes from fuel. Using a machine, such as a lawn mower or a car, to do a task saves time and personal energy.

It is important to note that, scientifically, no work is done if there is no movement in the direction of the force. For example, if a person pushes on a wall and the wall does not move, no work is done. However, if the wall breaks, slides, or dents, movement has taken place and work has occurred.

As people have attempted to make tasks easier to do, they have invented many helpful machines. Simple machines are any of the basic mechanical devices for applying a force. Using wheels and axles attached to a box clearly helps move the box across the floor more easily than does merely dragging the box across the floor. The simple machines presented in this chapter include the wheel and axle, the inclined plane, the lever, and the pulley. They all help make tasks easier to do because of the work they perform.

Introduction ✋

Wheel in the CART that is carrying the TAPE-sealed, TREAT-filled MYSTERY BOX. State that the box will be important for this new chapter. Encourage students to wonder what may be inside the box.

Directed Instruction ✋ ➕ ⚠

1 Ask students how the cart helped you bring the box into the classroom. (**You did not have to carry the box.**) What are some other helpful things people have made that make moving something easier to do? (**Possible answers: scooters, bikes, grocery carts, cars, airplanes, helicopters**) Discuss that God gave people the ability to invent.

2 Direct students' attention to the first student page. Read the top half of the page and have volunteers tell how each machine helps people. (*crane:* **moves pieces of heavy construction;** *sewing machine:* **moves a needle and thread to make clothes;** *helicopter:* **lifts things into the air**)

3 Ask students what moving the box on the cart and picking up a pencil both have in common. (**movement**) Remind them that movement is a change of position or place. Have students stand and do a few jumping jacks. Refer to the definitions on the board. Help students remember that they also learned about force in Chapter 5. Review that **force** means *a push or a pull.* Ask students if their feet pushed or pulled when they did a jumping jack. (**pushed**) Read that **work** refers to *an activity involving force and movement.* Explain that students have done work to complete the jumping jacks. Their feet provided the force to move their body off the ground. State that they are able to do jumping jacks because they have energy. **Energy** means *the ability to do work.* Share that food gives a person the ability to push a cart; pushing the cart results in work. Gasoline

96

gives a car the ability to move forward, resulting in work. Read the rest of the page. Assist students as needed in filling in the blanks.

4 Direct students' attention to the next page. Explain that a task is easier to accomplish when an activity does not require as much force and energy. Mention that some machines help people use less force to complete a task. Instruct students to circle the correct grocery cart and to explain how it helps make moving items easier to do. (**The wheels help the cart move more easily.**) Comment that not all machines have engines or motors.

5 Have students fan themselves for 1 min with a sheet of paper. Ask students how their hand and arm feel. (**tired, sore**) How would you feel if you had to do this all day? (**tired, no energy left to play**) What invention can people use to do the same work as the hand fan? (**an electric fan**) How does an electric fan help people? (**It does not use their energy.**) Where does the energy come from to do the work? (**electricity**) Read through the second half of the page. Have students circle the correct answer. Ask how the electric fan makes the work of moving air easier to accomplish. (**The fan uses electricity instead of the girl's energy to move the blades; the fan creates more force than the hand.**)

6 To review, direct pairs of students to do some kind of task in the classroom: organize a desk, pick up paper, or straighten a bookshelf. Encourage each pair of students to use the terms *work*, *energy*, and *force* to describe what they are doing. Point out that if they push against a wall or floor and it does not move, no work has been done.

⊕ Extension

Materials
• Video camera
• Internet

Throughout this chapter, use a video camera to record students constructing and demonstrating their machines. Interview students about what type of machine they are building and how it works. Present the video to the class in Lesson 6.7.

Search the Internet for online, student-appropriate videos and games about simple machines. View the material as a class and then allow students time in groups or individually to further explore the video or game.

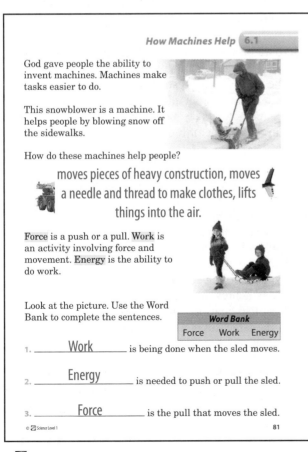

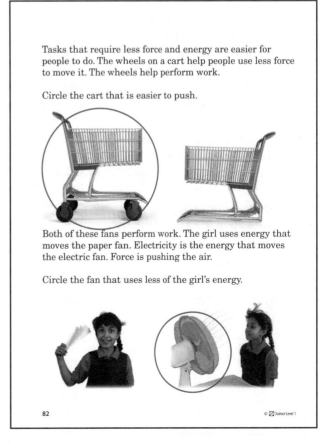

Objective

Students will apply knowledge of wheels and axles to create a machine that makes a task easier to accomplish because of the work the machine performs.

Materials

Introduction
• Cart, mystery box assembled in Lesson 6.1

Directed Instruction
• TM-6.2A Wheel and Axle or CP-6.2 Simple Machines Theme Park
• BLM 6.2A Sciencemobile, crayons, scissors, tape, straws, circular holed candy

Preparation

Place the CART holding the MYSTERY BOX assembled in Lesson 6.1 in the hallway by the classroom door. (*Introduction*)

Select **TM-6.2A Wheel and Axle** or **CP-6.2 Simple Machines Theme Park** for display. (*Directed Instruction*)

Assemble one Sciencemobile from **BLM 6.2A Sciencemobile**. Obtain the materials needed for each student to make a Sciencemobile: CRAYONS, SCISSORS, TAPE, 2 STRAWS, 4 CIRCULAR HOLED CANDIES. (*Directed Instruction*)

Alternatives

Instead of circular holed candies, use 2 toothpicks and 4 jelly beans. Cut the ends off the perpendicular straw halves and put a toothpick through each straw half. Push the end of a jelly bean into the toothpick ends.

Content

The combination of a wheel and an axle is a simple machine that turns the rotation of the wheel into a force on the axle. This machine consists of two circular objects: the wheel, which is a larger circle, and the axle, which is a small circular rod or bar. The axle is attached to the center of the wheel and turns the wheel by exerting effort or force. The wheel by itself is not a machine, but a friction-reducing device. The wheel helps reduce the friction of the work done, but it needs the axle to create a force. The wheel and axle helps move and lift objects. Pushing a box along a floor can be made easier by placing the box on a cart that has wheels and axles.

Introduction

Push the CART and MYSTERY BOX into the room. Mention that the wheels on the cart make pushing the mystery box around much easier. If possible, push the cart around the room and allow students to view the movement of the cart. Encourage students again to wonder what might be in the box.

Directed Instruction

1 Ask students what helped you bring the mystery box into the classroom. (**the cart**) How was the cart designed to help people use less energy when pulling or pushing? (**It has wheels.**) Explain to students that the wheels are attached to an axle, a small bar that allows the wheels to spin. A wheel and an axle together is a machine that turns to make things move.

Display **TM-6.2A Wheel and Axle** or present the slides about wheels and axles from **CP-6.2 Simple Machines Theme Park**. Point out the wheels. State that each wheel has an axle that it turns around to help it move. Have students identify axles.

2 Direct the class to turn to the first student page. Read the information regarding the wheel and axle. Have students place a finger on one of the wheels of the cart. Ask and discuss the question on the top of the page, and reinforce that something is moving in all these pictures. Help students understand that the wheel and axle makes moving things easier. Ask and discuss the question in the middle of the page. Then allow time for students to finish the page.

3 Guide students' attention to the second page and point out the chariot. State that wheels and axles are even mentioned in the Bible. Inform students that in Exodus the Israelites were slaves to the Egyptian people. God wanted to release the Israelites from slavery. He allowed them to escape, but then the Egyptians followed them. Point out that God gave Moses, the Israelite leader, the power to part the sea so the Israelites could pass through. But the Egyptians followed them. Read **Exodus 14:23–28** to share how God kept the Israelites safe. Elaborate on the fact that God made the wheels of the Egyptian chariots come off so that the Egyptians had difficulty driving and the Israelites could get away. Discuss how wheels and axles help vehicles move quickly.

Discuss the rest of the vehicles on the page. Ask students which vehicles they have seen or ridden in. Reiterate that wheels and axles make tasks easier to do by performing work. People use less energy riding in a truck than walking.

4 Prepare the class to make a Sciencemobile. Display the sample Sciencemobile that was made in advance. Distribute **BLM 6.2A Sciencemobile**, CRAYONS, SCISSORS, and TAPE. Read the following directions and assist students as needed:

1. Write your name on the bottom section of the Sciencemobile. Color and cut out the pattern. Fold on the gray lines. Tape the flaps together.
2. Cut a STRAW in half and tape each half parallel to the longer edges of the bottom of the Sciencemobile pattern. Cut the second straw and tape those halves perpendicular to the first straw halves.
3. Slide 2 CIRCULAR HOLED CANDIES onto both of the perpendicular straw halves. Wrap a piece of tape around each end of the straw (near the place where you want the candy to stay) so that the candy does not fall off. Be sure that the four pieces of candy are level. (Point out that the straws are the axles that help the wheels move. Without the straws, the candies could not move on their own. A wheel by itself is not a machine.)

Direct students to test their car in a manner that suits the classroom space. Ask students where the energy comes from to move the car. (**from me**) What forced the car to move? (**a push or a pull**) Reiterate that work was done because the car moved. Retain Sciencemobiles for reuse in Lesson 6.3.

⊕ Extension

Materials
- Book about machines
- "Little Red Wagon"

Read and discuss a book about machines with students, such as *Move It! Work It! A Song About Simple Machines* by Laura Purdie Salas (Picture Window Books, 2009).

Obtain and play an audio recording of the traditional children's song "Little Red Wagon." Point out the wheel and axle in the song. Reiterate that the wagon cannot move as easily with a broken wheel and axle. Have students brainstorm ways to fix the wagon.

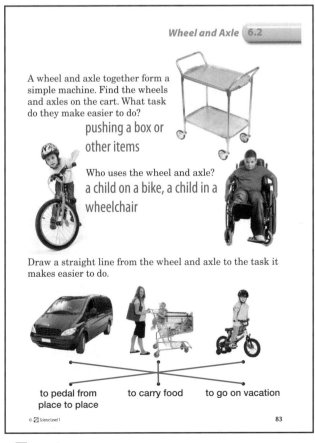

Wheel and Axle 6.2

A wheel and axle together form a simple machine. Find the wheels and axles on the cart. What task do they make easier to do?

pushing a box or other items

Who uses the wheel and axle?
a child on a bike, a child in a wheelchair

Draw a straight line from the wheel and axle to the task it makes easier to do.

to pedal from place to place   to carry food   to go on vacation

© Science Level 1   83

God made the wheels of the Egyptian chariots come off so the Israelites could escape. (Exodus 14)

Count how many wheels are on each machine. Can you see the axles?

4

1 or 2

4

8

18

84   © Science Level 1

6.3 Inclined Plane

Content

An inclined plane is a simple machine that helps move an object, a person, or an animal upward. Walking up an inclined plane, such as a gentle trail to a hilltop, takes longer than hiking up a steep slope but requires less effort (force). Increasing the distance by using the inclined plane or trail reduces the need for as much force. The same work is accomplished by climbing the steep slope, but more effort is needed for the shorter distance.

While a wheel and axle moves to carry a heavy load, an inclined plane raises a load. A wheel and axle reduces the friction it takes to do work; an inclined plane reduces the effort it takes to do the work.

Introduction

Point out the MYSTERY BOX and the CART at the front of the room. Ask the class to name some ways that the mystery box could be moved from the floor to the cart. (**Possible answer: pick it up and place it on the cart**) Convey that the box might be too heavy to lift. Ask students what might make the task easier. (**Answers will vary.**) Display the LONG BOARD. Set up the board as a ramp. Slide the box up the board and onto the cart. Exclaim how much easier it is to slide heavy things up instead of lifting them. Encourage students again to wonder what might be in the box.

Directed Instruction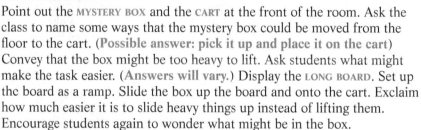

1 Ask students how the board made moving the mystery box easier. (**The board was used to slide the box up. You did not have to lift the box.**) Explain that the board was used as a simple machine called *an inclined plane* that made the task easier to do by performing work. Convey that *an inclined plane* means *a machine that is a flat, slanted surface that is used to lift an object*. A ramp is an example of an inclined plane. It connects a lower level to a higher level. Convey that an inclined plane is a simple machine; it does not require an engine or a motor.

2 Display **TM-6.3A Inclined Plane** or present the slides about inclined planes from **CP-6.2 Simple Machines Theme Park**. Point out the inclined planes and have a volunteer describe how the inclined planes perform work and help people do tasks. (**They help move objects more easily.**)

3 Direct the class to turn to the first student page. Read about the inclined plane and point out the inclined plane in each picture at the top. Also note that the ramp you used to move the mystery box is an inclined plane. Guide students to understand that the inclined plane was designed to move objects up easily. The object goes a longer way but with less effort. Ask and discuss the question at the end of the first paragraph. Then have students place a finger on the inclined plane—ramp—in the bottom picture of the truck and car. Check for understanding by asking how this inclined plane is being used. (**It helps the car move onto the truck more easily.**) Direct students to use the Word Bank to complete the sentences.

Have students turn to their second page. Note the inclined plane on the ark and ask who it would help enter the ark. (**Noah and his family, animals**) Guide students in circling the inclined planes on the page. Point out how each inclined plane helps accomplish a task in an easier manner by performing work. The inclined plane helps lift the skateboarder and the biker into their jumps; it moves people up the escalator; and it assists passengers onto a boat. Ask students in what direction the inclined planes are helping people move. (**up**) Reiterate that, by definition, inclined planes help move things up. Review the topic of inclined planes by using the question at the bottom of the page. Point out the wheels and axles on the bike and mention that the wheel and axle, as well as the inclined plane, helps the bike rider roll up the ramp and into a jump.

4 Explain that students will now make their own inclined plane. Distribute SCIENCEMOBILES from Lesson 6.2 and have students stack a few books on their desk. Direct students to try to roll their Sciencemobile over the books. Explain that if this were a real vehicle, it would be very difficult to drive over such a large obstacle. Distribute CARDBOARD STRIPS and TAPE to pairs of students, and instruct them to make an inclined plane that will make driving over the books easier to do. Allow time for partners to discuss and try out their ideas. Ask several pairs to demonstrate their inclined plane to the class and to share how it works.

Notes:

✚ Extension

Materials
- Long board, gallon jug, water
- Resources about Egyptian pyramids

Prop a long board on a chair. Fill a gallon jug with water and cap it tightly. Have a student slide the jug up the board to the seat of the chair. Then have him or her lift the jug from the floor to the seat of the chair. Ask which was easier to do. Invite other students to repeat the activity. Create a graph on the board comparing their results. (Sliding should be easier than lifting.)

Research with the class how ancient Egyptians used inclined planes to build pyramids. Have students draw a picture of what they learned.

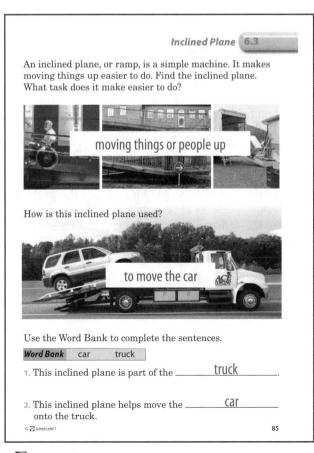

6.4 Lever

Content

A lever is a simple machine that helps lift or move a load. A crowbar is a well-known lever. It functions to pry or lift objects while resting on a prop called *a fulcrum*. Levers are categorized into three classes. A first-class lever like a seesaw or scissors is built with the fulcrum in the center and the load (L) and force (F) on opposites ends. A second-class lever, such as a wheelbarrow or nutcracker, holds the load in the center, and the fulcrum and force are on opposite ends. A broom, a baseball bat, and a human forearm represent the third class of levers. They all have the force, or effort, in the center, and the load and fulcrum are on opposite ends. The different classes of levers require different levels of force needed to move a variety of loads.

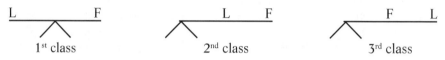

L F	L F	F L
1ˢᵗ class	2ⁿᵈ class	3ʳᵈ class

Introduction 🖐

Draw students' attention to the MYSTERY BOX on the CART and demonstrate how to use a PRY BAR to open the large outer box. Explain that using a pry bar as a lever helps open the box. Share that a lever is a machine that helps by lifting up the taped edge of the box. Allow students to peer into the large box to see what is inside. (**a small box**) State that in Lesson 6.5 students will assist in removing the smaller box from the larger one.

Directed Instruction 🖐 ➕

1 Direct students to turn to the first student page. Read the information about levers, and stress that levers can make tasks easier to do by helping people lift or move things. State that *a lever* refers to *a machine that is a stiff bar with a support*. Have students place a finger on the lever at the top of the page. Ask and discuss the question beside the box.

Have students look at the remaining pictures. Indicate that levers are found in many everyday items. Instruct students to draw a line to match each picture to the corresponding name of the lever. Ask students to describe what it might be like to try to remove the nail without the hammer. (**It would be very difficult.**)

Guide students to turn to the second page and to complete the activity at the top. Remind students that levers help people lift or move things. Have them analyze and discuss how each lever is helping a person lift or move something. When students have finished, ask them which lever also has a wheel and axle. (**the wheelbarrow**) Have students complete the page.

2 Display **TM-6.4A Lever** or present the slides about levers from **CP-6.2 Simple Machines Theme Park**. Discuss the levers and ask students to identify what is being lifted in each picture. (**people**)

3 Divide the class into pairs and instruct pairs to have a pencil available. In addition, provide each pair with a RULER, TAPE, two PAPER CUPS, a SMALL ROCK, and a handful of COINS. Guide pairs in following the directions below to make a lever:
   • Tape a pencil to the desk.
   • Tape the bottom of the cups to each end of a ruler.

- Set the ruler on the pencil, centered and perpendicular to the pencil.
- Place a rock into one of the cups.
- Count the coins, one at a time, as you drop them into the other cup.
- Record how many coins it takes to lift the rock.

Poll student pairs for the number of coins it took to lift each rock. Inquire why some levers took more coins to lift the rock. (**Answers will vary but should include that some rocks are heavier than others and needed more coins to lift them.**) Convey that the heavier rocks required more force in order to be moved. The coins provided the force needed to do the work of moving the rock. Ask students if they think moving the ruler would make a difference. (**Answers will vary.**)

Direct students to move the ruler so that the cup with the coins is closer to the pencil. Ask students if it will take more coins (more force) to move the rock. (**Yes.**) What do you think will happen if you move the ruler so that the cup with the rock is closer to the pencil? (**Answers will vary.**) Instruct students to test their prediction and then to calculate if it took more or fewer coins to lift the rock. (**fewer**)

Reiterate that the lever is the simple machine that helped move the rock. Different levers might have their support, like the pencil, in different places on the machine; each machine is designed for a different purpose. Convey that a seesaw, a nutcracker, and a broom are all levers, but all are designed differently. Have students share with their partner how the lever they created with the ruler and pencil helped move the rock.

⊕ Extension

Materials
- Clothespins, craft sticks, glue, tape, marshmallows, cups

Create marshmallow catapults to demonstrate levers. Before class, glue large craft sticks to the top of wooden clothespins so that one end of the stick lines up with the clamped end of the clothespin. Direct students to use two pieces of masking tape to stick the bottom of the clothespin to their desk. Have them place a small marshmallow on the free end of the stick. Instruct them to press the stick down and release. Place paper cups at the end of the desks and challenge students to launch their marshmallows into the cups.

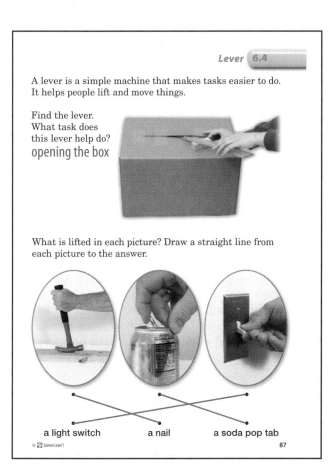

Lever 6.4

A lever is a simple machine that makes tasks easier to do. It helps people lift and move things.

Find the lever. What task does this lever help do? opening the box

What is lifted in each picture? Draw a straight line from each picture to the answer.

a light switch   a nail   a soda pop tab

© Science Level 1   87

Circle all the levers in these pictures.

Circle the word that best completes the sentence.

1. _____ is a push or a pull.
   (Force)   Energy   Work

2. A lever makes _____ easier to do. A lever performs work.
   force   energy   (tasks)

88   © Science Level 1

6.5 Pulley

Objective

Students will construct a pulley that will perform work.

Materials

Introduction
- Mystery box assembled in Lesson 6.1, cart, long board from Lesson 6.3

Directed Instruction
- Mystery box, rope, heavy tape, PVC pipe, broomstick, goggles
- TM 6.5A Pulley or CP-6.2 Simple Machines Theme Park
- Pulley materials
- Crayons

Preparation

Have available the MYSTERY BOX from Lesson 6.1 and CART , and the LONG BOARD from Lesson 6.3. (*Introduction*)

To create a pulley, tie a ROPE around the box inside the MYSTERY BOX. Wrap HEAVY TAPE around a 6 in. long PVC PIPE so that the tape is thick enough to act as a ridge to keep the rope on the pipe. Slip the pipe onto a BROOMSTICK. Obtain 3 GOGGLES for student volunteers. (*Directed Instruction*)

Select **TM-6.5A Pulley** or **CP-6.2 Simple Machines Theme Park** for display. Gather PULLEY MATERIALS (empty spools, rulers, pencils, yarn, straws, tissue boxes) for small groups. Obtain CRAYONS. (*Directed Instruction*)

Alternatives

Substitute a bottomless plastic cup for the PVC pipe. Or, make a pulley by wrapping the rope around a rolling pin.

Content

A pulley consists of a rope or cable wrapped around a grooved wheel. The pulley works by changing the direction of a force. For example, a person can pull on a pulley in a downward motion to lift a heavy object. A pulley on a flagpole is a fixed pulley because the pulley itself does not move; therefore, it does not add to the effort used to move the load (the flag). The pulley simply changes the direction of the force and makes lifting the load easier. A moveable pulley does not change the direction of the force, but instead increases the size of the force, so less effort is required to move the load. An example of a moveable pulley is a zip line. A pulley is a simple machine.

Introduction

Wheel the MYSTERY BOX on the CART around the room. Ask students what simple machine on the cart helps move the box easily around the room. (**a wheel and axle**) Display the LONG BOARD and ask what type of machine it is. (**an inclined plane**) Block the wheels of the cart, and then use the inclined plane to move the mystery box up and onto the cart. Ask students what machine helped open the box in Lesson 6.4. (**a lever**) What was inside the large box? (**a small box**) State that today students will learn about a machine that will help them remove the small box from the large one.

Directed Instruction

1 Direct the class to turn to the first student page. Share that there is another machine besides the lever that helps lift objects; this machine is a pulley. Explain that *a pulley* refers to *a machine that is a grooved wheel with a rope or cable around it*. Have students place their finger on the simplified pulley that the children are using. Point out the axle (the mop) on the pulley wheel. Ask and discuss the question in the purple box. Ask for volunteers to assist with the demonstration of a PULLEY. Pass out GOGGLES for the volunteers to wear to encourage a habit of safety during science experiments.

Emphasize that as one student pulls down on the rope, the box lifts. By using the pulley, the direction of the force is changed. The student in the center pulls down and the box goes up. Using this pulley makes lifting easier than having to bend and lift the box manually. Once the inner box has been lifted, remove the outer box. Have students slowly lower the inner box to the floor. State that in Lesson 6.7 they will use a machine to open the small box and reveal what is inside.

2 Read the top of the first student page aloud. Point out that the pulley makes the task of lifting the box easier because the pulley performs work. Allow students to share about pulleys they have seen or used. Encourage students to recognize pulleys around their school and neighborhood. Discuss what is being lifted in the pictures. Allow time for students to use the Word Bank to complete the sentences. Ask them how using a pulley helps the man in the picture. (**He does not need to climb the pole to raise the flag.**)

Direct students' attention to the second page. Read the directions and guide students in matching each term to the correct picture. Review each type of simple machine as necessary. Read the problem at the bottom of the page to students. Discuss the three choices and guide students in understanding that wheels and axles would help the suitcase move more easily. Point out that many suitcases are made with wheels and axles already. Also, some people move a large number of suitcases on a cart or dolly with wheels and axles.

3 Display **TM-6.5A Pulley** or present the remaining slides from **CP-6.2 Simple Machines Theme Park**. Discuss the examples and check for understanding. Ask students what the lever and the pulley help people do. (**lift or move things**) Have students look around the room for any examples of levers or pulleys. (**Possible answers:** *lever*: scissors, stapler; *pulley*: flag)

4 Inform students that they will have time to make the machine studied today. Distribute PULLEY MATERIALS to small groups. Allow groups time to make model pulleys and assist when needed. Assess students' understanding while observing students' involvement in the activity. If you choose, have groups volunteer to share their machine with the class.

5 Write the words *wheel and axle*, *inclined plane*, *lever*, and *pulley* on the board. Distribute CRAYONS and have students fold a sheet of drawing paper into fourths. Allow time for them to draw a picture of each of the machines they have studied in this chapter. Instruct students to label the pictures. Have them take their drawing home to share with a family member.

Notes:

Extension

Materials
• Magazines, scissors, glue, poster board
• Ball, bucket, classroom items

Ask students to cut pictures of machines from magazines and to glue them onto poster board. Display the poster of each type of machine in the classroom.

Divide the class into small groups and give them a task such as getting a ball into a bucket. Challenge groups to build a machine that will complete the task. Permit them to use classroom materials to assist with the task. Allow the ball to be pushed or pulled to start; and encourage students to be a part of the machine.

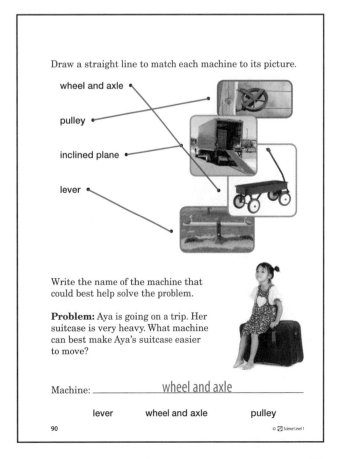

6.6 Tech Connect

Objective

Students will use materials to design a device that solves a problem.

Materials

Directed Instruction
• Boxes, small balls, items to complete a challenge

Preparation

Gather a BOX and a SMALL BALL for small groups or pairs of students. In each box, add several ASSORTED ITEMS for completing a challenge, such as rulers, connecting blocks, cardboard strips, straws, tape, pencils, and rubber bands. (*Directed Instruction*)

Content

NASA—the National Aeronautics and Space Administration—has been creating robots for years. From exploring space, to fixing spacecraft, to driving airplanes, robots have played an important role in developing and strengthening advances in outer space. Robonaut, a recent NASA invention, was designed to assist astronauts working in space. In 2012, Curiosity, a space rover, was launched onto Mars to collect data for scientists.

Robots are also helpful in making advances in medicine and physical therapy. Prosthetic limbs have assisted war veterans and physically challenged people in recovering and gaining control of their limbs. Prosthetics is not a new solution, but it continues to advance through new discoveries and technology. Recent advances enable some patients to control a robotic limb through a sensor attached to the motor cortex of their brain. This allows them the ability to complete tasks they may have never been able to do on their own.

Introduction

Encourage students to share about robots they have seen in movies, television shows, or comics. (**Answers will vary.**) What did the robots do? (**Possible answers: helped people, fought, built things**) State that many movies and comics about robots are make-believe but today, students will learn about some real robots that help people.

Directed Instruction

1 Direct students' attention to the first student page. Read the sentence at the top. Explain that many different types of robots help people and are each designed for a specific purpose. Explain that robots help scientists learn more about outer space. Robots help move, build, and fix equipment on space stations; they can also explore outer space. Read the second paragraph about Curiosity. Share that Curiosity can drive on the planet Mars and gather information about the planet's land and atmosphere. Scientists then use computers to get messages from Curiosity.

Inform students that scientists also use robots to fly planes. Since these planes do not need a pilot, they are able to travel to dangerous places, like volcanoes, and take pictures. State that scientists are still thinking of new ways that robots can help explore Earth and outer space.

2 Explain that robots can also help people who do not have use of their arms or legs. Move to the third paragraph and read it with students. State that doctors use robots to help certain people. Praise God that He gives doctors and scientists wisdom to design ways to help people.

3 Read the bottom of the page with students. Reiterate that scientists are designing new robots. Inform students that one new robot invention functions like an insect's exoskeleton. The robot is placed to fit around a person's body to help the person move and do amazing things. The exoskeleton robot is being designed for soldiers, firefighters, emergency workers, and industrial workers. It can help people carry heavier loads and to do more work with less effort.

4 Turn to the next page with students. State that competitions for making robots start as early as first grade. These students work together in groups to solve big challenges. These challenges may include saving energy, keeping food safe, and helping sick people get better. Each group finds information about their topic, shows their idea on a poster, and then makes a robot for their solution.

State that today, students will complete a small challenge about simple machines. Read the challenge on the page. Then distribute the BOXES of ASSORTED ITEMS for completing a challenge and divide the class into groups or pairs. Instruct students to create a machine that moves a BALL across a desk. State that the ball must go completely across but not fall off the side of the desk.

Have students draw their idea first and then try it out on a desk. Move through the room and provide assistance and redirection as needed. If students need help, point out that an inclined plane is a simple machine that moves things easily from one place to another.

When groups complete their challenge, have them demonstrate their machine to the class. Point out parts on each machine that worked well to move the ball. Instruct students in cleaning up the supplies. Then have them share with a partner some ways robots help people.

Notes:

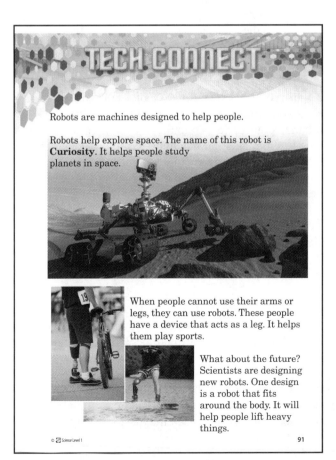

⊕ Extension

Materials
• *Internet*
• *Some Kids Use Wheelchairs*

Research national elementary robotic competitions, such as Jr. FIRST Lego Leagues for grades K–3 students. Consider starting a local team.

Refer to Internet sites that give updates on rovers like Curiosity. Share pictures and videos of outer space with the class.

Discuss with students the awareness and acceptance of others with physical disabilities. Point out how machines have helped those individuals move more easily. Read *Some Kids Use Wheelchairs* by Lola M. Schaefer (Capstone, 2008).

Materials

Introduction
• Mystery box, lever

Directed Instruction
• BLM 6.7A Machine Facts
• Tubs, assorted materials
• BLM 6.7B Chapter 6 Test

Preparation

Set the MYSTERY BOX on a table or desk for students to observe. Have available a LEVER for opening the box. (*Introduction*)

Write the definitions of *force*, *work*, and *energy* on the board. Replace a few words in the definitions with blank lines for students to fill in. (*Directed Instruction*)

Print **BLM 6.7A Machine Facts** for each student. (*Directed Instruction*)

Prepare 4 TUBS filled with ASSORTED MATERIALS for making machines (straws, tape, cardboard, yarn, circular candies, marshmallows, craft sticks, connecting blocks, scissors). (*Directed Instruction*)

Print **BLM 6.7B Chapter 6 Test** for each student. (*Directed Instruction*)

Introduction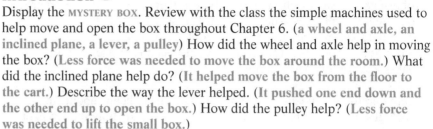

Display the MYSTERY BOX. Review with the class the simple machines used to help move and open the box throughout Chapter 6. (**a wheel and axle, an inclined plane, a lever, a pulley**) How did the wheel and axle help in moving the box? (**Less force was needed to move the box around the room.**) What did the inclined plane help do? (**It helped move the box from the floor to the cart.**) Describe the way the lever helped. (**It pushed one end down and the other end up to open the box.**) How did the pulley help? (**Less force was needed to lift the small box.**)

Ask a volunteer to suggest what simple machine can be used to open the small box. (**a lever**) Proceed to use a LEVER to open the small box and distribute the contents as you choose.

Directed Instruction

1 Read the definitions of *force*, *work*, and *energy* from the board. Invite students to fill in the missing words. (*force*: **a push or a pull**; *work*: **an activity involving a force and movement**; *energy*: **the ability to do work**) Allow students to demonstrate each vocabulary word. Have them use force to push or pull their chair behind their desk. Direct them to do work by moving an object such as a book or pencil across their desk. Then have them use energy by running in place.

Distribute **BLM 6.7A Machine Facts** and allow time for students to complete the worksheet. Have a volunteer read and answer a fact. Select another volunteer to explain the fact in his or her own words. Point out the merry-go-round at the bottom of the page. Ask what type of machine it is. (**a wheel and axle**) Have them locate the axle on the machine. Reiterate that a wheel needs an axle for it to become a machine. Ask what force is moving the merry-go-round. (**a push from the girls**)

2 Divide the class into four groups. Distribute a TUB of ASSORTED MATERIALS for making machines to each group. Assign each group a machine (a wheel and axle, an inclined plane, a lever, a pulley). Instruct groups to use the materials in the tub to make that machine. Remind students that the materials are for making the machines only. You may choose to allow students in each group to make their machine individually or in pairs, or to have them all make matching machines together.

When groups have finished, direct them to observe or identify another group's machine. Allow students to carefully try out their classmates' machines. Give students the opportunity to share about the machine they are observing. Assist in cleanup of the materials.

3 Use the student pages as review or pretest. Complete these pages with the class. Discuss ideas for the journal and list ideas on the board. Focus on the fact that both the lever and the pulley help people move things more easily.

You may use **BLM 6.7B Chapter 6 Test** for individual assessment. Read through this page with the class. Provide as much reading support as necessary. You may choose to use this blackline master as an oral assessment or not to do it at all.

4 Chapter 6 Machines has been completed. Staple the student pages and send them home as a booklet to share with a family member.

Notes:

⊕ **Extension**

Materials
• Video from Lesson 6.1
• Backpack, rope

Show the class video created during this chapter. If desired, present it to another class.

Bring a backpack, and escort students to the playground to discover simple machines. Point out wheels and axles (steering wheel, merry-go-round), inclined planes (slide, ladder, ramp), levers (seesaw, swing), and pulleys (zip line). Challenge students to think of ways to move the backpack around the playground: create a pulley to move the backpack up (provide rope), or push the backpack up an inclined plane. To check for comprehension, call out types of machines for students to find and play on.

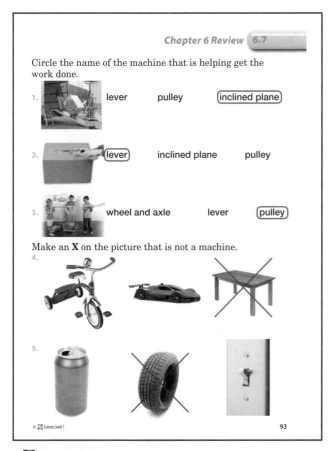

Chapter 6 Review 6.7

Circle the name of the machine that is helping get the work done.

1.   lever   pulley   (inclined plane)

2.   (lever)   inclined plane   pulley

3.   wheel and axle   lever   (pulley)

Make an **X** on the picture that is not a machine.

4.

5.

© Science Level 1   93

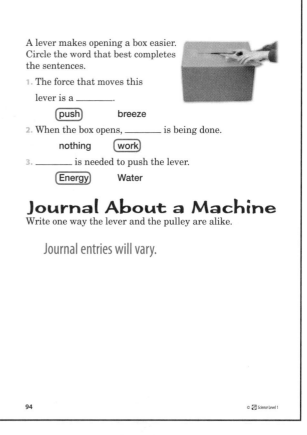

A lever makes opening a box easier. Circle the word that best completes the sentences.

1. The force that moves this lever is a _____.
    (push)   breeze

2. When the box opens, _____ is being done.
    nothing   (work)

3. _____ is needed to push the lever.
    (Energy)   Water

Journal About a Machine
Write one way the lever and the pulley are alike.

Journal entries will vary.

94   © Science Level 1

Unit 3

and Space
cience

Seasons and Matter

Chapter 7

Key Ideas

- Seasons affect plants, animals, and people.
- Three of the states of matter are solid, liquid, and gas. Water can be found in all three states.
- People use tools to measure weather conditions. Thermometers indicate temperature.

7.0 Chapter Preparation

season
matter

Looking Ahead

- For **Lesson 7.7**, record a local weather report from a television channel or obtain it from an online source.
- Begin collecting paper-towel tubes for each student to use in **Lesson 8.4**.

Introduction

The study of seasons brings understanding of things experienced every day. Students will examine God's design on the grand scale of the earth and the sun. They will learn attributes of each season. Students will become aware of the daily and seasonal changes around them. These changes may come in the form of weather and temperature. The influence of the seasons on plants and animals is important for a deeper understanding of the topic. Students will explore three common states of matter—solid, liquid, and gas. Thermometers, weather-radar technology, rain gauges, and wind socks monitor weather in a concrete way. This chapter will help students recognize God's provision of what people need in order to live.

About This Chapter

Lesson 7.1 – What Seasons Are
Materials
- Tape
- Scissors
- Glue

Lesson Content
A season is a time of year. In each season, the temperature and weather may change. People, animals, and plants may respond to each season differently.

Lesson 7.2 – Seasons and Plants
Materials
- Seeds
- Hand lenses
- Bags
- Paper towels
- Water
- Pot
- Soil
- Pinecones

Lesson Content
The seasons help plants grow. Some trees lose their leaves in fall and winter, and some, like the evergreen, keep their needles all year long.

Lesson 7.3 – Seasons and Animals
Materials
- Globe

Lesson Content
Animals survive winter in different ways. Some animals migrate, some hibernate, and some stay active. God's design of each animal allows it to survive the conditions of each season.

Lesson 7.4 – States of Matter
Materials
- Ice cubes
- Tablespoon
- Vinegar
- Bottle
- Funnel
- Baking soda
- Balloon
- Goggles
- Teaspoons
- Salt
- Sand
- Cups
- Water
- Spoons
- Marker

Lesson Content
The states of matter include solid, liquid, and gas. Water can be found in all three states. The water in a pond may be in a solid state in the winter but thaw to a liquid state in the spring.

Lesson 7.5 – Seasons and Weather
Materials
- Soap
- Plate
- Microwave
- Oven mitt
- Newspaper
- Shaving cream
- Cups
- Water
- Food coloring
- Eyedroppers

Lesson Content
Some substances dissolve in water. Water evaporates, cools, forms clouds, and falls back to the ground as rain.

Lesson 7.6 – Tools to Measure Weather
Materials
- Wind chime
- Fan
- Thermometer
- Cups
- Water
- Soil

Lesson Content
A thermometer can measure the temperature of water or air. A temperature can be read in degrees Fahrenheit or Celsius. A rain gauge and a wind sock are other tools used to measure weather.

Lesson 7.7 – Tech Connect
Materials
- Weather report

Lesson Content
Doppler radar and weather satellites are tools meteorologists use to predict the weather. These scientists can predict the weather and warn people of upcoming storms, like thunderstorms, tornadoes, and hurricanes.

Lesson 7.8 – Chapter 7 Review
Materials
- Camera
- Blue paper
- Tape

Teacher Resources

The AMS Weather Book: The Ultimate Guide to America's Weather by Jack Williams. University of Chicago Press and the American Meteorological Society, 2009.

Keeping God's Earth: The Global Environment in Biblical Perspective. Edited by Noah J. Toly and Daniel I. Block. InterVarsity Press, 2010.

Student Resources

Clouds by Anne Rockwell. HarperCollins, 2008.

Junior Meteorology DVD Set by Jason Lindsey. American Family Studios, 2011.

Seasons of the Year by Margaret Hall. Capstone Press, 2007.

Supplemental Materials

Blackline Masters
7.1A Season Cards
7.1B Which Season
7.1C Season Chart
7.1D Today the Weather Is
7.6A Thermometer
7.8A Season Facts
7.8B Chapter 7 Test

Transparency Masters
7.2A Seasons
7.2B The Life of an Apple Tree, Part 1
7.2C The Life of an Apple Tree, Part 2
7.6A Thermometer

7.1 What Seasons Are

Objective

Students will identify each season by its characteristics.

Materials

Introduction
• BLM 7.1A Season Cards, tape

Directed Instruction
• BLM 7.1B Which Season, BLM 7.1C Season Chart, scissors, glue

Preparation

Draw these 2 patterns on the board. (*Introduction*)

○△□○△□

4, __, 2, 4, 3, 2, __

Print and cut apart enough sets of **BLM 7.1A Season Cards** so each student has a card. Have TAPE available. (*Introduction*)

Write the definition of *season* on the board. (*Directed Instruction*)

Print **BLM 7.1B Which Season** and **BLM 7.1C Season Chart** for each student. Have SCISSORS and GLUE available. (*Directed Instruction*)

Content

Seasons are due to several factors: the angle of the sun's rays, the position of Earth in its orbit, and Earth's tilt.

• Angle: The sun's rays strike Earth at different angles. Rays that strike Earth at an angle close to 90°, as at the equator, cause that part of Earth to be hotter. Rays that strike Earth at an angle close to 45° spread over a larger area, causing that part of Earth to be colder.

• Position: The location of Earth in its orbit around the sun helps determine the season. Each orbit takes approximately 365 days.

• Tilt: Earth maintains a 23.5° tilt from a vertical orientation. In the study of seasons, teachers and students find it helpful to view Earth's Northern and Southern Hemispheres, which are separated by the equator, an imaginary line.

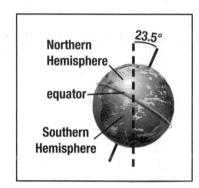

This illustration shows the position and tilt of Earth at each season.

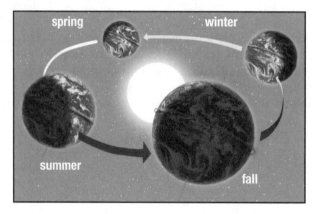

Introduction

Refer to the first pattern on the board. Say the shapes out loud so students hear as well as visualize the pattern to determine what comes next. (circle) For the second pattern, allow students time to figure out the missing numerals. Help them recognize that when a blank is toward the beginning, they need to look further for a pattern. (3, 4)

Distribute the precut **BLM 7.1A Season Cards**, and give a different season card to each student in groups of about four. Have students order the cards, starting with winter. Assist as needed. Check for accuracy. (winter, spring, summer, fall) Give each group of students TAPE to attach the cards together to make a section of a season pattern. Allow each group to tape its section to the classroom wall. Read the pattern aloud with the class to emphasize that the order is always the same.

Directed Instruction

1 Read the definition on the board—**season**: *a time of year*. Ask students which season they are in right now. (Answers will vary but should indicate the season for your location and time of year.) State that today

students will learn more about the seasons. Express that in each season the temperature changes by getting colder or hotter. Temperature tells how hot or cold something is. Convey that in different seasons, the weather may also change. State that weather can be rainy, snowy, sunny, cloudy, or windy. Lead a discussion about how students may notice snow in winter but not in summer.

Direct students' attention to the first page. Have a volunteer read the two sentences at the top. Read through the characteristics of winter and reiterate that many trees lose their leaves once a year. Have volunteers read through the other seasons on the first and second pages, and discuss what seasons are like where students live. (**Answers will vary.**) Ask students what their favorite activity is in each season. (**Answers will vary.**) Discuss the questions at the bottom of the second page with students.

2 Distribute **BLM 7.1B Which Season**, SCISSORS, and GLUE. Allow time for students to cut out each rectangle and to paste it on the correct season on **BLM 7.1C Season Chart**. Check for accuracy before students glue the rectangles to the paper.

Notes:

⊕ Extension

Materials
- BLM 7.1D Today the Weather Is, scissors, brass fasteners
- Clothing
- Internet, reference books

For each student, print **BLM 7.1D Today the Weather Is** or enlarge and print the page to display in the classroom. Provide scissors and brass fasteners. Have students observe, record, and graph the weather for the week.

Provide a variety of clothing for a seasonal fashion show. Have small groups dress for a particular season and model for the class.

Instruct small groups to research a country's seasons. Guide them in creating a travel brochure with information about the weather, seasons, and temperatures.

What Seasons Are **7.1**

A season is a time of year. The four seasons are winter, spring, summer, and fall.

Winter is the coldest season. The weather is rainy or snowy. Some trees lose their leaves. Some animals sleep all winter. People wear coats.

Spring is warmer than winter. Trees grow leaves and flowers. Some animals travel to their summer home. Farmers plant seeds.

© Science Level 1   97

Summer is the warmest season. The weather is sunny. Plants and flowers grow. Animals are active. Children play outside.

Fall is cooler than summer. Some trees lose their leaves. Some animals travel to warmer places. Other animals get food for the winter. Children go to school.

Discuss what the seasons are like where you live.
1. What is the weather like in each season?
2. Why do some animals move from place to place?
3. Why do plants grow well in the summer?

98   © Science Level 1

7.2 Seasons and Plants

Objective

Students will recognize seasonal changes in a variety of trees.

Materials

Introduction
• Bean seeds, hand lenses, ziplock bags, paper towels, water, pot, soil

Directed Instruction
• Pinecones
• TM-7.2A Seasons
• TMs-7.2B–C The Life of an Apple Tree, Parts 1–2

Preparation

Collect for small groups of students: a BEAN SEED, a HAND LENS, a ZIPLOCK BAG, and a PAPER TOWEL moistened with WATER. Have available a LARGE POT with SOIL. Hand lenses can be found in the ACSI Science Equipment Kit. (*Introduction*)

Obtain PINECONES with seeds on the cones for students to observe. (*Directed Instruction*)

Select **TM-7.2A Seasons** for display. (*Directed Instruction*)

Select **TMs-7.2B–C The Life of an Apple Tree, Parts 1–2** for display. (*Directed Instruction*)

Content

Deciduous trees—such as apple, oak, maple, elm, and aspen—lose their leaves annually and are classified as flowering plants. They produce flowers that die after pollination and fertilization, leaving a fruit or an enlarged ovary of seeds. A seed contains an embryo.

Conifer trees, such as pine, fir, and spruce, are not classified as flowering plants. Their seeds are not protected by a fruit but are located on the seed-bearing female cone. Most conifers lose and replace their needles (leaves) throughout the year. Since most conifers do not experience a bare period, they are typically called *evergreen*.

Introduction

Organize students into small groups and share that they will observe seeds growing. Distribute several BEAN SEEDS to each group. Allow time for students to use a HAND LENS to observe their bean seed. Distribute to each group a ZIPLOCK BAG and a PAPER TOWEL moistened with WATER. (To avoid mildew, be sure the paper towels are not too moist.) Instruct groups to slide the paper towel into the bag and to place the seeds on top of it. Do not seal the bag. Place the bags in a warm and sunny location that is suitable for promoting growth. Have students observe the progress of the seed growth over the next week. When the root and several leaves appear, demonstrate planting the seedlings in a LARGE POT filled with SOIL. Explain that the soil will provide the nutrients needed to continue growth. Ask students what the bean seeds need in order to grow. (soil, water, air, sun) Share that God has provided these things for plants.

Directed Instruction

1 Direct students' attention to the first page. Read the first sentence. Have volunteers read the description of the orange tree in each of the seasons. Discuss the following:
   • In the spring, orange trees grow white flowers or blossoms and new green leaves. Ask how the flowers smell. (sweet)
   • By summer, the flower petals have dropped and the center of the flower becomes the fruit. The fruit grows larger. Inside the fruit are seeds. Inquire what helps the fruit grow. (soil, water, air, sun)
   • Ask what happens to the orange fruit in fall and winter. (It is picked and eaten.) What do you think it feels like to pick and eat a fresh orange? (Answers will vary.) What can happen to the seeds inside each orange? (They can grow new orange trees.)
   • Have volunteers describe how people use their senses to observe oranges in each season.

2 Read **Genesis 8:22** on the student page. Discuss that one way God provides food for people is by plants like orange trees that grow and make fruit for people to eat. His design of the seasons provides plants with what they need to grow.

   Allow time for students to complete the exercise at the bottom of the first page. If needed, reread the top of the page to assist with student answers. Check for accuracy.

3 Display **TM-7.2A Seasons** and instruct students to follow along on their second page. Read the information about the oak tree from the page. Have students put a finger on each illustration as you name the season. Read the sentence about the pine tree. Compare and contrast the oak tree to the pine tree. Share that pine trees keep their leaves called *needles* all year. This is why pine trees are sometimes called *evergreen*. Ask students to describe how a pine needle feels. (**sharp, stiff**) Explain that the pine tree does not produce a flower or fruit, but it makes seeds. Explain that the seeds are on the pinecones. Display and allow students to observe PINECONES. Share that the seeds are on the outside of the cone. Have students compare and contrast the different types of trees.

Teach that *a group of events that repeats in a certain order over and over* is called *a cycle*. Ask students to name examples of cycles. (**seasons, changes in trees**) Discuss the questions at the bottom of the page. (**Answers will vary but should include that spring brings warmth and water.**)

4 Display **TMs-7.2B–C The Life of an Apple Tree, Parts 1–2**. Read about the life of the tree. If you have time, refer to some of the trees mentioned in the Bible.
- Tree of Life (Genesis 2:9)
- Tamarisk tree where Saul and his sons were buried (1 Samuel 31:13)
- Oak tree that Absalom was caught in (2 Samuel 18:9)
- Fig tree cursed by Jesus (Matthew 21:19)
- Sycamore tree that Zacchaeus climbed (Luke 19:4)
- Fig tree where Jesus saw Nathanael (John 1:48)
- The cross on which Jesus died (Acts 5:30)

⊕ Extension

Materials
- Book about seeds
- Orange seeds, plates, hand lenses, crayons, oranges

Select and read a book to students about planting seeds. Possible books include the following:
The Life Cycle of a Pine Tree by Linda Tagliaferro (Capstone Press, 2007).
The Tiny Seed by Eric Carle (Little Simon, 2009).

Distribute an orange seed on a plate to each student. Allow students to use hand lenses, paper, and crayons to observe and draw their orange seed. Distribute orange slices as a snack. Have students use their five senses to analyze the orange. Direct them to write about the orange. Check student records for possible allergies first.

Seasons and Plants 7.2

The seasons help an orange grow.

In spring, the orange tree has green leaves and white flowers. It smells sweet.

In summer, the flower petals fall off. A small orange grows.

In fall and winter, workers pick the oranges.

"As long as the earth endures, seedtime and harvest, cold and heat, summer and winter ... will never cease." Genesis 8:22

Match the season to how an orange grows.

spring • → • Oranges are picked.
summer • → • Flowers grow.
fall and winter • → • Oranges grow.

© Science Level 1   99

The oak tree grows new leaves in the spring. It loses leaves in the fall.

spring   fall
summer   winter

The needles on a pine tree stay all year long. How are the oak tree and pine tree alike? How are they different?

Events that repeat in a certain order form a cycle. The seasons occur in a cycle.

1. Why does a plant start to grow in the spring?

2. Tell about a plant that might grow in your yard in the spring.

100   © Science Level 1

7.3 Seasons and Animals

Objective

Students will explain the effects of seasonal changes on certain animals.

Materials

Directed Instruction
• Globe

Preparation

Draw this graphic on the board. (*Introduction*)

January February
December
March
winter
November
April
fall **spring**
October
May
summer
September
June
August July

Obtain a GLOBE. (*Directed Instruction*)

Content

God provided animals with ways to survive the winter season. For example, insects may find shelter in places like rotting logs and holes in the ground. They may even live in a gall, or swollen part, of a tree.

God created the snowshoe hare to survive in the cold winter forests. The hare's thick white coat helps it camouflage in the northern forests during the winter. In spring, the hare's coat changes to brown and it blends nicely with the forest ground. Though the white coat is quite useful in winter, the greatest asset a snowshoe hare may have is its long, webbed hind feet, from which the snowshoe hare got its name. Its snowshoe-like feet allow it to run and jump on top of the snow to quickly escape predators. God also designed this animal to be able to eat a variety of foods—plant stems, pine needles, tree bark—in order to survive the harsh, barren winters.

Introduction

Refer to the graphic drawn on the board. Discuss some special events that happen every year, such as Christmas in December and summer's start in June. Ask each student to name his or her birth month and place a check mark next to that month. Point to the hottest month or snowiest month in your region. Relate that the months of the year begin and end at the same place; they follow a cycle.

Directed Instruction

1 Review the definition of *cycle*. (**a group of events that repeats in a certain order over and over**) Ask students why the months of the year occur in a cycle. (**Events happen each year in a certain order; the year begins and ends in the same time frame, place, or month.**) Lead a discussion about cycles that students may be familiar with, such as the hands of a clock, the circulatory system, a school bus route, or a baseball player rounding the bases. Emphasize that in each example something began and ended at the same place or in the same time frame.

Remind students that the seasons occur in a cycle. Point out that the cycle of seasons affects animals in different ways. Use a GLOBE to show the location of the Shetland Islands—northeast of Scotland. Ask students if they like to go horseback riding. (**Answers will vary.**) Inform the class that a very special kind of horse comes from these islands. It grows to be approximately 3.5 ft tall only. Compare its height to the height of your students. Have students look at and describe the picture of the Shetland pony on the first student page.

Beginning with the icon for winter, have students place a finger on the name of each season as you read what happens to the pony during that season. Check for understanding by asking how the pony's shedding can help the pony in the summer. (**The pony can be cooler in the hot summer.**) How does its thick hair help it in the winter? (**The pony can be warmer in the cold winter.**)

Share that God designed other animals with different ways to survive in cold weather. Read and discuss the information on the page about geese, fish, and insects.

2 Direct students' attention to the second page. Share that animals need shelter to stay alive. As living things, they also need food, water, and air. Read about the elk. Convey that if all the animals were elk, they would all have to move from place to place to find food in the winter. Read the information about the chipmunk. Have a volunteer read the way in which a snowshoe hare survives the winter. State that a hare is similar to a rabbit.

Assist students in completing the chart. Then read the sentences at the bottom of the page and allow time for students to use the words from the chart to fill in the blanks.

3 Divide the class into three groups—elk, chipmunks, and snowshoe hares—and allow the groups to act out the winter behavior of each. The "elk" can move from place to place by walking to one corner of the room. The "chipmunks" might rest their heads on their desks. The "snowshoe hares" could stay active by walking around the room and blending in.

Remind the class that God designed all these animals to be able to survive the winter's cold in different ways. Have volunteers name an animal and describe the way it survives the winter. (**Possible answers: Some kinds of sandhill cranes fly to warmer areas to live during the winter; some frogs dig deep holes into the soil below the frost line.**)

Notes:

➕ **Extension**

Materials
• Chalk or white board markers
• *The Mitten, 20th Anniversary Edition,* sheet

Guide students in creating a graph of months on the board. Have students color a box in the month they were born. Then compare the months. You may choose to relate this activity to the seasons by dividing the months into their seasons and discussing the data.

Share with students *The Mitten* by Jan Brett (Putnam, 2009). Guide students to pretend to be the animals in the story, and use a sheet as the mitten. Discuss how animals sleep and find food and shelter during the winter.

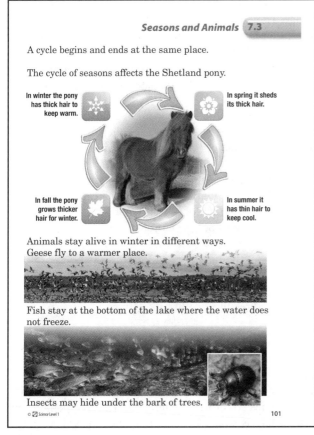

Seasons and Animals **7.3**

A cycle begins and ends at the same place.

The cycle of seasons affects the Shetland pony.

In winter the pony has thick hair to keep warm.

In spring it sheds its thick hair.

In fall the pony grows thicker hair for winter.

In summer it has thin hair to keep cool.

Animals stay alive in winter in different ways. Geese fly to a warmer place.

Fish stay at the bottom of the lake where the water does not freeze.

Insects may hide under the bark of trees.

© Science Level 1   101

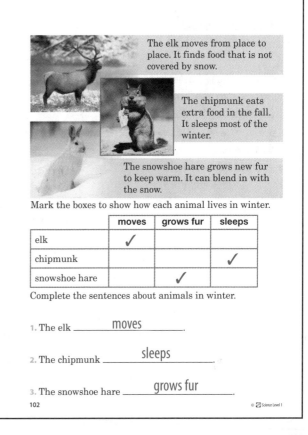

The elk moves from place to place. It finds food that is not covered by snow.

The chipmunk eats extra food in the fall. It sleeps most of the winter.

The snowshoe hare grows new fur to keep warm. It can blend in with the snow.

Mark the boxes to show how each animal lives in winter.

	moves	grows fur	sleeps
elk	✓		
chipmunk			✓
snowshoe hare		✓	

Complete the sentences about animals in winter.

1. The elk _____moves_____.

2. The chipmunk _____sleeps_____.

3. The snowshoe hare _____grows fur_____.

102   © Science Level 1

7.4 States of Matter

Students will observe and illustrate states of matter.

Materials

Introduction
• Ice cubes

Directed Instruction
• Tablespoon, vinegar, bottle, funnel, baking soda, balloon
• Goggles, teaspoons, salt, sand, clear plastic cups, water, spoons, marker

Preparation

Obtain 2 ICE CUBES. (*Introduction*)

Write the definition of *matter* on the board. (*Directed Instruction*)

Pour 4 TBSP OF VINEGAR into a clean BOTTLE. Use a FUNNEL to pour 1 TBSP OF BAKING SODA into a BALLOON. A funnel can be found in the ACSI Science Equipment Kit. Have items ready for a demonstration. (*Directed Instruction*)

Have Student Page 7.5 available so students can start an experiment they will finish in Lesson 7.5. Obtain GOGGLES, 2 TEASPOONS, 1 tsp SALT, 1 tsp SAND, 2 CLEAR PLASTIC CUPS, WATER, and 2 SPOONS for small groups or pairs of students. Have a MARKER available. (*Directed Instruction*)

Content

All matter is made of molecules. Three common states of matter are solid, liquid, and gas. States of matter have certain characteristics:
• Solids have a definite size and a definite shape. The temperature of an object indicates the speed at which its molecules are moving. The molecules of solids vibrate very slowly, but when heat is added, they move faster. Solid water is ice. If its molecules move fast enough, the solid changes to a liquid.
• Liquids have a definite size but not a definite shape. For example, liquid water has a definite size, but takes on the shape of its container. The molecules of liquids move more quickly than those of solids.
• A gas has no definite size or shape. It takes on the size and shape of its container, such as a balloon. Gaseous water is called *water vapor* and cannot be seen. The molecules of gases move more quickly than those of liquids. Examples of substances found naturally as a gas include carbon dioxide, nitrogen, and oxygen.

Introduction

Inform students that they will observe ice. Arrange them into a circle and show them TWO ICE CUBES. Direct students to pass around one ice cube. Set the other one on a desk. Ask students to predict which ice cube will melt first. (**Answers will vary.**) Play or sing a familiar song as students pass around the ice cube. They will notice that the ice cube they are passing melts faster than the ice on the desk. Convey that the warmth from students' hands made that ice cube melt faster. Have students return to their seat.

Directed Instruction

1 Read the definition of **matter**: *what things are made of.* Direct students' attention to the first page. Have a volunteer read the first two sentences. Emphasize that the most common states of matter are solid, liquid, and gas. Explain that ice is a solid. A solid has a its own shape. Have students name some solids and describe their shape. (**Possible answers:** *marble*: **round;** *pencil*: **long and thin**) Read the sentence about solids.

Invite a volunteer to read about liquids. Reiterate that a liquid takes the shape of its container. Ask students how the shape of the fruit punch changes. (**It changes from the shape of the cup to the container's shape.**)

Then have a student read the sentence about gas. Inform students that a gas fills what it is inside of. Clarify that the gasoline in a car is not the same as a gas. Discuss how air fills a balloon. Ask what happens if too much air goes into a balloon. (**It will pop.**) Demonstrate gas filling a balloon by placing the opening of the BALLOON with BAKING SODA over a BOTTLE with VINEGAR. Do not let the baking soda fall into the bottle until the balloon is secured over the bottle. Then tilt the balloon so the baking soda falls into the bottle. The baking soda will mix with the vinegar, creating carbon dioxide, and the balloon will inflate.

2 Guide students to turn to the second page. Read the sentence about water. Mention that an ice cube is water as a solid. Ask why an ice cube is a solid. (**It has a shape.**) Remind students of the demonstration with ice in the *Introduction*. Ask what happens when an ice cube is heated. (**It melts.**) Explain that it becomes water as a liquid. Ask what happens when the melted water boils. (**There is steam.**) Relate that steam is water that is

still in the liquid state, but water vapor, which cannot be seen, is the gaseous state.

Direct students' attention to the pictures of the pond on the page. Have students place a finger on each season of the pond as you discuss it. State that in winter, the water is frozen as a solid. In spring, the water melts as the temperature gets warmer. As the water heats up, it may be warm enough to swim in during summer. In fall, the water starts to freeze again. Allow time for students to draw pictures at the bottom of the page.

3 State that today students will start an experiment and will finish it in Lesson 7.5. Distribute GOGGLES, SALT, WATER, SAND, SPOONS, and CLEAR PLASTIC CUPS. Go through the first three steps on Student Page 7.5 with students:
1. Ask a question: Read the question that students will try to answer through the experiment.
2. Make a hypothesis: Ask students what they think will happen to the water. Have them write their guess. (**Answers will vary.**)
3. Plan and do a test: Explain that student groups will plan and do an experiment to test their hypothesis. Pour 1 tsp of salt into one cup of water, and 1 tsp of sand into another cup of water. Use different spoons to stir the sand and water. The salt will dissolve in the water, but the sand will not. Share that you will mark the beginning water level of each cup with a MARKER. Prepare a third cup with saltwater and cover it. Share that students will test water in this third cup that is covered to see what happens to the water in it. Place all the cups in a warm or sunny area. Explain that students will see the results tomorrow.

➕ Extension

Materials
• Cornstarch, water, food coloring, pan, speaker

Mix 2 parts cornstarch with 1 part water and add a few drops of food coloring to create a unique substance. Encourage a debate whether the substance is solid or liquid. Students will notice that it takes the shape of its container, but it also holds its own shape if students try to penetrate through it. The substance placed in a pan on a speaker will jump and vibrate on certain test frequencies (less than 50 Hz). Share that this cornstarch substance is called *oobleck*.

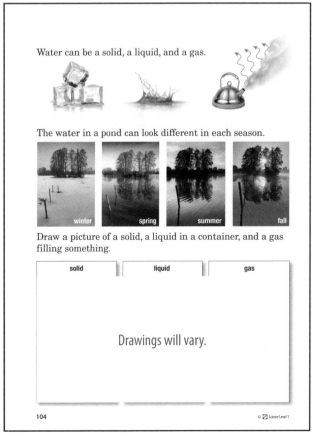

7.5 Seasons and Weather

Students will experiment with the properties of water and make a model of clouds.

Materials

Introduction
- Bar of Ivory soap, microwave-safe plate, microwave, oven mitt

Directed Instruction
- Newspaper, shaving cream, clear cups, water, blue food coloring, eyedroppers

Preparation

Purchase a fresh BAR OF IVORY SOAP. Have available a MICROWAVE-SAFE PLATE. Place a MICROWAVE in the classroom in a location where students can see it. Have an OVEN MITT available. (*Introduction*)

Gather NEWSPAPER as well as a can of SHAVING CREAM. The newspaper will be used to cover desks. For each student, obtain a CLEAR CUP of WATER, a CLEAR CUP of WATER tinted with BLUE FOOD COLORING, and an EYEDROPPER. (*Directed Instruction*)

Safety

Use caution when removing the hot plate and soap from the oven.

Food coloring can stain clothing and other objects. Caution students to be careful.

Content

Water moves between Earth and Earth's atmosphere in a continuous cycle. Water evaporates from plants, bodies of water, soil, and even humans. Liquid water changes to gaseous water called *water vapor*. Air containing water vapor can rise and cool. The water vapor can then condense onto dust particles, creating droplets that form a cloud. The droplets combine until a drop is formed that is too heavy to stay suspended in the air. The drop then falls to Earth as precipitation in the form of rain, snow, sleet, or hail, depending upon the temperature of the air. This movement of water from Earth to atmosphere and back completes one cycle.

Introduction

Place a fresh BAR OF IVORY SOAP on a MICROWAVE-SAFE PLATE. Heat the soap in a MICROWAVE for about 2 min. Students will notice the soap begin to foam and look like a cloud as it is heated. Remove the plate with an OVEN MITT. Since Ivory soap has pockets of air, the air expands when heated. (If you would like to repeat the experiment for small groups of students, cut a bar into smaller sections and microwave one section at a time.)

Directed Instruction

1 State that today students are going to learn about weather and clouds. Remind students of the experiment they started in Lesson 7.4. Gather the cups from the windowsill and ask students to observe any changes in the water. Have students complete the rest of the experiment on Student Page 7.5:

  4. Record and analyze your results: Ask students what happened to the water. (**It went down.**) Reinforce that the water levels are not the same as they were at the beginning of the experiment because some of the water evaporated. Convey that when water evaporates, it changes into gas and goes into the air. Ask students where the water is. (**in the air**) Where is the salt? (**on the sides of the cup**) Did the salt evaporate? (**No.**) Permit students to observe the remaining white salt deposits. Ask where the water is from the second cup. (**in the air**) Where is the sand? (**in the cup**) Did the sand evaporate? (**No.**) Where is the water level of the covered cup? (**the same as it was the day before**) Why did it not evaporate? (**The water could not get out of the covered container.**)

  5. Make a conclusion: Have students compare the results with their hypothesis. Reassure students that scientific inquiry is not about being right or wrong; it is about discovering something they did not know before or confirming something they do know.

  6. Share your results: Have students share with a classmate what they learned about water from their experiment.

  Reiterate that the water from the experiment evaporated, or changed into a gas, and went into the air. Convey that the water in the air can help form a cloud or can become rain, dew, frost, hail, sleet, or snow.

2 Have students turn to the second page. Invite a volunteer to read the sentences at the top of the page. Point out the gray clouds in the background of the picture.

  Direct students' attention to the calendar in the middle of the page. Guide students to use the calendar to fill in the graph at the bottom of their page. Ask questions to check for comprehension: Which season had the most rainfall? (**spring**) Which season had the least amount of rain? (**summer**) Which season had more rain—winter or fall? (**It rained the same amount both seasons.**) Why do you think flowers and plants grow well in spring? (**Answers will vary but should include that all the extra rain in spring helps them grow.**)

3 To demonstrate rainfall from clouds, cover desks with NEWSPAPER, and distribute a CLEAR CUP of WATER, a CUP of BLUE TINTED WATER, and an EYEDROPPER to each student. Fill the top of the clear cup with SHAVING CREAM. State that the shaving cream is like a cloud. Point out that when a cloud becomes heavy with water, it rains. Instruct students to add drops of blue water on top of the shaving cream until it falls below the cloud like rain. Advise students to be careful not to spill their cups of water.

Notes:

✚ Extension

Materials
• Lidded glass jar, hot water, ice, match, dark paper

Demonstrate how water can evaporate and condense into a cloud. Add ½ in. hot water to the jar. Turn the lid upside down and place ice in it. Set the lid on the jar. Encourage students to note the buildup of condensation on the sides of the jar. Light the match, blow it out, and quickly drop it into the jar. Immediately replace the lid. Hold the dark paper behind the jar and look for clouds to form inside. Remove the lid to allow the clouds to escape from the jar. Lead a discussion about how the liquid water turned to water vapor, which attached to the dust from the burnt match and then formed into a cloud.

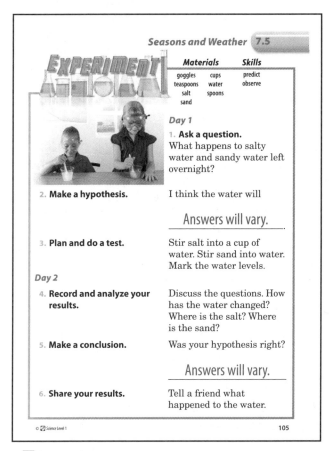

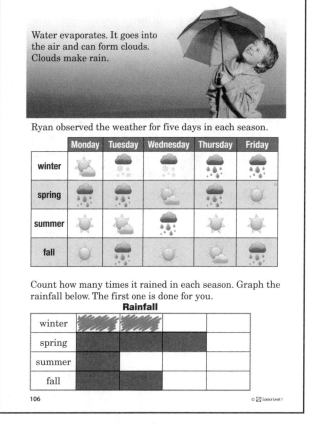

Content

Galileo Galilei is commonly credited as the inventor of the thermometer around 1592. Temperature scales were introduced by Daniel Gabriel Fahrenheit and Anders Celsius in the 1700s. Since then, a wide variety of thermometers have emerged for the purpose of reading temperatures in weather, medicine, and cooking. The typical mercury thermometer is starting to be phased out, especially in the home, because skin contact with mercury, which could occur if the thermometer is broken or not properly disposed of, is known to be poisonous. Most recently, digital and infrared thermometers are becoming the standard. New technology, such as highly accurate and quick-reading electronic thermometers, is constantly being developed.

Introduction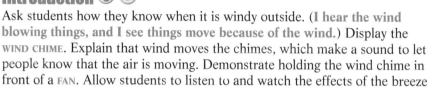

Ask students how they know when it is windy outside. (**I hear the wind blowing things, and I see things move because of the wind.**) Display the WIND CHIME. Explain that wind moves the chimes, which make a sound to let people know that the air is moving. Demonstrate holding the wind chime in front of a FAN. Allow students to listen to and watch the effects of the breeze blowing through the chime.

Directed Instruction

1 Review with students that temperature tells how hot or cold something is. Direct students' attention to the first page and read the first two paragraphs. Ask what is used to measure temperature. (**a thermometer**) Help students determine what number values the thermometer indicates. (**38, 100**) Count by tens and then by fives to draw students' attention to the increments of degrees. Display **TM-7.6A Thermometer**. Point out the °F at the top and explain that it stands for *degrees Fahrenheit*. Explain that the °C stands for *degrees Celsius*. People in the United States typically use the Fahrenheit scale to measure temperature. People in other parts of the world use the Celsius scale. Discuss the temperatures of a hot day and a cool day, and the temperature at which water freezes. Assist students in rereading the temperature of the thermometer on the page and stating the degrees with the correct scale. (**38°C, 100°F**)

2 Have a volunteer read the paragraph above the chart. Guide the class in completing the activity in the middle of the page. Use a THERMOMETER to measure the temperatures of the air in the classroom, a CUP of WATER, and a CUP of SOIL. Allow time for students to enter these temperatures onto their chart. Place the 2 cups outside for 2 hr and then record all three outdoor temperatures. Discuss the results. Direct students to count up from the lesser value to the greater value or to subtract the lesser value from the greater value to get the difference of the higher and lower temperatures. Guide students to answer the questions at the bottom of the page.

Share that a special kind of thermometer may be used by a parent or doctor to determine whether a person has a fever. State that a person's normal body temperature is around 98.6°F, but a person who is sick may have a higher temperature.

3 Direct students' attention to the second page. Read the sentence at the top. Share that after a rain gauge fills with rain, a person can record how

much rain has fallen over a period of time. State that many rain gauges are now digital. Have a volunteer read the information about making a rain gauge. You may choose to make a rain gauge as a class project by using a cup and a ruler or opt to encourage students to do this at home. Then read the information about a windsock. Point out the compass for students to identify the direction of the wind. (**from the east to the west**)

4 Distribute **BLM 7.6A Thermometer** to each pair of students. Allow time for pairs to work—one student saying a temperature and the other pointing to it on the thermometer. Have partners discuss what season it might be if the temperature outside were 100°F (**summer**), 60°F (**spring or fall**), and 20°F (**winter**).

Notes:

⊕ Extension

Materials
• String, sticks, small items
• Bottle, food coloring, water, straw, clay, trays

Have students make a few strings of small items (like keys, beads, shells, and washers). Direct students to tie the strings of items to a stick to make a wind chime.

Make your own thermometer. Fill a small bottle two-thirds full of tinted cold water and insert a clear straw to 2 in. below the water level. Tightly seal clay around the upright straw and bottle lip. After several minutes, the water level will move up or down the straw depending on the surrounding temperature. Try placing the jar in a tray of hot water or cold water, near a window, or in the refrigerator.

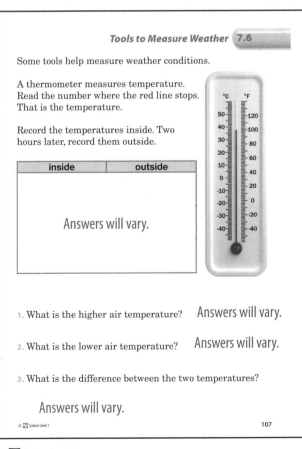

Tools to Measure Weather 7.6

Some tools help measure weather conditions.

A thermometer measures temperature. Read the number where the red line stops. That is the temperature.

Record the temperatures inside. Two hours later, record them outside.

inside	outside

Answers will vary.

1. What is the higher air temperature? Answers will vary.

2. What is the lower air temperature? Answers will vary.

3. What is the difference between the two temperatures?

Answers will vary.

© Science Level 1   107

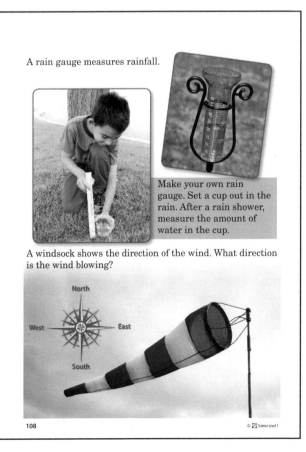

A rain gauge measures rainfall.

Make your own rain gauge. Set a cup out in the rain. After a rain shower, measure the amount of water in the cup.

A windsock shows the direction of the wind. What direction is the wind blowing?

108   © Science Level 1

Objective

Students will evaluate how technology helps people prepare for different kinds of weather.

Materials

Introduction
• Weather report

👋 Preparation

Record a local WEATHER REPORT that contains a Doppler radar image. The report may be obtained from a television station or from an online source. Prepare to show the report to students. (*Introduction*)

Content

Scientists measure weather conditions in many ways. Their measurements help predict weather. The prediction allows people to make necessary preparations that can ultimately save lives. Doppler radar equipment is used to make an image. The colors of the image indicate the intensity and type of precipitation. Doppler radar was first introduced in the early 1990s. Since then, Doppler technology, such as duel polarization, has advanced to give scientists more accurate and timely forecast information. A tracking system of Doppler radars called *NEXRAD* is able to detect details of storms and weather across the United States. Besides Doppler radar, weather satellites play an important role in detecting weather conditions from the satellites' orbits about 22,000 miles above Earth. These satellites locate not only cloud systems and weather conditions, but also pollution, sandstorms, and ocean currents by using infrared and visual imagery.

Introduction 👋

Play a WEATHER REPORT from a local news station for students. Point out the Doppler radar images on the screen. Demonstrate how to tell what the current weather is and how to predict what weather may come on the basis of the radar image. Point out any rain or storms in the area.

Directed Instruction ➕

1 Ask students how they might be able to notice that a storm is coming without using a weather report. (**Possible answers: The sky gets dark; it gets windy; it gets cold; people go inside.**) Share that God designed people with the ability to observe by using their senses. By observing and recognizing signs of an approaching storm, people know to take shelter. Share that some people with special training and equipment can predict what the weather will be like a few days from now.

2 Write *meteorologist* on the board in syllables (*me·te·o·ro·lo·gist*). Have students repeat the word several times. Direct students' attention to the first page. Read the first paragraph. Point out that people who report the weather on television may be meteorologists. These scientists use tools that help determine what the weather conditions are and what they might be in the days to come.

Have students place a finger on the white dome in the first photo. Explain that this picture shows the outside of Doppler radar equipment. Point out the different colors of the second picture—the Doppler radar image. The colors show where and how hard it is raining. Read the caption. Ask how Doppler radar pictures can help people. (**The pictures tell people what the weather is like now and what weather is coming.**) Explain that sometimes a meteorologist studies a Doppler radar picture that indicates the formation of a big storm. He or she can then warn people about the storm.

Point out the third image. State that as this weather satellite moves around Earth, it monitors weather conditions. This satellite can detect wind, snow, and other types of weather. Point out the satellite image of Hurricane Irene. This hurricane affected the United States and the Caribbean in 2011.

Then have students share in pairs what it would be like to be a meteorologist. Their discussion might include use of some of the equipment shown in this lesson. They may also discuss what it might feel like to help save lives by warning people of dangerous weather.

3 Guide students to turn to their second page. Convey that the page includes examples of dangerous weather. When meteorologists warn people of possible severe weather, the people can prepare themselves. Read through the section on thunderstorms. State that if students hear thunder or see lightning, they should go indoors immediately. Being around trees and water is especially dangerous during thunderstorms.

Move to the next section about tornadoes. State that meteorologists are usually able to warn people before a tornado approaches. Sometimes a warning siren sounds. Emphasize that during a tornado students should find shelter away from windows and go to the lowest place in the shelter, like a basement. Review tornado drill procedures for your school.

Read the section about hurricanes. State that hurricanes affect people on the coast the most because they are closest to the ocean. Some cities may even have to evacuate, or go to a safer place, until a hurricane passes.

Reiterate that weather technology and meteorologists can help warn people and prepare them for severe weather. Discuss the questions at the bottom of the page. Then emphasize that God also protects His people and is with them through any storm. Read a few of the following Bible verses as reassurance: **Deuteronomy 31:6**; **Nahum 1:7**; **Psalm 46:1–3**, **7**; **Psalm 107:29**; **Luke 8:24**; **1 Peter 5:7**. Allow students time to share with a partner one way God has protected them or their family.

➕ Extension

Materials
• Jar, water, dish soap
• Mirror, glass, water, flashlight

Plan for a class field trip to a local news station.

Create a tornado in a jar of water. Add a drop of liquid dish soap to the water. Screw on the lid and swirl for about 5 sec.

Share the Bible truth about Noah and God's promise evidenced through the rainbow. Place a small mirror in a large, clear glass of water. Darken the classroom. State that when Christians find themselves in dark and scary places, God is still with them. Shine a flashlight onto the mirror; notice the colors of the rainbow appear on the opposite wall. (Adjust mirror as necessary.)

TECH CONNECT

Meteorologists study the weather. They use technology to predict the weather. They can tell if it might rain or snow.

Here is a Doppler radar tower.

This weather satellite goes around Earth.

The yellow and red colors show that it is raining.

This image of Hurricane Irene was taken from a satellite.

TECH CONNECT

A thunderstorm has wind, rain, lightning, and thunder. Keep away from trees.

A tornado has spinning winds and a funnel-shaped cloud. Keep away from windows.

A hurricane has powerful winds. It can have rain, thunder, and lightning. Go to a shelter or another safe place.

1. How does Doppler radar help people?
2. How can people stay safe in a thunderstorm? a tornado? a hurricane?

Materials

Introduction
• Video camera (optional)

Directed Instruction
• Blue construction paper, tape
• BLM 7.8A Season Facts
• BLM 7.8B Chapter 7 Test

Preparation

If desired, obtain a VIDEO CAMERA to record student videos. Obtain parental consent. (*Introduction*)

Write the word *evaporate* on the board in large letters. Place a cloud cut from BLUE CONSTRUCTION PAPER on each letter and attach the paper to the board with TAPE. (*Directed Instruction*)

Draw the following Creation web on the board. (*Directed Instruction*)

God's Purposeful Design

Earth

Seasons

Winter   Spring   Summer   Fall

Print **BLM 7.8A Season Facts** for each student. (*Directed Instruction*)

Print **BLM 7.8B Chapter 7 Test** for each student. (*Directed Instruction*)

Introduction 🖐

Divide students into four groups. Assign each group a season. Have groups write a weather report for that season. Direct them to state the temperature and to tell if the day is cloudy, sunny, windy, foggy, or snowy. Have the groups describe what trees might look like during their assigned season. Encourage students to present their report as a television meteorologist would. Have students share their report. Use the reports as an opportunity to assess students' understanding of the characteristics of seasons. You may choose to use a VIDEO CAMERA to record the groups and then share their presentations on your school's website or in an e-mail to parents.

Directed Instruction 🖐 ➕

1 Play the game Season Trivia. Explain that students should try to identify the hidden word on the board. For each question a student answers correctly, that student will get to remove one cloud made of BLUE CONSTRUCTION PAPER to reveal a letter of the hidden word. Read each clue and allow students to guess the answer and remove a cloud.

1. I show numbers. I tell you if something is hot or cold. (**a thermometer**)
2. I am a weather tool. I measure how much rain there has been after a rain shower. (**a rain gauge**)
3. I am a big, dangerous windstorm. I am shaped like a funnel. (**a tornado**)
4. I am something that has many colors. I can be seen in the sky mainly in the summer after a rainstorm. (**a rainbow**)
5. I am matter that you can see and touch. I have my own shape and size. (**a solid**)
6. I am a dangerous storm with very high winds. I usually form over the ocean. (**a hurricane**)
7. I am a mammal. My thick coat of hair helps me survive in the cold. I shed my thick coat in the spring. I am three and one-half feet tall. (**a Shetland pony**)
8. I am a weather tool. I make a picture so a meteorologist can predict the weather. (**Doppler radar**)
9. I am made of water. Soon the water in me may get too heavy and drop to the ground. (**a cloud**)

Ask students to read the hidden word together. (**evaporate**) Remind them that when water turns from a liquid to a gas, it evaporates and forms water vapor. The water vapor may then form a cloud. Ask students what water does when it turns from a liquid to a solid. (**It freezes.**) What must water do to turn from a solid to a liquid? (**melt or warm up**)

2 Review the definitions of *season* and *matter*. (*season*: **a time of year,** *matter*: **what things are made of**) Distribute **BLM 7.8A Season Facts** to each student.

Read the words in the Word Bank. Read the facts and say "blank" for the missing word. Give students time to fill in the words. When students have completed the page, ask a volunteer to read each fact with the answer. Ask another volunteer to explain the fact in his or her own words.

3 Direct students' attention to the Creation web on the board. Remind students that God purposefully designed Earth. Most people live in locations where there are four seasons. Ask students to name the four seasons. (**winter, spring, summer, fall**) What is the temperature like in each of these seasons? (**Winter is the coldest season. Summer is the hottest. Spring and fall both have milder temperatures.**)

4 Use student pages as a review or pretest. Complete these pages with your class. Have students brainstorm about seasons before they write their journal response. Write suggested words on the board. Have students listen as you read **Song of Solomon 2:11–12a** from the student page. Continue to read verses 12b and 13a. Ask students which season is described in the phrases *winter is past, flowers appear, the cooing of doves is heard*, and *the fig tree forms its early fruit*. (**spring**)

You may use **BLM 7.8B Chapter 7 Test** for individual assessment. Read through this page with your class. Provide as much reading support as necessary. You may choose to use BLM 7.8B as an oral assessment or not to do it at all.

5 Chapter 7 Seasons and Matter has been completed. Its pages can be stapled and sent home as a booklet to be shared with a family member.

Notes:

 Extension

Materials
- *To Everything There Is a Season*
- Construction paper, crayons

Read with students *To Everything There Is a Season* by Jude Daly (Eerdmans, 2009). Discuss the words cited from Ecclesiastes on each page. Discuss how just as the earth has seasons, people have seasons of their life as well.

Have students make a minibook by folding a piece of construction paper in half. On the front, have students write *Thank God for the Seasons*. In the center of the book, have them write a sentence thanking God for clouds, rain, sunshine, plants, water, oceans, or lakes. Allow time for students to draw and to color a picture that shows what they have written.

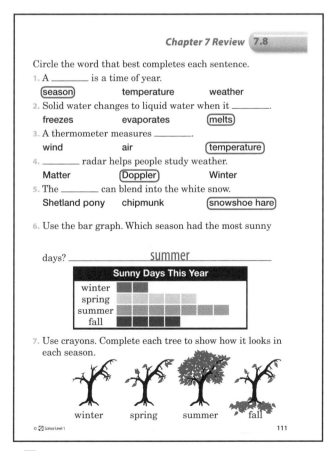

Space
Chapter 8

Key Ideas

- Earth and seven other planets each follow an orbit around the sun.
- Earth's orbit accounts for days, seasons, and shadows on Earth.
- Many people have explored space.
- Scientists and other people have created many inventions because of space exploration.

8.0 Chapter Preparation

Space

Vocabulary

orbit
space
telescope

Looking Ahead

- In **Lesson 8.4**, each student will need a paper-towel tube.
- Plan for students to create a space exhibit in **Lesson 8.7** if desired.

Introduction

Jeremiah 32:17 inspires an observational and imaginative study of outer space: "Ah, Sovereign Lord, You have made the heavens and the earth by Your great power and outstretched arm. Nothing is too hard for You." In this chapter, students start with the study of the mechanics of day and night and seasons, and then they learn the location of Earth's atmosphere and outer space. An introduction of things in space, including the planets, the moon, and the stars, helps students better understand what they are observing in the night sky. Inventions developed during the course of space missions add another dimension to the need for and relativity of this area of science. A time line of space exploration challenges students to dream and to "reach for the stars."

About This Chapter

Lesson 8.1 – Earth

Materials

- Globe
- Flashlight
- Balloons
- Markers
- Scissors
- Tape
- Card stock
- Paper clips
- Magnets

Lesson Content

Day and night occur as Earth rotates in one complete cycle each day. Earth's movement around the sun also accounts for the seasons. The sun creates shadows that differ depending on the time of day and the angle of the sun's rays on Earth's surface.

Lesson 8.2 – Atmosphere and Space

Materials

- Boots

Lesson Content

The atmosphere surrounds and protects Earth. Beyond Earth's atmosphere is space. Scientists have discovered stars, planets, moons, and meteoroids in space. People can look at space through telescopes.

Lesson 8.3 – Sun, Planets, and Moon

Materials

- Scissors
- Brass fasteners

Lesson Content

The sun is Earth's nearest star. It provides heat and light for all living things. Eight planets orbit the sun. One moon orbits Earth. A phase of the moon is determined by the sunlit portion as seen from Earth.

Lesson 8.4 – Stars

Materials

- Crayons
- Tape
- Aluminum foil
- Paper-towel tubes
- Construction paper
- Flashlights

Lesson Content

Stars are balls of hot gas. Throughout history, people have looked at the stars in the night sky. Sometimes people have looked at a group of stars and have imagined that the stars formed a shape of something they knew. These groups of stars, such as the Big Dipper, have been identified and labeled.

Lesson 8.5 – Exploring Space

Materials
- Tape
- Scissors

Lesson Content

Scientists have been sending spacecraft into outer space since the early 1900s. Many discoveries have been made by dedicated scientists, and new discoveries continue to increase through the use of technology.

Lesson 8.6 – Tech Connect

Materials

• Paper clips	• Rulers	• Straw	• Bags
• Crayons	• Tape	• Balloons	
• Yarn	• String	• Goggles	

Lesson Content

Exploring space has led to many different inventions, including cell phones and Doppler radar. A class experiment further explains the mechanics of one invention, the rocket.

Lesson 8.7 – Chapter 8 Review

Materials
- Construction paper
- Scissors
- Hole punch
- String
- Tape (optional)
- Poster board

Teacher Resources

Carrying the Fire: An Astronaut's Journeys by Michael Collins. Farrar, Straus and Giroux, 2009.

The Heavens Proclaim His Glory: A Spectacular View of Creation Through the Lens of the NASA Hubble Telescope. Thomas Nelson, 2010.

The Privileged Planet. DVD. Illustra Media, 2010.

Student Resources

Astronaut Handbook by Meghan McCarthy. Knopf, 2008.

National Geographic Little Kids First Big Book of Space by Catherine D. Hughes. National Geographic Society Children's Books, 2012.

One Giant Leap by Robert Burleigh. Philomel, 2009.

Supplemental Materials

Blackline Masters
8.1A Girl
8.1B Earth's Orbit
8.2A Recipe: Solar S'mores
8.3A "All Eight Planets"
8.3B Moon Phases, Part 1
8.3C Moon Phases, Part 2
8.5A Rocket
8.7A Stars
8.7B Space Facts
8.7C Chapter 8 Test

Transparency Masters
8.2A Atmosphere
8.4A The Big Dipper
8.4B Bear
8.4C Swan, Part 1
8.4D Swan, Part 2

Computer Presentation
8.2 Space

8.1 Earth

Objective

Students will observe and discuss how Earth's rotation causes days, seasons, and shadows.

Materials

Introduction
• BLM 8.1A Girl, globe, flashlight

Directed Instruction
• BLM 8.1A Girl, balloons, markers, scissors, tape, flashlight
• BLM 8.1B Earth's Orbit, card stock, scissors, tape, paper clips, small magnets

Preparation

Print one copy of **BLM 8.1A Girl** and cut out the figure. Obtain for a demonstration a GLOBE and a FLASHLIGHT. (*Introduction*)

Have available for small groups a copy of **BLM 8.1A Girl**, a BALLOON, a MARKER, SCISSORS, and TAPE. Obtain an extra set of supplies for yourself. Obtain 1 FLASHLIGHT. (*Directed Instruction*)

Write the definition of *orbit* on the board. (*Directed Instruction*)

Print **BLM 8.1B Earth's Orbit** onto CARD STOCK for each student. Gather SCISSORS, TAPE, a PAPER CLIP, and a SMALL MAGNET for each student. (*Directed Instruction*)

Safety

Inform students that it is very dangerous to stare at the sun.

Content

Earth makes one complete rotation in approximately 24 hours. As Earth rotates, it revolves around the sun. Earth's rotation accounts for day and night; Earth's tilt, angle, and orbital position create the seasons.

A shadow forms when an opaque object blocks light. The position of Earth in relationship to the sun affects the position and length of the shadow.

Introduction 🖐

Tape the figure from **BLM 8.1A Girl** on the equator of the GLOBE. Choose a volunteer to shine a FLASHLIGHT on the equator and explain that it represents the sun. Turn the classroom lights off to make this more effective. Turn the globe counterclockwise from the north in one complete rotation. As the paper figure faces the sun, state that it is day for people who live there. As the paper figure faces away from the sun, convey that it is night for people who live there. Share with the class that the paper figure just went through day and night. For real people, day and night happen over a 24-hour time period. Repeat several rotations of the globe. Ask how this shows a cycle. (**A repeating pattern of day and night occurs.**)

Directed Instruction 🖐

1 Reiterate that Earth completes a cycle in one day and one night. Direct students' attention to the first student page; read the first paragraph. Inform students that they will complete the activity that the children in the picture are doing to show how Earth's rotation makes day and night. Distribute **BLM 8.1A Girl**, a BALLOON, a MARKER, SCISSORS, and TAPE to small groups of students. Demonstrate how to draw a line around the balloon with a marker to represent the equator. Then, ask them to cut out the picture of the girl and to tape it to the balloon. Pick a volunteer to hold the FLASHLIGHT and, as with the globe, rotate the balloon to show one day and night cycle. Assist the groups as they prepare for the activity. Move from group to group and shine the flashlight on the equator as they rotate the balloon. Assess understanding by stopping the rotation with the paper person toward the flashlight and ask if it is day or night for the people who live there. (**day**) Rotate the balloon, stop it with the paper person away from the flashlight and ask if it is day or night for the people who live there. (**night**)

2 State that while Earth spins, it also follows a path, called *an orbit,* around the sun. Read the definition from the board—**orbit**: *the path a planet takes around the sun.* Convey that Earth is a planet and it moves around the sun. Earth's orbit around the sun creates the seasons. Demonstrate this by holding the balloon. Have a student stand with the flashlight while you walk around the student, spinning the balloon. Tilt the balloon slightly toward the light and state that the earth is tilted as well. Point out that the part tilted toward the sun is being warmed by the sun and is having summer. Ask students what season the people on the opposite side of Earth would be having, where the sun is not warming as much. (**winter**) Point out that even though the student with the flashlight has to move to keep the light on the balloon, the sun shines light in all directions; it does not spin. Allow students to practice moving their balloon around the flashlight and pointing out who would be having summer and winter on their balloon. Direct students' attention to the bottom of the page. Read and discuss the information about seasons.

3 Instruct students to turn to the second page. Explain that because Earth rotates, people see the sun in the eastern sky each morning. Read the first two sentences. Have students place a finger on the picture of the sunrise as a volunteer reads the next two sentences and students circle the correct answers for morning, noon, and evening.

Read the information about shadows. Have students place a finger on the first house and its shadow. Reiterate that this shadow is short. The sun is high in the sky; it is noon. Direct students' attention to the second house, which has a long shadow. Ask if the sun is high or low in the picture. (low) The sun's position indicates that it is morning or evening. Discuss how shadows can change throughout a day. Remark that the shadow in the picture is the shape of the house. Then answer the questions together.

Allow students to pick an object to make a shadow. Shine the flashlight onto a wall. Allow each student to place an object in front of the flashlight. Ask if the shadows look like the objects. (Yes.) Can you tell what the object is by looking at its shadow? (Yes, in most cases.) Share that when the sun shines, it makes shadows all over Earth.

4 The following activity will help students understand that Earth moves around the sun. Distribute **BLM 8.1B Earth's Orbit**, SCISSORS, TAPE, a PAPER CLIP, and a SMALL MAGNET. Ask students to cut out Earth at the bottom of BLM 8.1B, to tape it to a paper clip, and to place it on the orbit line on the CARD-STOCK copies. Direct students to place the magnet under the line so that the magnet attracts the paper clip. Guide them to move the magnet counterclockwise around the sun. Allow students to work with a partner.

➕ Extension

Materials
• Clay, toothpicks
• Sidewalk chalk

Have students make a clay model of Earth. Direct them to stick a toothpick through the center to represent the axis through the poles. Guide students to hold up their fist as the sun and to rotate their clay ball as they revolve it around the sun.

Take the class outdoors in the early morning. Have students use sidewalk chalk to trace around a partner's shadow. Take the class outdoors again at noon. Ask student pairs how the two shadows are different. (The noon shadow is shorter than the morning shadow.) How are the two shadows alike? (They are both shadows of the student.)

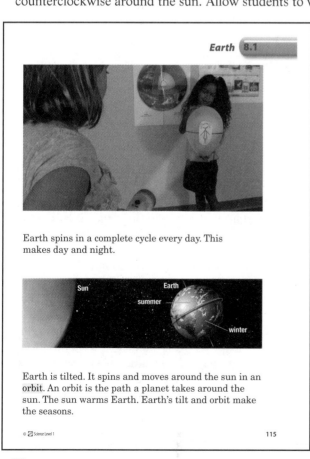

Earth 8.1

Earth spins in a complete cycle every day. This makes day and night.

Earth is tilted. It spins and moves around the sun in an orbit. An orbit is the path a planet takes around the sun. The sun warms Earth. Earth's tilt and orbit make the seasons.

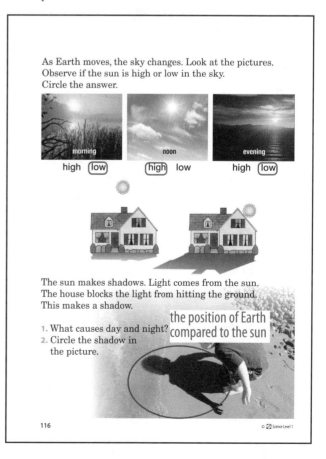

As Earth moves, the sky changes. Look at the pictures. Observe if the sun is high or low in the sky. Circle the answer.

morning — high (low)
noon — (high) low
evening — high (low)

The sun makes shadows. Light comes from the sun. The house blocks the light from hitting the ground. This makes a shadow.

1. What causes day and night? the position of Earth compared to the sun
2. Circle the shadow in the picture.

8.2 Atmosphere and Space

Objective

Students will distinguish between Earth's atmosphere and space.

Materials

Introduction
• Pair of rain boots

Directed Instruction
• TM-8.2A Atmosphere

Preparation

Obtain a PAIR OF RAIN BOOTS for a demonstration. (*Introduction*)

Select **TM-8.2A Atmosphere** for display. (*Directed Instruction*)

Write the definitions of *space* and *telescope* on the board. (*Directed Instruction*)

⚠ Safety

Remind students that it is very dangerous to stare at the sun.

Content

A blanket of air—the atmosphere—surrounds Earth. The components of the atmosphere at sea level include 78% nitrogen, 21% oxygen, and small amounts of other gases, including argon and carbon dioxide. The atmosphere thins, or is less dense, at locations farther from Earth's surface. The point at which the atmosphere ends and outer space begins is a bit vague. Layers of the atmosphere (approximate heights measured at sea level) include the following:

• Troposphere—from Earth's surface to about 6 to 10 miles; location of most weather
• Stratosphere—from 10 to 31 miles; contains the ozone layer
• Mesosphere—from 31 to over 50 miles
• Thermosphere—from about 50 to about 400 miles above Earth's surface

God's design of the atmosphere allows life on Earth to exist. The ozone layer in the stratosphere protects life on Earth from harmful gamma rays and X-ray radiation. The atmosphere is a source of oxygen, and it also protects Earth from objects such as meteoroids—small, solid objects that move through space. Meteoroids that enter the atmosphere are called *meteors* if they burn up in the atmosphere. If the meteoroids reach Earth without burning up, they are called *meteorites*.

Introduction

Display a PAIR OF RAIN BOOTS. Ask students how rain boots are useful. (**They keep my feet from getting wet.**) Explain that rain boots are made of a special material that stops water from coming into the boots. The boots also keep the feet warm. Share that similarly, God designed Earth with a sky, or atmosphere, to protect it. Read **Genesis 1:6–8** and lead a class discussion about the creation of the sky.

Directed Instruction

1 Display **TM-8.2A Atmosphere**. State that the atmosphere is all around Earth. Point out the height of the tall mountains, the clouds, the plane, and the huge distance to the beginning of space.

Direct students' attention to the first student page. Have a volunteer read the first three sentences. Ask volunteers to read the three bulleted sentences about how the atmosphere protects Earth. Stress that the atmosphere blocks only some of the harmful rays of the sun. Since some rays do reach Earth, it is important that people protect themselves with proper clothing or sunscreen when they are outside.

Reread the sentence about meteoroids. Ask students to describe what a shooting star looks like. (**a streak of light**) Share that a shooting star is not actually a star; it is usually a tiny piece of rock—a meteoroid, which can be the size of a pea or grain of sand—that is coming toward Earth's surface. Explain that the meteoroid lights up because it is burning up in the atmosphere. If it burns up completely, it is a meteor—a shooting star. If it hits Earth, it is a meteorite. Convey that the atmosphere causes most meteoroids to burn up before they hit Earth. Share that the moon has craters because it has no atmosphere; it is not protected from meteoroids.

2 Read the definition of the word **space**: *the area outside Earth's atmosphere*. Direct students to read it aloud with you from their page.

Draw students' attention to the pictures and offer some of the following information to encourage your class discussion:

- Star: Most stars are far away and are glowing balls of gas. The sun is Earth's closest star.
- Earth: It is shaped like a ball, or sphere, and has an atmosphere that can support life.
- Moon: Earth's moon orbits Earth. Its surface is bumpy and has craters from meteoroids hitting it.
- Mars: This is a planet near Earth. Mars is sometimes called *the red planet* because it looks red.
- Man-made satellite: This object orbits Earth and may be used for communication, such as taking pictures or sending phone or television signals around the world.
- *International Space Station*: This man-made space laboratory is where scientists perform many experiments.
- Hubble Space Telescope: This is a high-powered telescope that is orbiting Earth while taking photos of faraway objects in space.

3 Ask which of the five senses students would use to observe space. (**I would use my eyes to look.**) Have students turn to the second page. Read the sentences at the top, including the definition of **telescope**: *a tool that makes things that are far away appear closer and larger.* Ask students what a person might see in space when looking through the telescope. (**Possible answers: planets, moon, stars, chunks of rock, meteoroids, satellites**) Observe with students the pictures in the center of the page. Point out the details in the pictures that cannot be seen by the human eye from Earth. Answer the questions at the bottom with the class.

➕ Extension

Materials
- CP-8.2 Space
- BLM 8.2A Recipe: Solar S'mores, ingredients for s'mores

Present the slides about the atmosphere and telescopes from **CP-8.2 Space**.

Print **BLM 8.2A Recipe: Solar S'mores** and make the recipe with students. Discuss how the sun warms the s'mores just as it warms Earth. Convey that the aluminum foil and black paper help heat the food. Check student records for possible allergies.

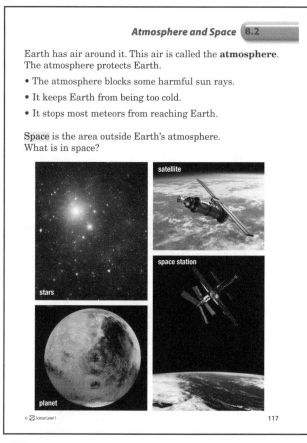

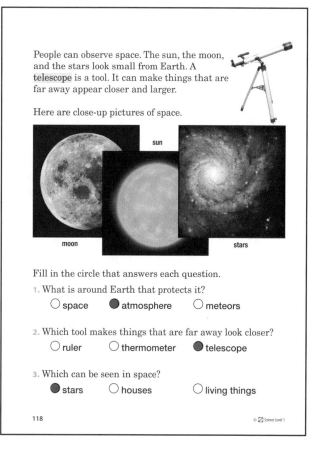

8.3 Sun, Planets, and Moon

Space

Objective

Students will compare the planets' orbits around the sun and compare the phases of the moon.

Materials

Introduction
• BLM 8.3A "All Eight Planets"

Directed Instruction
• BLMs 8.3B–C Moon Phases, Parts 1–2; scissors; brass fasteners

Preparation

Print **BLM 8.3A "All Eight Planets"** for each student. (*Introduction*)

Print **BLMs 8.3B–C Moon Phases, Parts 1–2**; scissors; and a BRASS FASTENER for each student. (*Directed Instruction*)

Content

The sun is Earth's closest star, and it provides heat and light to the whole solar system. The sun accounts for over 99% of the total mass of the solar system. The sun is a giant ball of gas, creating a massive amount of energy. The sun's core is over a million degrees hot. Because of its scorching temperature, no solid or liquid can exist on or near the sun.

The moon, the second brightest object seen from Earth, does not make its own light or heat. The light illuminated on the moon comes from the sun. Scientists' knowledge and exploration of the moon have assisted in predicting tides and creating the calendar. The moon and Earth have a strong gravitational pull toward each other. The orbits of the moon, Earth, and the sun account for solar and lunar eclipses.

Introduction

Engage students in singing a song about the sun and the planets from **BLM 8.3A "All Eight Planets"** to the tune of "Mary Had a Little Lamb."

Directed Instruction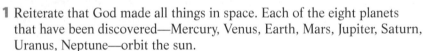

1 Reiterate that God made all things in space. Each of the eight planets that have been discovered—Mercury, Venus, Earth, Mars, Jupiter, Saturn, Uranus, Neptune—orbit the sun.

Have students turn to the first student page. Read the first paragraph about the sun. Explain that just as each student in this classroom has his or her own special name, this star has its own special name—*the sun*. Share that God made the sun and that the sun provides for life on Earth by giving off heat and light.

2 Remind students of the song from the *Introduction*. Ask how many planets travel around the sun. (**eight**) State that each planet travels in an orbit, just as Earth does.

Reiterate that Earth is one of the eight planets. Ask a volunteer to read the second paragraph—the one about Earth and the other planets. Direct students' attention to the image. Say the names of the eight planets and have students repeat the names after you. (Note that the distances from the planets to the sun in the illustration are not drawn to scale. Also, the planets do not line up in the same location in their orbits as shown.)

3 Read the questions about planets and allow time for volunteers to answer. Read and discuss **Genesis 1:16** from the page. Ask the class what the greater light is. (**the sun**) What is the lesser light? (**the moon**) Convey that the moon reflects the sun's light.

4 Direct students' attention to the second page. Select volunteers to read about the moon phases at the top of the page. Have students place a finger on the full moon, and have them describe how the moon looks. (**Answers will vary.**) Point out the second moon picture and ask if the moon changes shape. (**No.**) Can you see the whole circle in each picture? (**Answers will vary.**) Challenge students to see the rest of the moon that is in shadow. Reiterate that the lit part has light from the sun shining on it. Read the rest of the sentences about the moon. Complete the questions together.

5 Distribute **BLMs 8.3B–C Moon Phases, Parts 1–2**, SCISSORS, and BRASS FASTENERS. Read the directions for students to complete the activity. Assist students with the brass fasteners that join the two pieces. Guide students in turning the wheel to see each of the moon phases. Encourage them to share their wheel with a family member. Challenge students to also look outside for the moon before bed and to observe what it looks like.

Notes:

Sun, Planets, and Moon 8.3

The sun is a star. It heats and lights Earth. Plants, animals, and people need the sun.

Earth is one of the eight planets. The planets travel around the sun in an orbit.

Observe the distance from each planet to the sun.

1. Which planet is the closest to the sun? Which is the farthest?
   Mercury, Neptune
2. Which planet is the largest? Which is the smallest?
   Jupiter, Mercury
3. Which planet would you like to visit? Why?
   Answers will vary.

> God made two great lights—the greater light to govern the day and the lesser light to govern the night. He also made the stars.
> Genesis 1:16

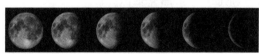

Earth has one moon. The moon orbits Earth.

The moon cannot make its own light. The light on the moon is from the sun.

The moon is round like a ball. Sometimes only part of the moon shows. Sometimes the moon does not show at all.

There is no air or water on the moon.

There are no living things.

The moon has deep holes, mountains, and flat space.

The first person to walk on the moon was Neil Armstrong.

Fill in the circle beside the answer.

1. Where does the light on the moon come from?
   ○ Earth   ● sun   ○ lamp

2. Are there living things on the moon?
   ○ yes   ● no

8.4 Stars

Content

Stars are large spheres of gas. Every star is unique, and scientists categorize stars by their magnitude of brightness. Atomic reactions keep a star hot until it burns out and dies.

The night sky is divided into 88 constellations. Though constellations are named after imagined configurations in the night sky, they are useful in tracking satellites and identifying and locating stars. Every known star can be associated with a constellation and thus assigned its place in the sky.

Introduction

Lead a class discussion from **Matthew 2:1–12** about the star that led the wise men to Jesus. Reinforce that God used a star to give people direction.

Directed Instruction

1 Ask a volunteer to describe what the stars in the night sky look like. (**Answers will vary.**) Direct students' attention to the first page. Have a volunteer read the question and the description of stars in the first paragraph. Discuss the information with students. Remind them that the sun is a star; it looks larger because it is closer than the other stars. Share that throughout history, people have looked at the stars in the night sky. Sometimes people would look at a group of stars and imagine the stars to be a shape of something they knew about. They imagined drawing lines from star to star to make an outline of a person, an animal, or an object. Share that one group of stars is called *the Big Dipper*. Ask a student to read the second paragraph. Display **TM-8.4A The Big Dipper**. Explain that people thought this group of stars looked like a dipper, or a ladle. Have students use a finger to trace the shape of the dipper made by the stars. Compare the pattern of stars to the picture of the dipper, or ladle.

2 Direct students to turn to the second page. Ask the question and read the directions at the top of the page. Display **TM-8.4B Bear** or present the section about the Bear from **CP-8.2 Space**. Use TM-8.4B or CP-8.2 as a guide to show students how to connect the stars. Allow time for students to complete the exercise and permit them to use a CRAYON to connect the stars. Convey to students that some lines have already been drawn for them. Challenge students to find the Big Dipper in the Bear. Point out the Big Dipper on the image you have displayed.

3 Read **Job 9:9** from the student page. Reinforce that God made the stars and people have used their imagination to see shapes inspired by the position of the stars. Discuss that the group of stars called *Bear* is mentioned in the Bible.

4 Display **TM-8.4C Swan, Part 1** or present the first slide about the swan from CP-8.2. Have the class observe the stars. Ask students if they see a pattern that could be something they know. (**Answers will vary.**) Share that many years ago, people imagined seeing a swan. Point out the wings and long neck of the imaginary swan. State that you will show them a picture that will help them see the imaginary swan. Show the swan from **TM-8.4D Swan, Part 2** or the next slide from CP-8.2. Explain that people used their imagination to make star pictures, or shapes, using God's placement of the stars.

5 Display the prepared star picture. Read the directions from the student page about how to make a star picture. Encourage students to see the star pattern on the black paper the girl is holding. Convey that students will now make their own star patterns. Assist each student in using TAPE to attach a 4 IN. SQUARE OF ALUMINUM FOIL to one end of a PAPER-TOWEL TUBE. After students think of a pattern for a picture, direct them to very carefully use a pencil point to make holes in the foil. Assist students in using a FLASHLIGHT to shine through the tube onto a sheet of DARK CONSTRUCTION PAPER to see a star picture. Turn off the lights in the classroom to make this more effective. Allow time for students to interact and to discuss their star pattern.

Notes:

➕ Extension

Materials
- *Twinkle, the Star of Bethlehem*
- Black construction paper, star stickers, white crayons

Share with students *Twinkle, the Star of Bethlehem* by Christine Faith Hoffman (CreateSpace, 2010). This fictional book shares how Twinkle was chosen for a special task of leading the wise men and others to Jesus, and how God also has a purpose for each of His children.

Have students draw a pencil outline of an animal on black construction paper. Then instruct them to place 10 star stickers on the animal. Guide students to use a white crayon to draw lines to connect the stars to make an outline of their animal.

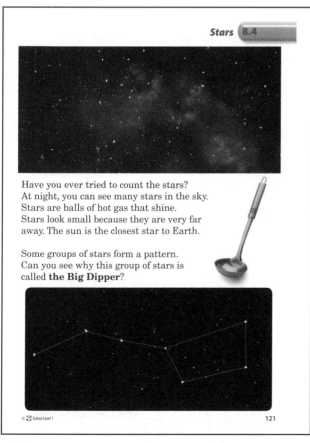

Stars 8.4

Have you ever tried to count the stars? At night, you can see many stars in the sky. Stars are balls of hot gas that shine. Stars look small because they are very far away. The sun is the closest star to Earth.

Some groups of stars form a pattern. Can you see why this group of stars is called **the Big Dipper**?

© Science Level 1   121

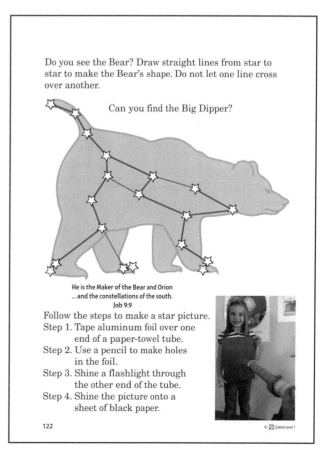

Do you see the Bear? Draw straight lines from star to star to make the Bear's shape. Do not let one line cross over another.

Can you find the Big Dipper?

He is the Maker of the Bear and Orion ... and the constellations of the south.
Job 9:9

Follow the steps to make a star picture.
Step 1. Tape aluminum foil over one end of a paper-towel tube.
Step 2. Use a pencil to make holes in the foil.
Step 3. Shine a flashlight through the other end of the tube.
Step 4. Shine the picture onto a sheet of black paper.

122   © Science Level 1

8.5 Exploring Space

Content

Dr. Robert Goddard sent up the first liquid-fueled rocket in 1926. His was the first of many rockets of its type. This technology was used to further the course of space exploration.

Spacecraft may be manned or unmanned. Some of the more famous spacecraft include the following:
- *Sputnik 1* (unmanned)—This was the first artificial Earth satellite, launched by the former Soviet Union in 1957. In 1961 the Soviets also launched the first human to go into space—Yuri Gagarin.
- *Apollo 11* (manned)—The crew included Neil Armstrong and Buzz Aldrin, the first people to land on the moon.
- *Mariner 9* (unmanned)—This spacecraft was the first to orbit another planet—Mars.
- *Space Shuttle* missions (manned)—These shuttles launched from Earth and returned from space, accomplishing many tasks to enhance the quality of life on Earth.
- *International Space Station* (manned)—The first crew set out in 2000. Plans are in place for other crews to continue manning the spacecraft until at least 2020. The United States and Russia combined their space stations into a single model and have received assistance from the European Space Agency and Japan.
- *Curiosity*, a Mars Science Laboratory rover (unmanned)—This rover landed on the surface of Mars in 2012. Its exploratory purpose is to search for organic molecules and to investigate whether conditions have been favorable for microbial life. It also searches for clues in Mars' rocks about possible past life.

Introduction ✋

State that today students will be studying spacecraft. Distribute **BLM 8.5A Rocket**, TAPE, and SCISSORS. Assist students with the activity. In order for the rocket to stand, be sure students make a gap between the two papers at the rocket's base. (If needed, stuff the gap with a rolled piece of paper to provide stability.)

Directed Instruction ⊕

1 Ask students what it might feel like to go to space in a big rocket. (**Answers will vary.**) Then share with the class that not all spacecraft were designed to carry people. As an introduction to space history, convey that the first rocket reached space in 1926. It was invented by Dr. Robert Goddard. Share also that the *Sputnik 1* satellite made the first orbit of Earth in 1957.

Have students turn to the first page. Introduce students to a time line by reading the sentences above the time line. Have students place a finger on each color shown. Explain that each large block of color marks a 10-year period. State the time period that each color represents. Share that within each 10-year period, many space-related events occurred. One event is listed in each time period of this time line.

Direct students to place a finger on each picture as you name the event. Announce the year that each event occurred. Help students find the year noted on the time line by counting each dot by ones to the yellow dot. Refer to the following information as you discuss each event.

- 1969—Neil Armstrong is the first person to walk on the moon.
- 1971—*Mariner 9* is the first spacecraft to orbit another planet—Mars.
- 1981—The *Space Shuttle* missions begin.
- 1998—The *International Space Station* project begins.
- 2004—The Mars rover *Opportunity* lands on Mars. Share that another Mars rover—*Curiosity*—landed on Mars in 2012.

2 Have students turn to the second page. Direct them to place a finger on the picture of the astronauts in the *International Space Station* (*ISS*). Read the top of the page with students. Share the following information about the *ISS* with students:

- In 1998, the first two modules, or parts, of the *ISS* were launched and joined together.
- There have been over 125 launches to the *ISS*. Launches have been made by Russians, Americans, Europeans, and Japanese. The *ISS* has traveled over 1.5 billion miles—the same as eight round trips to the sun.
- The *ISS* weighs almost a million pounds (as much as 320 cars). Its length is just a bit longer than a football field, and its living area is bigger than a five-bedroom house.
- Fifty-two computers control the *ISS*. The power comes from an acre of solar panels.

3 Read the exercise on the second half of the page. Brainstorm ideas with the class and write some of the words on the board. Allow time for students to complete the page. Assist with spelling. If you choose, allow volunteers to read their story to a partner or to the class.

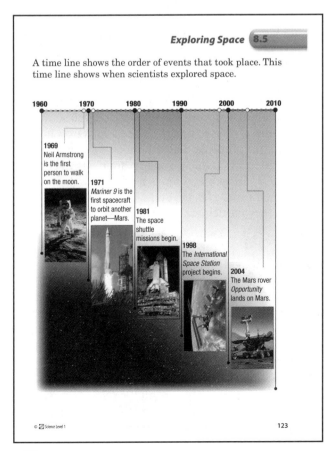

Exploring Space 8.5

A time line shows the order of events that took place. This time line shows when scientists explored space.

1960 1970 1980 1990 2000 2010

1969 Neil Armstrong is the first person to walk on the moon.

1971 *Mariner 9* is the first spacecraft to orbit another planet—Mars.

1981 The space shuttle missions begin.

1998 The *International Space Station* project begins.

2004 The Mars rover *Opportunity* lands on Mars.

Scientists continue to explore space. The *International Space Station* travels around Earth. Astronauts experiment and perform tests in space.

Aki Hoshide, Yuri Malenchenko, and Suni Williams aboard the *International Space Station*

Pretend you are in a space station. Write about what you see and do.

Answers will vary.

© Science Level 1   123

124   © Science Level 1

Objective

Students will examine how space exploration has influenced advances in technology and investigate how a rocket goes into space.

Materials

Introduction
• Paper clips, crayons, yarn, rulers, tape

Directed Instruction
• Tape, kite string, straw, paper clips, balloons, goggles
• Ziplock bags

Preparation

Gather PAPER CLIPS, CRAYONS, YARN, RULERS, and TAPE for small groups of students. (*Introduction*)

Use TAPE to attach 3 KITE STRINGS to the wall. Tape 1 string about 3 ft up, the second to the top of the wall, and the third to the ceiling. Make sure when strings are extended, they are not in the way of students. Cut a STRAW into three sections and slide the sections onto the taped pieces of string. Tie the loose ends of the strings to PAPER CLIPS to keep the straws from slipping off. Have ready 3 BALLOONS, and provide GOGGLES for any students participating. Also, compile ROCKET PACKETS consisting of a string, a balloon, a paper clip, and a small section of straw for students to take home and try out the experiment with their family. Place the materials inside a ZIPLOCK BAG for each student. (*Directed Instruction*)

Content

People have benefited from the work done in space science. The field of medicine is one area in which these benefits are reflected. Improvements have been made in breast-cancer detection, laser angioplasty procedures, and pacemaker monitoring. Developments have also been made in art preservation, forest management, and school-bus design. Other ways in which people have benefited from space exploration include the development of cell phones and the inventions of Fisher space pens, freeze-dried foods, Doppler radar technologies, effective race-car parts, fire-resistant clothing, memory foam, bendable ski boots, and fogless glasses. The knowledge gained about space also increases appreciation, wonder, and understanding of God's creation.

Introduction

State that Thomas Edison invented lightbulbs. Ask how people's lives would be different without lightbulbs. (**Answers will vary.**) Share that this and other inventions took time and experimentation by the inventors. Convey that students will work in groups to invent something. Arrange students into small groups. Distribute PAPER CLIPS, CRAYONS, YARN, RULERS, and TAPE. Direct students to use the materials to make an invention. Allow time for students to work. Have each group share their invention with the class.

Directed Instruction

1 Share that people have invented many things because of their study of space. Have students turn to the first page. Convey that because astronauts have performed experiments in space, people have new helpful inventions. Read the first paragraph and then have a volunteer read the sentence about cell-phone cameras. Read the paragraph about the space pen and ask how it would help people. (**It would help scientists write as they are working in space, underwater, or in other situations.**)

2 Drop a pencil on the floor. State that gravity pulls things down. Share that in space there is less gravity, or pull, so things float around. Because of this, scientists had to invent a way for astronauts to eat in space so that their food would not float around. Have students place a finger on the picture of dehydrated foods. Tell students that one way to prepare food is by taking out the water. Later, when the astronauts are ready to eat, they can add water to the food. Dehydrated foods tend to be lighter and take up less space than normal food. This is also helpful for people who must carry their food when they participate in activities such as fishing or hiking.

3 Have students place a finger on the Doppler radar tower, and read the sentence together. Share with the class that this technology was developed when people studied space. Ask students what Doppler radar helps meteorologists do. (**predict the weather**) Share with the class that space exploration has even led to advances in race cars and the drivers' clothing. Ask students what other kinds of people may need fire-resistant clothing. (**Possible answers: firefighters, military**) Read the sentences and have students underline as directed in the last sentence. Check for accuracy.

4 Guide students to turn to their second page. Inform them that they will be doing an experiment about an invention called *a rocket*. Read each step:

1. Ask a question: Read the question that students will try to answer through the experiment. Encourage them to think about what would make a rocket go up into the air.
2. Make a hypothesis: Have students write their guess.
3. Plan and do a test: Point out the 3 KITE STRINGS taped to the wall and ceiling. Explain that you will inflate 3 BALLOONS and launch them at different angles. Inflate the first balloon and hold it closed with your fingers. Select a volunteer to tape the side of the balloon to the end of the STRAW on the lowest string. Stretch the string with your other hand so that it makes a straight, angled path toward the wall. Encourage students to predict what the balloon will do when released. Release the balloon. Repeat the process for the other strings. You may choose to allow volunteers to assist with launching each balloon. Provide GOGGLES for each participant first.
4. Record and analyze your results: Give students time to make check marks to indicate their answer for each launch.
5. Make a conclusion: Encourage discussion about how the balloon moved across the room. **(The air pushed it.)** Compare the air moving the balloon to the gas inside a rocket. Point out the exhaust from the burning gas at the bottom of the rocket in the picture. State that the gases inside the rocket push it up into the air. Have students compare the results with their hypothesis. Remind students that scientific inquiry is not about being right or wrong; it is about discovering something they did not know before or confirming something they do know.
6. Share your results: Distribute ROCKET PACKETS to students to take home and try with their family. Encourage students to explain to their family members how a rocket works like the balloon.

Extension

Materials
- Apple slices (dried and fresh)
- Water bottle, lemon juice, baking soda, toilet paper, cork, goggles

Invite students to compare and taste dried and fresh apple slices. Check student records for possible allergies.

Construct a cork rocket in a plastic water bottle. Fill the bottle halfway with lemon juice. Wrap 1 tbsp of baking soda in a square of toilet paper and drop it in the bottle. Quickly place a cork on top. The baking soda will react with the lemon juice, causing the cork to shoot high into the air. Make sure all students are wearing goggles and are standing at least 4 ft away. Conduct this experiment outdoors.

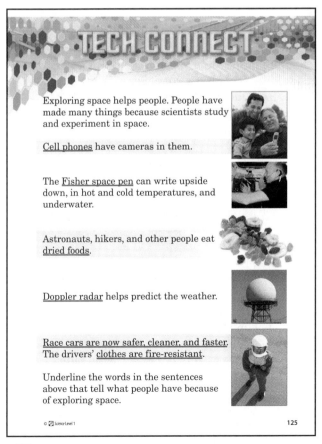

TECH CONNECT

Exploring space helps people. People have made many things because scientists study and experiment in space.

<u>Cell phones</u> have cameras in them.

The <u>Fisher space pen</u> can write upside down, in hot and cold temperatures, and underwater.

Astronauts, hikers, and other people eat <u>dried foods</u>.

<u>Doppler radar</u> helps predict the weather.

<u>Race cars are now safer, cleaner, and faster</u>. The drivers' <u>clothes are fire-resistant</u>.

Underline the words in the sentences above that tell what people have because of exploring space.

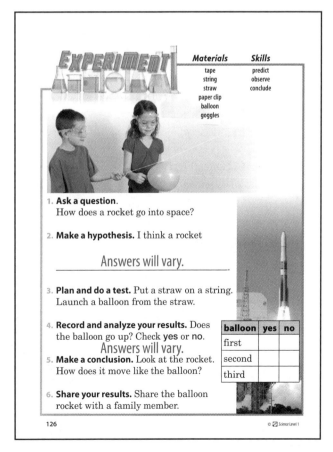

EXPERIMENT

Materials	Skills
tape	predict
string	observe
straw	conclude
paper clip	
balloon	
goggles	

1. **Ask a question.** How does a rocket go into space?

2. **Make a hypothesis.** I think a rocket

   Answers will vary.

3. **Plan and do a test.** Put a straw on a string. Launch a balloon from the straw.

4. **Record and analyze your results.** Does the balloon go up? Check **yes** or **no**.
   Answers will vary.

balloon	yes	no
first		
second		
third		

5. **Make a conclusion.** Look at the rocket. How does it move like the balloon?

6. **Share your results.** Share the balloon rocket with a family member.

Introduction
- BLM 8.7A Stars, yellow construction paper, scissors, hole punch and string (or tape)

Directed Instruction
- BLM 8.7B Space Facts
- BLM 8.7C Chapter 8 Test
- Poster board

Preparation

Print several double-sided copies of **BLM 8.7A Stars** on YELLOW CONSTRUCTION PAPER. Cut stars apart with SCISSORS. Use a HOLE PUNCH and STRING to attach each one to the ceiling, or use TAPE to attach them to the walls in the classroom. Space the stars far apart from each other. (*Introduction*)

Draw this Creation web on the board. (*Directed Instruction*)

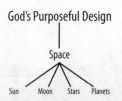

God's Purposeful Design

|
Space

Sun Moon Stars Planets

Print **BLM 8.7B Space Facts** for each student. (*Directed Instruction*)

Print **BLM 8.7C Chapter 8 Test** for each student. (*Directed Instruction*)

Obtain POSTER BOARD for small groups of students. (*Directed Instruction*)

Introduction

Complete a listening activity with students. Read each of the following Bible verses and have students stand under one of the STARS (made from **BLM 8.7A Stars**) that has a word from the verse (shown in green below). After all students are standing under a star, reread the verse and have them say the word from the star.

- "Ah, Sovereign Lord, You have made the heavens and the **earth** by Your great power and outstretched arm. Nothing is too hard for You." (Jeremiah 32:17)
- He took him outside and said, "Now look toward the heavens [the sky], and count the **stars**, if you are able to count them." And He said to him, "So shall your descendents be." (Genesis 15:5)
- The **sun** rises and the sun sets, and hurries back to where it rises. (Ecclesiastes 1:5)
- Every good and perfect gift is from above, coming down from the Father of the heavenly lights, who does not change like shifting **shadows**. (James 1:17)
- "He spreads out the northern skies over empty **space**; He suspends the **earth** over nothing." (Job 26:7) For this verse, have students move from one star to the other.

Direct students to return to their seat.

Directed Instruction

1 Review the definition of each vocabulary word. (*orbit*: the path a planet takes around the sun; *space*: the area outside Earth's atmosphere; *telescope*: a tool that makes things that are far away appear closer and larger) Distribute **BLM 8.7B Space Facts**. Read the facts and say "blank" for the missing word. Allow time for students to fill in the words from the Word Bank. Then have volunteers read each fact with the answer.

2 Direct students' attention to the Creation web on the board. Share that God purposefully designed space. Select a volunteer to name things in space shown on the web. (**sun, moon, stars, planets**) Ask students to name other things in space. (**Possible answers: satellites,** *International Space Station*)

3 Use student pages as a review or pretest. Complete these pages with your class. Allow time for students to write their journal entry. You may use **BLM 8.7C Chapter 8 Test** for individual assessment. Read through this page with your class. Provide as much reading support as necessary. You may choose to use BLM 8.7C as an oral assessment or not to do it at all.

4 Prepare for a space exhibit. This will necessitate an extra science class. Allow students time in class to prepare. Some preparation will need to be made at home. Discuss with students that, in small groups, they will prepare a special presentation for other classes and parent visitors. When visitors arrive, the visitors will move from table to table as student groups share their posters, props, and information. The presentations will be given for small groups of visitors at each table concurrently rather than to one large audience.

Select a time for the space exhibit. You may choose to send home a letter to parents explaining the details—purpose, date, time, and their child's topic. Ask for parent volunteers to assist on the day of the exhibit. Pick a topic for small groups from the following list. Allow students to use their student pages for information and ideas.

Topics may include the planets and their orbit around the sun, Earth and its atmosphere, stars, space foods, astronauts, missions, space-related inventions, meteorites, comets.

Distribute POSTER BOARD to each group. Allow time for students to make drawings that illustrate their topic. Share with the class that they may bring in props. Remind them that they must be prepared to share their information when visitors arrive at their table. If you choose, have students write a Bible verse on their poster.

Other ideas are as follows:
• Have students organize pictures or drawings of astronauts or other famous people in space history.
• Guide students in making and displaying clay models of planets.
• Let students dress up as astronauts.
• Assign students to make travel guides for planets. Allow time for students to gather information about a particular planet.
• Ask students and parents to provide a variety of refreshments: star-shaped cookies and dehydrated foods like beef jerky and dried fruit. Label this presentation area *Space Restaurant*.

5 Chapter 8 Space has been completed. Its pages can be stapled and sent home as a booklet to share with a family member.

➕ Extension

Materials
• CP-8.2 Space
• Scale, calculators

Present and discuss the remaining slides from **CP-8.2 Space**. Review other slides as desired.

Being sensitive to students' preferences, let each student weigh himself or herself on a scale. Then teach students how to divide their weight by 6 on a calculator to solve for their weight on the moon. Guide them to multiply their weight by 28 to determine how much they would weigh on the sun.

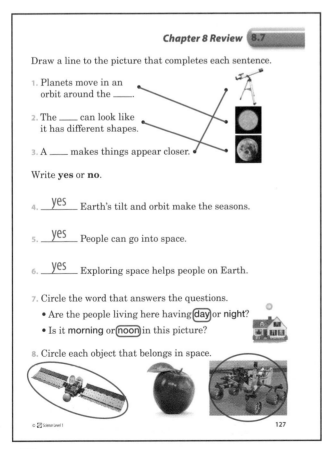

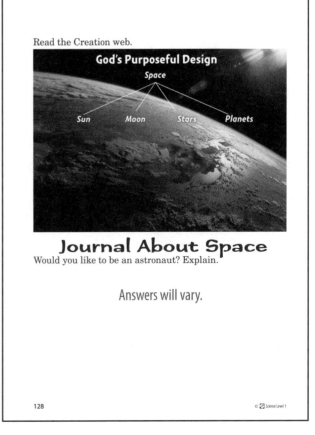

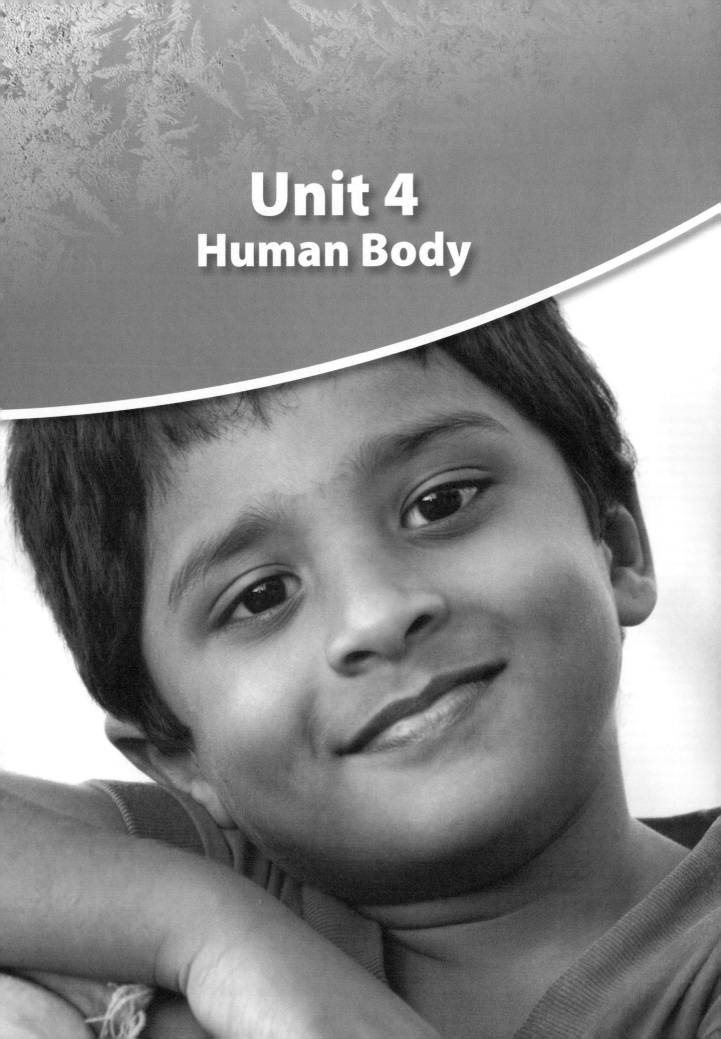

Unit 4
Human Body

Teeth

Chapter 9

Key Ideas
- God designed teeth as tools to help people eat, talk, and smile.
- People have different types of teeth that help chew food.
- It is important to keep teeth healthy by eating healthy food, brushing, flossing, visiting the dentist regularly, and wearing mouth protection while participating in sports.

9.0 Chapter Preparation

Introduction

The study of teeth shows a clear connection between science and growth patterns occurring in a child's body. Students will relate to the presence of primary and permanent teeth, while understanding that the timing of growth may differ from one person to another. A study of tooth anatomy will help them gain an appreciation of the importance of maintaining healthy teeth through proper diet, appropriate mouth protection while participating in sports, and good oral hygiene. The concept of God's purposeful design comes into focus again as students learn about the types of teeth and their functions. Information about the dental office and what to expect during a visit will help prepare students who may not have experienced a dental appointment. Earning a healthy teeth certificate at the end of the chapter may motivate students to be good stewards of their teeth.

About This Chapter

Lesson 9.1 – What Teeth Are

Materials
• Kitchen tools   • Scissors
• Crackers   • Crayons
• Card stock

Lesson Content
God created people to have teeth so they could eat, talk, and smile. As children grow, their teeth grow too.

Lesson 9.2 – Sets and Parts of Teeth

Materials
• Box   • Gloves   • Apple
• Clothing   • Crayons   • Scissors
• Mirrors   • Knife   • Glue

Lesson Content
Permanent teeth replace primary teeth. Teeth have two main parts: the crown and the root. Enamel covers the crown. Dentin, found beneath the enamel and all around the interior pulp, makes up most of the tooth. The pulp holds blood vessels and nerves that send messages to the brain.

Lesson 9.3 – Types of Teeth

Materials
• Knife   • Mirrors   • Cheese
• Fork   • Gloves
• Spoon   • Crayons

Lesson Content
There are three types of primary teeth: incisors, cuspids, and molars. Each type helps fulfill a different purpose in eating.

Lesson 9.4 – Healthy Teeth

Materials
• Bowls   • Glove   • Egg   • Scissors
• Frosting   • Toothbrush   • Glass   • Glue
• Crackers   • Paper towel   • Cola
• Water   • Yarn   • Craft sticks

Lesson Content
Eating healthy food, brushing and flossing, getting dental exams, and wearing mouth protection during sports are habits that keep teeth healthy.

Lesson 9.5 – The Dental Office

Materials
- Toothbrush
- Toothpaste
- Class photograph

Lesson Content

Regular visits to the dentist promote good dental health. The dentist cleans teeth, fills cavities, provides fluoride, and encourages proper teeth care. The dentist and dental hygienist use many different kinds of tools, including an explorer, a mirror, and an X-ray machine to help them do their work.

Lesson 9.6 – Chapter 9 Review

Materials
- *George Washington's Teeth*
- Crayons

Teacher Resources

Dental Health Education: Lesson Planning and Implementation by Lori Gagliardi. Prentice Hall, 2006.

Science Through the Year, Grades 1–2 by Laurie Hansen. Teacher Created Resources, 2007.

Understanding Teeth: An Illustrated Overview of Dental Concepts for Patients by Stephen F. Gordon. CreateSpace, 2011.

Student Resources

I Lost My Tooth in Africa by Penda Diakité. Scholastic, 2006.

Teeth by Sneed B. Collard III. Charlesbridge, 2008.

The Tooth Book: A Guide to Healthy Teeth and Gums by Edward Miller. Holiday House, 2009.

Supplemental Materials

Blackline Masters
9.1A Missing Tooth Graph
9.1B Dental Bookmark
9.1C Dental Data
9.2A Parts of a Tooth
9.2B Teeth
9.3A Animals
9.4A Puppets

9.6A Teeth Facts
9.6B Chapter 9 Test
9.6C Dental Certificate
9.6D Take a Bite

Transparency Masters
9.2A Teeth X-rays
9.2B Parts of a Tooth

9.3A Teeth Types
9.5A A Dental Visit

Computer Presentation
9.6 Teeth

9.1 What Teeth Are

Students will identify three basic functions of teeth.

Materials

Introduction
• Kitchen tools

Directed Instruction
• Crackers
• BLM 9.1A Missing Tooth Graph, BLM 9.1B Dental Bookmark, card stock, scissors, crayons
• BLM 9.1C Dental Data

✋ Preparation

Collect an assortment of KITCHEN TOOLS, such as a fork, a spoon, a measuring cup, a potato masher, and a cheese grater. (*Introduction*)

Write the definition of *teeth* on the board. (*Directed Instruction*)

Obtain a CRACKER for each student. (*Directed Instruction*)

Print 1 copy of **BLM 9.1A Missing Tooth Graph**. Enlarge the graph if you choose. Print double-sided copies of **BLM 9.1B Dental Bookmark** on CARD STOCK to make a bookmark for each student. Cut apart with SCISSORS. Obtain CRAYONS for students. (*Directed Instruction*)

Print **BLM 9.1C Dental Data** for each student. (*Directed Instruction*)

⚠ Safety

Check student records for possible allergies.

Content

God designed the human body to have tools for acquiring things—such as oxygen, food, and water—that are necessary for life. Teeth, one of the tools God provides, enable people to chew and break apart the food they eat.

This chapter continues to explore the purposeful design of God's creation through the study of form and function as it relates to the human body. Students will explore God's design of teeth and the particular functions they serve—eating, talking, and smiling. First graders should understand that it is perfectly normal for some of them to have a few permanent teeth while others do not. Each child's body grows and changes in its own way.

Introduction 🖐

Ask the class to name a tool. (**Possible answers: screwdriver, hammer, saw**) Display several KITCHEN TOOLS such as a fork, a spoon, a measuring cup, a potato masher, and a cheese grater. Ask volunteers to describe how each tool's form is perfectly suited to the function it was designed to do. (*fork*: **has pointed tines to stick into food;** *spoon*: **has shallow scoop to collect food;** *measuring cup*: **has lined space to hold a measured amount of food;** *potato masher*: **has flat parts to mash cooked potatoes;** *cheese grater*: **has sharp holes to scrape cheese into tiny pieces**)

Directed Instruction 🖐

1 Explain that God designed some kinds of living things, including people, to have teeth that help them chew food. Direct students' attention to the first student page. Make a comparison between the kitchen tools on display, which are used for specific functions, and teeth, which God designed to help people cut and chew food. Discuss that animals and even some nonliving things have teeth also. Ask students to look at the pictures at the top of the first student page and to tell how the different kinds of teeth are useful. (**Gears turn with the help of teeth; the teeth of a zipper help join two pieces of fabric, such as in closing a coat; a dog's teeth help the dog eat; the teeth of a saw cut wood.**)

2 Read the section on growth and change. One kind of change is how teeth grow. Discuss how the infant grows from a toddler to a boy. As his body grows, his teeth develop too. Ask and discuss the question at the bottom of the page. Then read **Psalm 139:14a**. Relate how God made each part of the human body. Convey that each part grows and works with other parts of the body to make the whole body.

3 Share that God designed parts of the human body, such as teeth, to be used as tools. Ask what jobs teeth do. (**Answers will vary but should include that they help people eat, talk, and smile.**)

4 Choose six volunteers to come to the front of the classroom. Hand the first two students a CRACKER and ask them to demonstrate the first job of teeth: eating. Have the next two volunteers demonstrate the second job: talking. Ask the last two volunteers to demonstrate the third job: smiling. Distribute crackers to the rest of the class and have them notice how their teeth accomplish the job of eating. Ask students how their teeth help them eat. (**Teeth bite, chew, and grind.**) Then give students a minute to talk to

and smile at their neighbors. Conclude by reviewing the functions or jobs of teeth. (**eating, talking, smiling**)

5 Have students refer to the front of their book for information about the five senses. Discuss each picture. Then, direct students' attention to the second student page. Read the definition of **teeth**: *tools that help people eat, talk, and smile*. Have students complete the exercises at the top of the page, reminding students that eating involves the sense of taste. Then direct students to answer the questions at the bottom of the page.

6 Display **BLM 9.1A Missing Tooth Graph**. State that this chart will be a place for the class to keep a record of the number of teeth students lose throughout the year. Distribute a CARD-STOCK bookmark from **BLM 9.1B Dental Bookmark** to each student. Allow time for students to color the bookmark with CRAYONS and to sign the back as a pledge to take care of their teeth. Consider laminating the bookmarks for durability.

7 Distribute **BLM 9.1C Dental Data**. Inform students that they should take this chart home, share it with an adult, and check the boxes as they eat healthy foods, brush, and floss. Request that students bring this chart back to school for Lesson 9.6.

Notes:

+ **Extension**

Materials
• "Brush Your Teeth"

Obtain and play an audio recording of "Brush Your Teeth" by Kids Choir (Star Song Music, 2009). Sing with students to encourage them to get excited about this chapter on teeth.

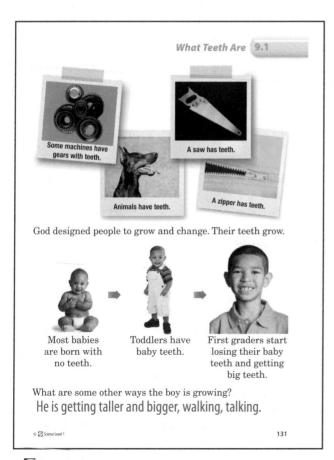

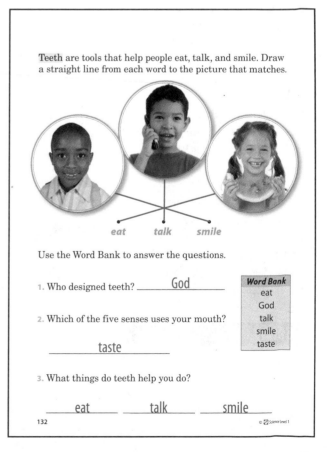

.2 Sets and Parts of Teeth

Objective

Students will differentiate between primary and permanent teeth and label the parts of a tooth.

Materials

Introduction
• Box, adult-sized clothing

Directed Instruction
• Small mirrors, latex gloves
• TM-9.2A Teeth X-rays, TM-9.2B Parts of a Tooth, pink crayons, knife, apple
• BLM 9.2A Parts of a Tooth, scissors, glue

Preparation

Select an open area in which students can run. Fill a BOX with ADULT-SIZED CLOTHING. (*Introduction*)

Write the definitions of *primary teeth* and *permanent teeth* on the board. Obtain a SMALL MIRROR and LATEX GLOVES for each student. Mirrors are in the ACSI Science Equipment Kit. If enough mirrors are not available, plan to have students work in groups. (*Directed Instruction*)

Select **TM-9.2A Teeth X-rays** and **TM-9.2B Parts of a Tooth** for display. Have PINK CRAYONS available for students. (*Directed Instruction*)

Use a KNIFE to cut an APPLE from top to bottom. (*Directed Instruction*)

Print **BLM 9.2A Parts of a Tooth** for each student. Gather SCISSORS and GLUE. (*Directed Instruction*)

Safety

Caution students about running in adult clothes.

Check student records for latex allergies.

Content

Before birth, a baby has special cells, like seeds in his or her gums, that will grow into teeth. Proper nutrition from the mother during pregnancy promotes tooth development for the baby before the baby is even born. Primary or baby teeth, usually the lower incisors, begin to erupt at approximately six months of age. In a child's second or third year of life, the upper secondary molars, the last of the primary teeth, erupt. Babies develop teeth as their diet shifts from exclusively milk to the addition of solid foods—a wonderful example of God's purposeful design. The first primary tooth is lost at approximately age 6. In this process, the permanent tooth pushes on the roots of the baby tooth, causing the roots to resorb, or dissolve. The baby tooth then falls out and the permanent tooth erupts. By age 12 or 13, a child may have 28 of the 32 permanent teeth. The third molars commonly known as *wisdom teeth* are the last to erupt.

A tooth has two main parts: the crown, which is the visible part of the tooth, and the root, which is hidden under the gingiva, or gum, and extends into the jaw bone. Enamel, which is the hardest substance produced by the human body, covers the crown. Dentin, found beneath the enamel and all around the pulp, makes up most of the tooth. It covers and protects the pulp. In the pulp are blood vessels that supply nourishment to the tooth, and nerves that send messages to the brain.

Introduction

Guide students to an open area of the room or an open space on campus. Point out the BOX of ADULT-SIZED CLOTHING. State that students will play a game involving the clothing. Divide the class into two equal teams and direct each team to form a line facing the box. Explain that when you say go, the first student on each team will run to the box, put on an article of clothing, and then run back and tag the next student's hand. Teams will continue to race and put on clothing until the last student in each line has made it back to the line. The winning team is the team that finishes first.

Direct students back to their seat and ask what was challenging about the game. (**Answers will vary but should include that dressing and running quickly in adult clothes was hard to do.**) Why do you think it is better for children to wear child-sized clothes? (**They fit better.**) As children grow, what happens to their clothes? (**Children have to get rid of their old clothes and get new clothes in a bigger size.**) State that today students will learn about a part of their body that develops and gets replaced as they get older.

Directed Instruction

1 Share with the class that teeth change as people grow. Share that most babies are born without teeth. Babies drink milk or formula. As babies grow, their teeth start to come in because children need teeth to chew food. Point to the definitions on the board and explain that this *first set of teeth* is called **primary teeth**, or baby teeth. At about age six, **permanent teeth**, meaning *the second set of teeth*, start to take the place of the baby teeth. The new teeth push on the primary teeth until the primary teeth fall out. Remind students that God designed the permanent teeth to last for the rest of a person's life, so it is very important to take care of them! Ask students to raise a hand if they have ever lost a tooth. (**Answers will vary.**) Emphasize that God purposefully designed bodies to grow and change.

2 Direct students' attention to the first page. Read and discuss the paragraph at the top. Ask a volunteer to count the number of teeth shown in the picture. (20) Mention that some students may already have six-year molars, which are permanent teeth. Six-year molars are in the very back of the mouth. Stress that if a student does not have these teeth yet, they will be coming in very soon. Distribute SMALL MIRRORS and LATEX GLOVES. Allow time for students to complete the exercises.

Display the top part of **TM-9.2A Teeth X-rays**. The X-ray shows the primary teeth and the hidden permanent teeth. Remind the class that the permanent teeth push on the roots of the primary teeth; this action helps the primary teeth fall out. The bottom X-ray is of permanent teeth.

3 Show **TM-9.2B Parts of a Tooth**. Point to the crown, root, and gum. Have students turn to their second page. Read the sentences at the top. Distribute PINK CRAYONS and give time for students to complete the page.

Hold up the cut APPLE. Convey that the apple has different parts inside and so does a tooth. Point out the enamel, dentin, and pulp on TM-9.2B and on the students' second page. Enamel covers and protects the tooth's crown; dentin makes up much of the tooth, and it covers and protects the pulp; within the pulp are blood vessels and nerves that send messages to the brain. Have students complete the exercises.

4 Distribute **BLM 9.2A Parts of a Tooth**, SCISSORS, and GLUE. Read the directions; provide help if needed. Let students refer to their student page.

⊕ Extension

Materials
• Camera
• Newspaper, BLM 9.2B Teeth, smocks, toothbrushes, floss, paint

Take a picture of each student's teeth. Keep track of which student goes with each picture. Display the photographs on a bulletin board. Encourage students and parents to match the pictures to the students.

Lay out newspaper to protect the desks. Provide a tooth cutout from **BLM 9.2B Teeth** and a smock for each student. Have students paint designs on the tooth using an old toothbrush and floss. They can drag the floss through the paint across their picture, and paint with the toothbrush or spread the bristles apart to splatter the paint.

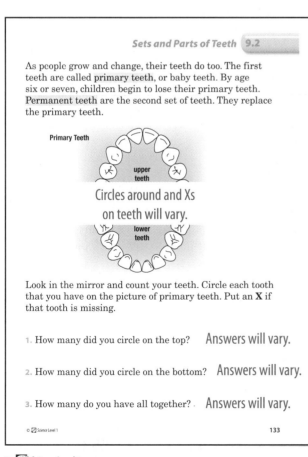

Sets and Parts of Teeth 9.2

As people grow and change, their teeth do too. The first teeth are called **primary teeth**, or baby teeth. By age six or seven, children begin to lose their primary teeth. **Permanent teeth** are the second set of teeth. They replace the primary teeth.

Primary Teeth

upper teeth

Circles around and Xs on teeth will vary.

lower teeth

Look in the mirror and count your teeth. Circle each tooth that you have on the picture of primary teeth. Put an **X** if that tooth is missing.

1. How many did you circle on the top?   Answers will vary.

2. How many did you circle on the bottom?   Answers will vary.

3. How many do you have all together?   Answers will vary.

© Science Level 1   133

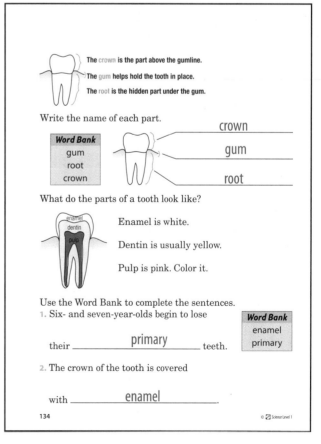

The crown is the part above the gumline.
The gum helps hold the tooth in place.
The root is the hidden part under the gum.

Write the name of each part.

Word Bank
gum
root
crown

crown

gum

root

What do the parts of a tooth look like?

enamel
dentin
pulp

Enamel is white.

Dentin is usually yellow.

Pulp is pink. Color it.

Use the Word Bank to complete the sentences.
1. Six- and seven-year-olds begin to lose

their _____ primary _____ teeth.

Word Bank
enamel
primary

2. The crown of the tooth is covered

with _____ enamel _____.

134   © Science Level 1

9.3 Types of Teeth

Teeth

Objective

Students will locate the incisors, cuspids, and molars and be able to explain the function of each.

Materials

Introduction
- Plastic knife, fork, and spoon

Directed Instruction
- TM-9.3A Teeth Types
- Small mirrors, latex gloves
- Crayons
- Cheese cubes

✋ Preparation

Gather a PLASTIC KNIFE, FORK, and SPOON for a demonstration. (*Introduction*)

Select **TM-9.3A Teeth Types** for display. (*Directed Instruction*)

Obtain a SMALL MIRROR and LATEX GLOVES for each student. Gather mirrors from the ACSI Science Equipment Kit. If enough mirrors are not available, plan to have students work in groups. (*Directed Instruction*)

Collect CRAYONS for students. (*Directed Instruction*)

Obtain a CHEESE CUBE for each student. (*Directed Instruction*)

⚠ Safety

Check student records for possible allergies.

Content

As a child develops, his or her permanent teeth replace the primary teeth. A person's permanent teeth provide the means to eat a variety of foods.

God designed the shape and placement of teeth to help with the biting and chewing process:
- Incisors are located in the front of the mouth. These 8 teeth have a sharp edge and are designed to bite and cut.
- Cuspids are located back beyond the incisors. These 4 teeth have a sharp pointed cusp and are designed to bite and tear.
- Premolars are located farther back beyond the cuspids. These 8 teeth have 2 cusps (points) and are designed to grind and chew. Premolars are also known as *bicuspids* because of their 2 cusps.
- Molars are located farthest back. These 12 teeth have 3 to 5 cusps and are designed to grind and chew.

Teeth vary in form and function. God's design of human teeth matches the food God designed for humans to eat. God's design of animal teeth also fits their form and function. Some animals are known for their most prominent type of teeth. A rabbit has incisors that continue to grow throughout its lifetime so that the rabbit can acquire the vegetation God has provided. Jaguars and dogs are known for their sharp, pointy cuspids, or canines, that stab and tear the meat that God provides. Elephants have large incisors called *tusks* that are used to dig up roots and fulfill other survival purposes.

Introduction ✋

Show students a PLASTIC KNIFE, FORK, and SPOON. Ask them to name foods a knife would be used for. (**Possible answers: cheese, peanut butter, meat**) What are some foods a fork would be used for? (**Possible answers: mashed potatoes, salad, vegetables**) What are some foods a spoon would be used for? (**Possible answers: ice cream, yogurt, soup**) Why would it be hard to eat pudding with a knife? (**Possible answers: The pudding would slide off of the knife; the knife might cut my tongue.**) What might happen if you tried to use a fork to eat soup? (**The fork would not pick up the liquid.**) Share with students that people use all of these utensils when they eat, but each utensil serves a different purpose.

Directed Instruction ✋

1 Emphasize that although people use all of their teeth when they eat, God made some teeth for biting, some for tearing, and others for chewing. God designed different kinds of teeth to help people eat the different kinds of foods He has provided. Teeth cut and grind food into small pieces so that it can be swallowed.

2 Direct students' attention to the first page. Read the descriptions of incisors, cuspids, and molars. Explain that the top arch of teeth on the page represent a child's upper teeth; the bottom arch represents the lower teeth. Display **TM-9.3A Teeth Types**. Reiterate that incisors bite and cut food. Ask students if incisors should be sharp or dull. (**sharp**) Point to the incisors. Convey that the word *incisors* is similar to *scissors*, which is also a sharp tool that cuts. Ask where the incisors are located in the mouth. (**front**) Point to the cuspids. Ask what tooth shape is best for tearing. (**pointed**) Have students place a finger on each upper cuspid and then on each lower cuspid. Point to the molars and ask why they are good for

160

grinding and chewing. (**They are big and wide.**) Give time for students to complete the exercises at the bottom of the page.

3 Distribute SMALL MIRRORS and LATEX GLOVES. Refer to TM-9.3A, and point to each tooth type. Direct students to look at each kind of tooth in their mouth.

4 Direct students' attention to the second page. Read and review the shapes of the teeth. Share that God's design of each tooth helps people eat the food He has provided. Allow time for students to use CRAYONS for the coloring activity on this page. Then have students complete the rest of the page.

5 Distribute CHEESE CUBES. Instruct students to press their upper teeth into the cheese but not to bite through. Circulate around the room and point out the marks made by incisors, cuspids, and molars. Allow students to show each other the bite marks and then to eat their own pieces of cheese.

Notes:

⊕ Extension

Materials
• Paper plates, crayons, glue, miniature marshmallows
• BLM 9.3A Animals

Distribute a paper plate to each student and demonstrate folding it in half to make a mouth. Have students color lips on the outside and a tongue on the inside. Instruct them to glue 20 miniature marshmallows inside the mouth to represent teeth—10 on the top and 10 on the bottom.

Print **BLM 9.3A Animals** for each student. Talk about how some animals have teeth. Have students name animals that do not. (**Possible answers: birds, insects**) Work through the page with students.

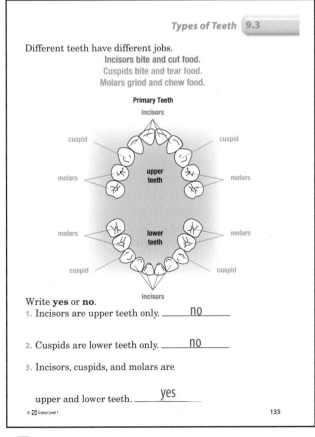

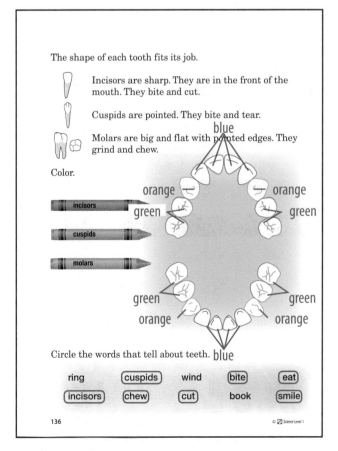

9.4 Healthy Teeth

Content

In order to keep teeth healthy, dentists recommend brushing twice a day, flossing once a day, and visiting a dentist every six months. Foods with sugar promote tooth decay because they feed the bacterial population present in the mouth. The bacteria in turn produce an acid that breaks down tooth enamel. Dentists recommend avoiding sugary foods or limiting the intake of them to occur at meals only.

An egg and cola experiment yields a stained egg that can be brushed in an effort to remove the stain. This experiment helps students relate to the fact that what they eat can affect the color and health of their teeth.

Introduction

Inform the class that they will learn why it is important to brush and floss. Ask for a volunteer to put on the WHITE LATEX GLOVE. Instruct the student to keep his or her gloved fingers together during the course of the demonstration. Share that in this demonstration, the fingers represent teeth.

Follow these steps:
1. Direct the student volunteer to dip his or her gloved fingers into a BOWL of CHOCOLATE FROSTING.
2. Next, have the student place his or her gloved fingers in a BOWL of CRUSHED CRACKERS. Direct the student to move his or her gloved fingers to mash the food like teeth.
3. Have another volunteer brush the gloved fingers with a TOOTHBRUSH over a BOWL of WATER as the gloved fingers are kept together. Wipe off the fingers with a PAPER TOWEL after brushing. Ask the class if the fingers are clean now. (**Answers will vary.**)
4. Direct the first volunteer to hold up his or her hand and to spread the gloved fingers apart. Point out the food between the fingers. Explain that brushing did not clean all the surfaces of the fingers, just as brushing does not adequately clean between the teeth.
5. Ask students how they can clean between their teeth. (**by flossing**) Emphasize how important it is to use floss every day. Have the student close his or her fingers once again, and use WHITE YARN to demonstrate how floss does a thorough job of cleaning between the teeth.

Directed Instruction

1 Emphasize the importance of learning how to take care of teeth. Ask the class to name some ways they have learned to care for their teeth so far. (**by brushing, by flossing**) How does brushing help take care of teeth? (**It takes the food off the front, back, and tops of the teeth.**) How does flossing help take care of teeth? (**It cleans between the teeth.**) Express that flossing also helps gums stay healthy.

2 Share that besides brushing and flossing, people should do other things to take care of their teeth. Eating healthy foods and drinking healthy drinks—those containing no sugar or low amounts of it—keep teeth strong. Wearing a mouth guard during sports protects teeth from injury.

3 Have students turn to the first page. Read the sentence at the top and discuss the statements about eating healthy foods, brushing, flossing, and wearing mouth protection. Then give students time to complete the page.

4 Continue to the second page. Explain that this experiment will be started today and finished during Lesson 9.5. Display the GLASS of COLA and the HARD-BOILED EGG WITH SHELL, and read the skills to be used. Share that in this experiment, the egg represents a tooth.

Read the problem: *Will cola stain an egg?* Explain that this experiment will show if cola will stain an egg over a period of time. Read the segment for Day 1 and give students time to answer Exercise 2. Place the egg in the cola. Retain student pages for Lesson 9.5, when students will complete the experiment.

5 State that if students do not take proper care of their teeth, they could end up with a cavity, a hole in their tooth that a dentist must fill. Convey that students will learn more about the dentist in Lesson 9.5. To reinforce dental care, engage students in a puppet show. Use the puppets on **BLM 9.4A Puppets** and read the following story about Wally. After you have finished, distribute BLM 9.4A, CRAFT STICKS, SCISSORS, and GLUE. Allow time for students to cut out the puppets, to glue them to the sticks, and to perform a show for their classmates. You may choose to have students present a show for a partner or to have small groups perform for the class.

Wally the Tooth

Wally the Tooth was a happy tooth. His owner, Mike, had taken good care of him. Then Mike forgot about brushing and flossing, and Wally got a cavity. Wally began to hurt, so Mike went to his dentist for help. Mike's dentist fixed the cavity with a filling. Now Wally feels much better, and Mike is careful to eat healthful foods and to brush and floss every day.

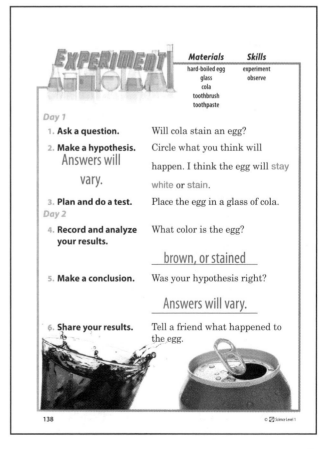

9.5 The Dental Office

Objective

Students will identify the various tasks a dentist performs.

Materials

Directed Instruction
- TM-9.5A A Dental Visit
- Toothbrush, toothpaste
- Class photograph

Preparation

Verify that all is in order for the planned field trip to a local dentist's office before today's lesson, or verify that the invited dentist or hygienist is ready to be the guest speaker. Work with students to make a list of questions that students can ask. Prior to the trip, clarify with the dentist how he or she prefers to field questions. (*Introduction*)

Select **TM-9.5A A Dental Visit** for display. (*Introduction*)

Have available student pages and the egg in cola from Lesson 9.4. (*Directed Instruction*)

Select a TOOTHBRUSH and TOOTHPASTE for a demonstration. (*Directed Instruction*)

Obtain or take a CLASS PHOTOGRAPH of students smiling to give the dentist. Ask parents and guardians for permission to send the photo. (*Directed Instruction*)

Advise students to bring in **BLM 9.1C Dental Data** to be used in Lesson 9.6.

Content

A child's dental check-up is usually a pleasant experience. The dentist counts and examines the teeth. Sometimes he or she takes X-rays. The dentist or dental hygienist cleans the teeth and, when necessary, applies fluoride to strengthen them. Tools at the dental office allow the dentist to do his or her job, which includes checking for cavities and diseases of the teeth and gums.

Introduction

Display **TM-9.5A A Dental Visit** and talk about the progression of a dental visit: waiting in the waiting room, being taught dental hygiene, getting teeth checked and cleaned, and ending with a smile.

Directed Instruction

1 If a field trip to a dental office was not possible, introduce the dental professional to the classroom. Ask the visitor to speak about his or her job, the dental equipment, the importance of visiting the dentist, and how to care for teeth at home. Encourage a dialogue with the visitor using questions chosen previously by students. Encourage students to ask additional questions.

If a speaker is unavailable, teach the class these techniques:
- Brush with a soft toothbrush twice a day. Brush all teeth making small circles at the base of the tooth on the outer and inner sides.
- Floss with an 8- to 12-in. piece of dental floss once a day. Bring it carefully between the teeth. Slide the floss up and down between the teeth, scraping the sides. The floss should gently slide slightly below the gumline.

Share with the class that it is important to do these things to prevent cavities and keep gums healthy. It is important to visit a dentist every six months.

2 After the visitor has finished, direct students to turn to their first page and reinforce the concepts learned from the visit. Discuss the jobs of the dentist and how he or she helps people.

Discuss the use of gloves, a coat, glasses, and a mask to keep germs from spreading. Talk about how the dentist and dental hygienist use many different kinds of tools, including an explorer, an X-ray machine, and a mirror to help them do their work. Each of these tools has a special job.

3 Direct students' attention to the second page. Give time for students to locate and circle all of the objects. Then complete Exercise 2 together.

4 Inform the class that it is time to find out the answer to the experiment begun in Lesson 9.4. Distribute student pages from Lesson 9.4. Ask a volunteer to share what he or she predicted on Day 1. (**Answers will vary.**) You may choose to take a poll of the class' predictions.

Direct students' attention to the Day 2 section. Inform students that they will now collect the data. Read *What color is the egg?* Remove the egg from the cola and allow the class to see the change in color. Give students time to write the color of the egg that was placed in cola and their conclusion to the question. Remind students that scientific inquiry is not about being right or wrong; it is about discovering something they did not know before or confirming something they do know. Have students share their conclusion with a partner.

Convey that similar to the staining of the egg, items such as cola, tea, coffee, and other drinks and foods can stain teeth as well. Ask students what can help teeth look white and clean. (**brushing them**) Do you think brushing the egg would make it white and clean too? (**Answers will vary.**) Proceed by brushing the eggshell with a TOOTHBRUSH and TOOTHPASTE. Show students the results. Help them process this information and develop a conclusion. Students should discover that brushing the tooth helps clean it, but the egg is not as white as it was before the cola. Ask a volunteer to share whether his or her prediction was right.

5 Remind students that it is important to care for their teeth. Check for understanding by asking volunteers to describe the things they can do to protect their teeth. (**brush, floss, visit a dentist, eat healthy foods, wear a mouth guard**) Reiterate that wearing a mouth guard helps prevent injuries to the face and keeps teeth from getting chipped or knocked out. Mouth guards are needed in many sports, including hockey, baseball, football, basketball, soccer, and roller blading.

6 Have students write thank-you notes to the dental office or to the visitor. If possible, attach a CLASS PHOTOGRAPH of students smiling.

⊕ Extension

Materials
• BLM 9.2B Teeth, markers, toothbrushes, play dough, blocks, yarn
• BLM 9.2B Teeth

Guide students in proper brushing and flossing techniques. Print and laminate **BLM 9.2B Teeth** so each student has a laminated tooth. Draw spots of decay on the teeth with dry-erase markers. Have students use a toothbrush to clean their tooth. Next, press bits of play dough into the crevices of large connecting blocks. Have students use yarn to floss the play dough from the blocks.

Print **BLM 9.2B Teeth** so each student has a tooth. Direct students to draw and to label the parts of the tooth (enamel, dentin, pulp) on their cutout.

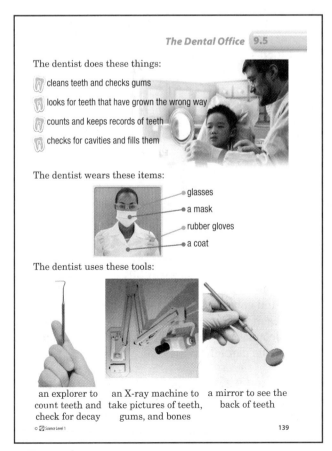

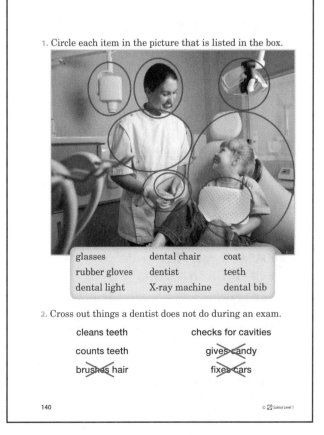

9.6 Chapter 9 Review

Materials

Introduction
• *George Washington's Teeth*

Directed Instruction
• BLM 9.6A Teeth Facts
• TM-9.2B Parts of a Tooth
• BLM 9.6B Chapter 9 Test, blue, orange, and green crayons
• Completed BLM 9.1C Dental Data, BLM 9.6C Dental Certificate

Preparation

Obtain *George Washington's Teeth* by Deborah Chandra and Madeleine Comora (Square Fish, 2007). (*Introduction*)

Write the definitions of *teeth* on the board. Scramble the letters of some of the words. Print **BLM 9.6A Teeth Facts** for each student. (*Directed Instruction*)

Draw the following Creation web on the board. (*Directed Instruction*)

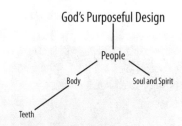

God's Purposeful Design

Select **TM-9.2B Parts of a Tooth** for display. (*Directed Instruction*)

Have BLUE, ORANGE, AND GREEN CRAYONS available. (Directed Instruction)

Print **BLM 9.6B Chapter 9 Test** for each student. Have BLUE CRAYONS available for students. (*Directed Instruction*)

Verify that students have their completed copy of **BLM 9.1C Dental Data** distributed in Lesson 9.1. Print and sign **BLM 9.6C Dental Certificate** for each student. (*Directed Instruction*)

Introduction

Read *George Washington's Teeth* to the class. This book shares what happened to George Washington's teeth as recorded in historical records and Washington's letters and diaries. Ask students to think about what they have learned in this chapter and to give suggestions of how George Washington could have taken better care of his teeth. (**Answers will vary but should include eating healthy foods, brushing, flossing, and going to see his dentist.**)

Directed Instruction

1 Draw students' attention to the definition of *teeth* on the board. Have students help unscramble the letters. Read the definition as a class. (*teeth*: **tools that help people eat, talk, and smile**) Review the definitions of *primary teeth* and *permanent teeth*. (*primary teeth*: **the first set of teeth**, *permanent teeth*: **the second set of teeth**) Distribute **BLM 9.6A Teeth Facts**. Read the directions. Have a volunteer read a fact and provide the answer. Select another volunteer to explain the fact.

2 Direct students' attention to the Creation web on the board. Share that God purposefully designed people with a body, and a soul and a spirit. One part of the human body shown on the web is teeth. Ask students to name other parts of the body. (**Possible answers: arms, legs, eyes, ears**) Inform students that they will learn about more parts of the body in upcoming lessons.

Display **TM-9.2B Parts of a Tooth**. Check for understanding by reviewing the gum, root, and crown. Review the parts of a tooth: enamel, dentin, pulp. Ask students why enamel is important. (**It covers and protects the tooth's crown.**) What makes up most of the tooth? (**dentin**) What does the pulp do? (**It has the blood supply for the tooth and the nerves that let the tooth feel.**)

3 Remind the class how teeth help people eat the kinds of foods God purposed them to eat—incisors for biting and cutting, cuspids for tearing, and molars for chewing and grinding.

4 Ask several volunteers to name some ways that they can care for their teeth. (**eat healthy foods, brush my teeth two times a day, floss once a day, visit the dentist twice a year, wear a mouth guard during sports**)

5 Use student pages as a review or pretest. Distribute BLUE, ORANGE, AND GREEN CRAYONS to students. Guide the class in completing these pages. Ask a volunteer to read the Creation web. Brainstorm words to include in their journal. List these words on the board. Then have students make a chart entitled *My dentist* and columns labeled *is*, *has*, and *can*. Direct students to fill in ideas for each column and then use the chart to write their journal entry. (**Possible answers: I learned that my dentist is helpful. My dentist has tools. He or she can fill cavities.**)

You may use **BLM 9.6B Chapter 9 Test** for individual assessment. Read through this page with the class. Provide as much reading support as necessary. Distribute a BLUE CRAYON to each student. You may choose to use BLM 9.6B as an oral assessment or not to do it at all.

6 Direct students to take out their completed **BLM 9.1C Dental Data**. Ask them to share the results and to discuss how they enjoyed doing this activity. Award certificates from **BLM 9.6C Dental Certificate** to all students and congratulate students on finishing the teeth chapter. Remind them that teeth are part of God's perfect design for the body. People should choose to eat healthy foods and keep their teeth clean so that their teeth will last a lifetime.

7 Chapter 9 Teeth has been completed. Staple it and send it home as a booklet to be shared with a family member.

Notes:

➕ Extension

Materials
• CP-9.6 Teeth
• BLM 9.6D Take a Bite, scissors, glue

Present and discuss **CP-9.6 Teeth**.

Print **BLM 9.6D Take a Bite** for students and distribute the copies, scissors, and glue. Have students work in pairs to complete the page. Ask volunteers to share their answers. Discuss that God designed these animals with teeth that allow them to eat the foods they eat: *hippopotamus*: grasses and water plants; *chimpanzee*: leaves and fruit; *donkey*: grasses; *Tyrannosaurus rex*: other animals. Discuss the different types of teeth (incisors, cuspids, molars) the animals use to eat their food.

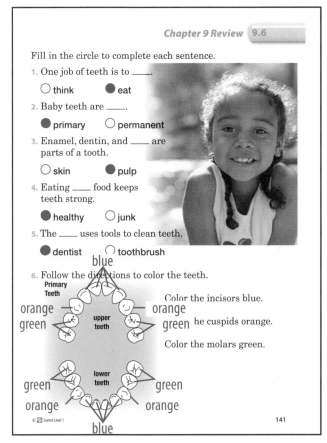

Chapter 9 Review 9.6

Fill in the circle to complete each sentence.

1. One job of teeth is to ____.
   ○ think   ● eat
2. Baby teeth are ____.
   ● primary   ○ permanent
3. Enamel, dentin, and ____ are parts of a tooth.
   ○ skin   ● pulp
4. Eating ____ food keeps teeth strong.
   ● healthy   ○ junk
5. The ____ uses tools to clean teeth.
   ● dentist   ○ toothbrush
6. Follow the directions to color the teeth.

   Primary Teeth
   blue
   orange
   green   upper teeth
   orange
   green   lower teeth
   green   green
   orange   orange
   blue

   Color the incisors blue.
   Color the cuspids orange.
   Color the molars green.

© Science Level 1   141

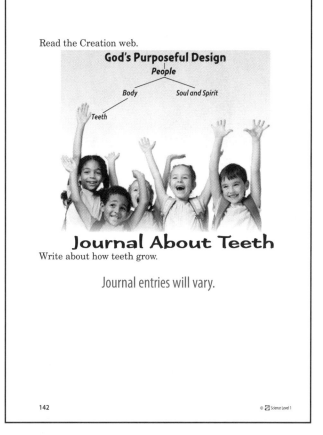

Read the Creation web.

God's Purposeful Design
People
Body   Soul and Spirit
Teeth

Journal About Teeth
Write about how teeth grow.

Journal entries will vary.

142   © Science Level 1

Bones and Muscles

Chapter 10

Key Ideas

- God designed bones, muscles, and joints to help people move.
- Bones connect and make up the skeleton, which gives the body its shape.
- People keep their bones and muscles strong by eating a variety of healthful foods and by exercising.

10.0 Chapter Preparation

Bones and Muscles

Vocabulary

bone
muscle
joint

Looking Ahead

- The skeleton found in the ACSI Science Equipment Kit will be used throughout the chapter. If the skeleton is not available, be prepared to display **TM-10.1A Skeleton** instead.
- Ask parent volunteers to make the hand-bone cookies for the *Extension* activity in **Lesson 10.4**.
- In **Lesson 11.1** of the Heart and Blood chapter, you will need a paper-towel tube for each student. Ask students or other teachers to help you collect the tubes.
- For an *Extension* activity in **Lesson 11.3**, arrange for the school nurse to come talk to the students about first aid and taking care of cuts.

Introduction

This chapter begins by studying the bones and muscles of the human body. Students will learn names of some bones like the *femur*, *skull*, and *stapes*. They will be introduced to some functions of bones and muscles including protection and movement. Maintenance of healthy bones through a healthy diet, exercise, and appropriate protection in sports is stressed as a means of caring for the body. Students will be challenged to study and identify the bones and muscles in order to better understand how God purposefully designed the human body.

About This Chapter

Lesson 10.1 – What Bones Are
Materials
- Adhesive putty
- Skeleton (optional)
- Chair
- Blanket
- Scissors
- Glue
- Construction paper

Lesson Content
A bone is a hard part of the body that gives the body shape and helps it move. God designed all the bones of the human body so that they fit together to make a skeleton. The human skeleton enables people to move in many different ways.

Lesson 10.2 – Muscles and Joints
Materials
- Skeleton (optional)

Lesson Content
Muscles and joints help people move. A muscle is a part of the body that helps the body move by moving bones. A joint is where bones meet. A hinge joint, such as the knee, moves to a certain point and then stops. The ball and socket joint in the shoulder allows for full arm rotation.

Lesson 10.3 – Bones Protect
Materials
- Nuts
- Banana
- Nutcracker
- Balloon
- Helmet (optional)
- Skeleton (optional)
- Yarn
- Pasta
- Tape
- Bags

Lesson Content
Hard bones inside the body protect organs and other soft places. For example, the skull protects the brain; the ribs shield the heart and lungs; and the backbone encases the spinal cord.

Lesson 10.4 – More About Bones
Materials
- Connecting cubes
- Straws
- Skeleton (optional)
- Rulers (optional)
- Scissors
- Tape

Lesson Content
The skeleton contains 206 bones working together to help the body move and give it shape. The stapes, the smallest bone, is located in the ear and aids in hearing. The longest bone is the femur, located in the leg. The bones in the fingers and toes are called *phalanges*.

Lesson 10.5 – Healthy Bones and Muscles

Materials
- Rulers (optional)
- Crayons
- Clay

Lesson Content
Exercise and a variety of healthful foods help keep bones strong and healthy. Calcium, found in dairy products, provides nutrients to the bones. When a bone breaks, a doctor will take X-rays of the bones and may apply a cast to help the bone heal.

Lesson 10.6 – Chapter 10 Review

Materials
- Skeleton (optional)   • Glue
- Crayons
- Scissors

Teacher Resources

Body of Evidence: Skeletal System, Cartilage, and Bone by Dr. David Menton. DVD. Answers in Genesis, 2011.

Scripture Insights from Science and Archaeology by Paul McCoy. WinePress, 2010.

Student Resources

Bones and Muscles by Angela Royston. Sea to Sea, 2011.

The Bones You Own by Becky Baines. National Geographic Society, 2009.

Jessica's X-ray by Pat Zonta. Firefly Books, 2002.

Supplemental Materials

Blackline Masters
10.1A Puzzle: Skeleton
10.1B "Many Bones"
10.4A Inch Ruler
10.4B Bone Role-Play
10.4C Recipe: Phalanges Cookie
10.5A Chart
10.5B Food Groups

10.6A Bone and Muscle Facts
10.6B Chapter 10 Test
10.6C Gear Cutouts

Transparency Masters
10.1A Skeleton
10.4A Hand Bones

10.1 What Bones Are

Objective

Students will identify bones as a body part that gives shape to a person and helps a person move.

Materials

Introduction
- BLM 10.1A Puzzle: Skeleton, adhesive putty

Directed Instruction
- Skeleton or TM-10.1A Skeleton
- Chair, blanket
- BLM 10.1A Puzzle: Skeleton, scissors, glue, construction paper

Preparation

Print 1 copy of **BLM 10.1A Puzzle: Skeleton**, enlarging it 200%. Cut puzzle pieces apart. Attach ADHESIVE PUTTY to the back of each piece. (*Introduction*)

Write the definition of *bone* on the board. (*Directed Instruction*)

Have the SKELETON from the ACSI Science Equipment Kit available or select **TM-10.1A Skeleton** for display. (*Directed Instruction*)

Cover a CHAIR with a BLANKET. (*Directed Instruction*)

Print **BLM 10.1A Puzzle: Skeleton** for each student. Gather SCISSORS, GLUE, and CONSTRUCTION PAPER. (*Directed Instruction*)

Content

The adult human skeleton is made up of 206 bones. A child is born with more, but as he or she grows, some bones fuse. Each bone is unique in form and serves a specific function; for example, three tiny bones in the ear—the stapes, malleus, and incus—assist in hearing.

The following are some functions of the skeletal system:
- Protecting internal organs
- Providing a framework for the human shape
- Serving as a place of attachment for muscles, tendons, and ligaments
- Making blood cells

Introduction

Distribute an adhesive-backed puzzle piece from **BLM 10.1A Puzzle: Skeleton** to each student or to pairs of students. Explain that students will be putting together all of the puzzle pieces to build a skeleton. Designate a spot on the board or a blank wall for the class to assemble the puzzle. Allow students with the top parts of the skeleton to stick their pieces on first. When all 14 pieces have been added to the puzzle, explain that the finished product shows a human skeleton made up of many bones.

Directed Instruction

1 Read from the board the definition of **bone**: *a hard part of the body that gives the body shape and helps it move.* Explain that God designed all the bones of the human body so that they fit together to make a skeleton. Read **Colossians 1:16–17**. Explain that bones are not invisible, but they are hidden from sight by muscle, skin, and hair.

2 Direct students' attention to the first student page. Ask volunteers to read all of the sentences about bones. Discuss that God designed people's bones to be inside the body, fit together to make up the skeleton, and grow. Allow students time to trace the skeleton with their finger.

Read the verses from **Job 10:8a, 11b** at the bottom of the student page. Reinforce that God designed the body to move.

3 Display the SKELETON or **TM-10.1A Skeleton**. Point to bones that show a variety of shapes and sizes. State that students will learn the names of some specific bones throughout the chapter.

4 Ask students what people would look like if they did not have bones. (**a blob, a lump with no shape**) Point out that another job of the human skeleton, besides movement, is to give people a special shape. Display the CHAIR that is covered by the BLANKET. Ask what is under the blanket. (**chair**) How do you know what is under it? (**It is easy to tell that there is a chair's shape under the blanket.**) Share that, just as they could see the shape of the chair, God's design of the human body includes bones that give humans shape.

5 Instruct students to turn to the second page. Reiterate that one job of the skeleton is to help people move. Discuss some ways that the human body moves. Ask students to share their favorite way to move. (**Possible answers: run, walk, bend, twist, stretch, hop**) Guide students to match each of the three words at the top of the page with the correct picture. Ask students to identify which bones they would use to draw. (**finger and hand bones**) What bones do you use to dance? (**Possible answers: arm and leg bones, the entire skeleton**) Which bones help you run? (**leg and feet bones**)

Guide students to complete the exercises at the bottom of the page. Check for accuracy.

6 Distribute BLM 10.1A, SCISSORS, and GLUE to each student. Instruct students to cut out the pieces and to place them onto a piece of CONSTRUCTION PAPER. Direct students to glue the pieces together after you have checked the placement of the puzzle pieces for accuracy. If time is an issue, have students complete the puzzle at home with a family member, and then have them bring the completed puzzles back to school. Display the puzzles in the classroom.

Notes:

➕ **Extension**

Materials
• BLM 10.1B "Many Bones"
• *I Dig Dinosaurs! Buddy Davis' Amazing Adventures*

Print **BLM 10.1B "Many Bones"** for each student. Sing the song to the tune of "Jingle Bells." Schedule a time when your students can perform the song for other classes.

Show the video *I Dig Dinosaurs! Buddy Davis' Amazing Adventures* (Answers in Genesis, 2011) and discuss dinosaur bone findings.

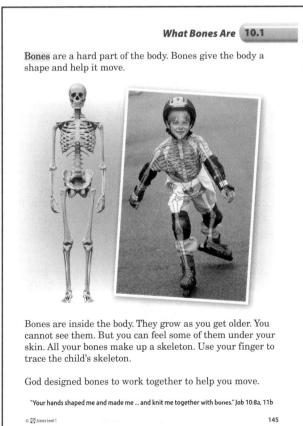

What Bones Are 10.1

Bones are a hard part of the body. Bones give the body a shape and help it move.

Bones are inside the body. They grow as you get older. You cannot see them. But you can feel some of them under your skin. All your bones make up a skeleton. Use your finger to trace the child's skeleton.

God designed bones to work together to help you move.

"Your hands shaped me and made me … and knit me together with bones." Job 10:8a, 11b

© Science Level 1   145

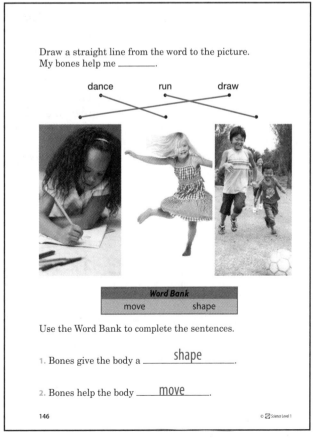

Draw a straight line from the word to the picture.
My bones help me _____.

dance   run   draw

Word Bank
move   shape

Use the Word Bank to complete the sentences.

1. Bones give the body a ____shape____.

2. Bones help the body ____move____.

146   © Science Level 1

10.2 Muscles and Joints

Objective

Students will locate muscles and joints in the human body.

Materials

Directed Instruction
• Skeleton or TM-10.1A Skeleton

✋ Preparation

Write the definitions of *muscle* and *joint* on the board. (*Directed Instruction*)

Have the SKELETON from the ACSI Science Equipment Kit available or select **TM-10.1A Skeleton** for display. (*Directed Instruction*)

Content

There are over 650 muscles in the human body. Skeletal, smooth, and cardiac are the three types of muscle tissue, and each type serves a unique function. Skeletal, or striated, muscles such as biceps allow voluntary movement, which is controlled by a person's will. Muscles move when the brain sends them a message. The message travels through nerves, across nerve cells called *neurons*, to the muscles. The skeletal muscles pull the attached bones, causing the corresponding body part to move. Smooth muscles and the cardiac muscle, on the other hand, function involuntarily. Smooth muscles are located in the walls of the intestines, bladder, and other internal organs; the cardiac muscle is only in the heart.

Muscles and joints serve various functions in the human body:
• Muscles allow people to close their eyes and blink. Muscles involuntarily change the size of the eye's pupil.
• A spasm in the muscle called *the diaphragm* causes a hiccup.
• It takes approximately 17 muscles to smile.
• Connective tissues, such as tendons and ligaments, hold parts of the body together. Tendons connect muscle to bone. Ligaments connect bone to bone or bone to cartilage.
• Joints are where bones meet. Different kinds of joints, such as hinge joints and ball-and-socket joints, serve different purposes. Hinge joints, such as knees, elbows, and finger joints, can be described as working like a door hinge. Ball-and-socket joints, such as the shoulder and hip, are designed with an end, or ball, of one bone fitting into the socket of the other. This allows for full movement in all directions. For example, the ball of the femur fits into the socket in the pelvis, creating the hip joint.

Introduction

Invite a few volunteers to the front of the room to flex their muscles for the class. Exclaim how big each volunteer's muscles are. Ask the class to stand and perform these activities as you name each one: running in place, jumping up and down, sitting in a chair, smiling, chewing, blinking, breathing. Repeat the list above. Ask students which actions they think use their muscles. (**Answers will vary but should include all.**) State that today students will learn how muscles help the body move.

Directed Instruction ✋ ➕

1 Direct students to feel their cheeks while they are not smiling. Ask how the cheeks feel. (**soft, relaxed**) Have students make their biggest smile and feel their cheeks. Ask how their cheeks feel now. (**stiff, hard**) Explain to students that they are feeling muscles at rest and then at work or tensed.

2 Read from the board the definition of **muscle**: *a part of the body that helps the body move.* Direct students' attention to the first page. Read the text about muscles, verifying that each student has flexed their arm muscle and pointed to an arm muscle of the boy roller blading. State that God designed people to have more than 650 muscles. Each of these muscles is a different size and shape and has a special job to do.

3 Read from the board the definition of **joint**: *a part of the body where bones meet.* Read and discuss the information about joints on the page. Point to the knee on the SKELETON or on **TM-10.1A Skeleton**, and direct students to observe how their knees move. (**out and in, open and close**) Explain that this kind of a joint is called *a hinge joint*. It works like the hinge of a door. Demonstrate the movement of a classroom door hinge.

4 Direct students' attention to the second page. Read about and discuss the illustration of the hinge joint of the knee and the image of the door hinge. Read and discuss the question in the middle of the page. Explain that the knee joint allows the leg to move and then stops the leg once it is straight. Convey that the elbow is also a hinge joint. Have students bend their arm at the elbow. Help them notice that the arm stops when it is straight.

Point to the hip joint (top of the leg where the femur meets the pelvis) on the skeleton or on TM-10.1A. Have the class move their hip joint (leg) and describe how it moves. (**all around, not just out and in**) Point out that the shoulder also moves this way.

Share that the hip and shoulder joints are called *ball-and-socket joints*; one end is like a ball, and the other end is like a socket or bowl. Refer to the graphics of the hip joint and the faucet. Convey that the faucet handle moves freely from hot to cold water and from a little to a lot of water because of a ball-and-socket joint. The ball-and-socket joint in the hip allows for a range of movements. Direct students to make a cup with one hand and a fist with the other and to put them together. Ask a volunteer to describe how this is like a ball-and-socket joint. (**the way it moves**)

5 Complete the exercises at the bottom of the page together. Direct students to share with a classmate what helps the body move. (**muscles, joints**)

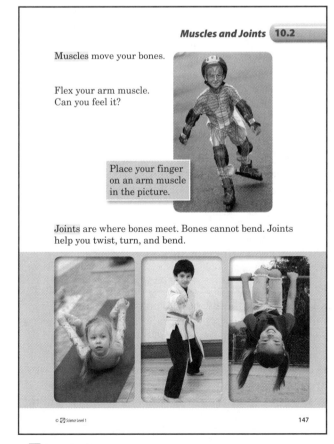

Muscles and Joints 10.2

Muscles move your bones.

Flex your arm muscle. Can you feel it?

Place your finger on an arm muscle in the picture.

Joints are where bones meet. Bones cannot bend. Joints help you twist, turn, and bend.

© Science Level 1   147

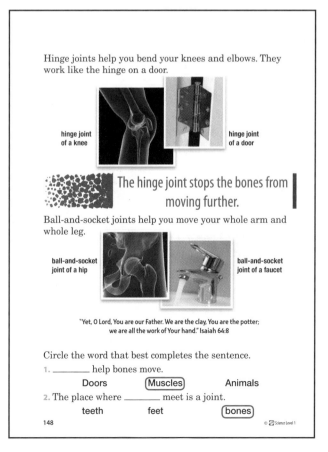

Hinge joints help you bend your knees and elbows. They work like the hinge on a door.

hinge joint of a knee

hinge joint of a door

The hinge joint stops the bones from moving further.

Ball-and-socket joints help you move your whole arm and whole leg.

ball-and-socket joint of a hip

ball-and-socket joint of a faucet

"Yet, O Lord, You are our Father. We are the clay, You are the potter; we are all the work of Your hand." Isaiah 64:8

Circle the word that best completes the sentence.
1. _____ help bones move.
   Doors   (Muscles)   Animals
2. The place where _____ meet is a joint.
   teeth   feet   (bones)

148   © Science Level 1

10.3 Bones Protect

Objective

Students will examine how certain bones protect specific parts of the body.

Materials

Introduction
- Pistachio nut, walnut, banana, nutcracker

Directed Instruction
- Balloon, helmet (optional)
- Skeleton or TM-10.1A Skeleton
- Yarn, penne pasta, tape, small bags

Preparation

Obtain a PISTACHIO NUT, a WALNUT, a BANANA, and a NUTCRACKER for a demonstration. (*Introduction*)

Inflate a BALLOON for a demonstration. (*Directed Instruction*)

Bring in a HELMET (optional). Have the SKELETON from the ACSI Science Equipment Kit available or select **TM-10.1A Skeleton** for display. (*Directed Instruction*)

Cut an 18 in. piece of YARN for each student. Tie a piece of PENNE PASTA (or ziti) to one end of the yarn, and wrap a piece of TAPE around the other. Place each prepared string of yarn in a SMALL BAG along with 9 additional pieces of pasta. (*Directed Instruction*)

Safety

Check student records for possible allergies.

Content

God's design of the human skeleton provides protection for many internal organs. The skull protects the brain; the rib cage shields the heart and lungs; and the vertebrae of the backbone encase the spinal cord.

- The skull is made up of 22 bones: 8 cranial bones and 14 facial bones.
- There are 12 pairs of ribs—all attached to the vertebral column in the back. The first 7 are attached in the front to cartilage connected to the sternum, or breastbone. The next 3 ribs attach to each other via cartilage and then to the seventh rib. They are known as *false ribs*. The last 2 ribs, which are also known as *false ribs*, are uniquely called *floating ribs* because they attach to muscle in the abdominal wall.
- The backbone is made up of separate or fused vertebrae: 7 cervical (neck region); 12 thoracic (chest area); 5 lumbar (lower back); 5 in the sacrum (which are fused in adults); and 4 fused at the base, or coccyx. Inside the backbone rests the delicate spinal cord, a bundle of nerve fibers.

Introduction

Hand a PISTACHIO NUT, a WALNUT, and a BANANA to three volunteers. Ask the volunteers what the hard or thick outer part does. (**Answers will vary but should include protect, keep safe, or keep clean the inner part.**) Ask the class to define the word *protect*. (**Possible answers: to keep safe, to take care of, to help**) Assist volunteers in removing the outer covering of the nuts and fruit. Use a NUTCRACKER to crack the walnut open. Have each volunteer describe for the class how these coverings help protect the nut or fruit.

Directed Instruction

1 Review with students the definition of *bone* from Lesson 10.1. (**a hard part of the body that gives the body shape and helps it move**) Inform the class that God designed bones to protect some of the parts on the inside of the body. Mention that the brain, heart, and lungs are some parts on the inside of the body. Instruct students to touch the top of their head. Explain that a bone called *the skull* protects the brain. Have students place their hands over their heart and lungs. Convey that ribs are bones that protect the heart and lungs.

2 Remind the class that their muscles and joints help them play sports and do fun activities. Ask students when people should wear a mouth guard to protect their teeth. (**when playing sports**) In which sports do people wear a helmet? (**Possible answers: football, baseball, bicycle riding**) Why is it important for people playing these sports to wear a helmet? (**to protect their brain**) By God's design, the brain works in very important ways. Since it is very delicate, it needs protection. Display an inflated BALLOON and discuss how both the balloon and brain are soft and delicate.

3 Direct students' attention to the first page and read the information and questions at the top. Lead the class to the conclusion that the helmet protects the balloon like the skull protects the brain. If you chose to bring a HELMET to class, demonstrate putting the balloon inside the helmet.

Display the SKELETON or **TM-10.1A Skeleton** and point out the skull, ribs, and backbone. As a volunteer reads the remaining text on the student page, instruct students to put a finger on the corresponding bone(s) in the picture. Read and discuss the Bible verse at the bottom of the page.

4 Explain that the backbone is actually many bones. Direct students to bend forward and to feel their backbone. Point out that each bump is a separate, small bone. Convey that one job of the backbone is to protect the spinal cord. Compare the spinal cord to a headphone or earbud cord. The spinal cord carries messages between the brain and the body similar to the way a headphone cord carries music from a musical source to the ears.

5 Have students turn to their second page. Read and discuss the sentence and question at the top. Point out the backbone model and exclaim that students will make one today. Distribute SMALL BAGS of prepared PENNE PASTA materials. Instruct students to thread the YARN through the pasta and then tie on the last piece of pasta. Assist as needed. Circulate through the classroom, and individually assess students' understanding of the backbone. (**It is made of many small bones. It protects the spinal cord.**)

Ask how the pasta pieces are like bones. (**They are hard.**) What is the pasta protecting? (**the soft yarn inside**) How is the yarn like the spinal cord? (**Both are soft and delicate.**) Have students carefully move the model to test its ability to stand up straight, bend over, and do a somersault. Explain that if the backbone were one big bone, people could not bend and twist the way they do. Point out the way God purposefully designed the skeleton to protect humans and allow them to move in many ways. Direct students to take their model home and to describe how the backbone works.

6 Help students prepare for writing their journal entry by brainstorming words about bones. Have students complete the page.

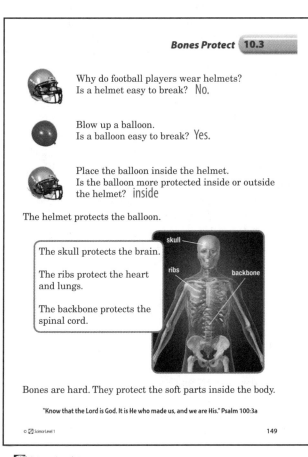

Bones Protect **10.3**

Why do football players wear helmets? Is a helmet easy to break? No.

Blow up a balloon. Is a balloon easy to break? Yes.

Place the balloon inside the helmet. Is the balloon more protected inside or outside the helmet? inside

The helmet protects the balloon.

The skull protects the brain.

The ribs protect the heart and lungs.

The backbone protects the spinal cord.

skull

ribs

backbone

Bones are hard. They protect the soft parts inside the body.

"Know that the Lord is God. It is He who made us, and we are His." Psalm 100:3a

© Science Level 1   149

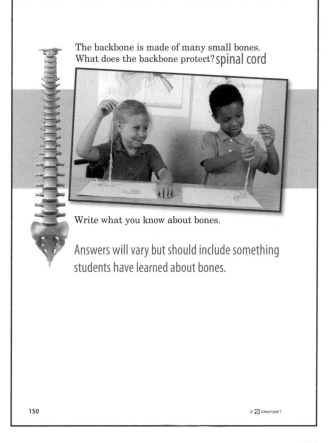

The backbone is made of many small bones. What does the backbone protect? spinal cord

Write what you know about bones.

Answers will vary but should include something students have learned about bones.

150   © Science Level 1

Objective

Students will recognize and compare specific bones in the body.

Materials

Introduction
• Connecting cubes

Directed Instruction
• Straws
• Skeleton or TM-10.1A Skeleton
• Rulers or BLM 10.4A Inch Ruler, scissors, tape
• BLM 10.4B Bone Role-Play

Preparation

Obtain enough CONNECTING CUBES so each student and yourself have 10. Cubes can be found in the ACSI Math Manipulatives Kit. (*Introduction*)

Cut several STRAWS into halves, thirds, or fourths to make a total of 206 parts. (*Directed Instruction*)

Obtain the SKELETON from the ACSI Science Equipment Kit or select **TM-10.1A Skeleton** for display. (*Directed Instruction*)

Collect a RULER or print **BLM 10.4A Inch Ruler** for each student. Have SCISSORS and TAPE available. (*Directed Instruction*)

Print and cut apart 1 copy of **BLM 10.4B Bone Role-Play**. (*Directed Instruction*)

Content

The number, size, shape, and organization of bones in a skeleton display God's purposeful design. Some special bones of the human body include:

• Stapes ('stā·pēz): the smallest bone. It is one of the three bones used in hearing, and it is located in the middle ear. The stapes is approximately 3 mL long. It is also called *a stirrup* because its shape resembles that of a stirrup.
• Femur (or thighbone): the longest, largest, and strongest bone.
• Phalanges (fā·'lan·jēz): the bones of the fingers, thumbs, and toes. There are 2 phalanges in each thumb and 3 in each finger; there are 2 phalanges in each big toe and 3 in each remaining toe. The bones of the hand are metacarpals; of the wrist, carpals; of the foot, metatarsals; and of the ankle, tarsals.

Introduction

Display **10 CONNECTING CUBES**. Arrange them in a shape of your choice in front of the class. Ask students what the parts are that make up this model and give it a shape. (**the connecting cubes**) Distribute connecting cubes to students to make a model. State that the cubes connect to build a model like bones connect to make a skeleton.

Directed Instruction

1 Direct students to turn to the first page, and read the question at the top. Have students write their answer. Guide students to observe the bones of the skeleton shown on the page. Compare these bones to the scattered bones on the page. Ask the next question on the page, Do you think there are more bones in the skeleton or around the skeleton? (**Answers will vary.**) State that the number of bones in the skeleton is the same as the number of bones around it. Point out that in the skeleton, the bones are all put together; those that are scattered do not make a shape. Explain that God designed bones to fit in exactly the right places in the body.

2 Inform students that the next activity will help them learn how many bones are in the human body. Give each student approximately 8 to 10 STRAW PIECES. In groups of four, have students write down the number of straw pieces each student has and the sum for their group. Check the calculations made by each group and write these numbers on the board. Add the totals to get 206. State that there are 206 bones in the human body. Have each student carefully add his or her straw parts to one pile on the floor of the classroom. Remind the class that there are the same number of straw parts in the pile as there are bones in the human body. Reiterate that God designed people's bones to fit together to make a skeleton. Allow students to complete the final blank on their page.

3 Use the SKELETON or **TM-10.1A Skeleton** to reinforce that bones form a skeleton, which gives the body a shape. There are many different sizes and shapes of bones. The smallest bone in the body is found in the head. Have students guess where that bone is found. (**Answers will vary.**)

4 Direct students' attention to the second page to find out the answer. Have students put a finger on the area of the skeleton's ear. Say the word *stapes* and have the class repeat it. Instruct students to put a finger on the larger picture of the stapes. Inform students that the stapes helps them hear. Compare this picture to the smaller stapes picture, the actual size of the stapes in the body. Compare the stapes to the femur or thighbone, which is the largest bone in the body. Say the word *femur* and have the class repeat it. Point out both femurs on the skeleton or on TM-10.1A. Distribute RULERS or **BLM 10.4A Inch Ruler** (which students assemble using SCISSORS and TAPE). Allow time for students to measure one of their femurs and to record it on their page. Share that the femur is about 20 in. long in an average adult man. Collect the rulers for Lesson 10.5.

5 Direct students to look at the skeleton on the page and to touch the bones of the fingers, thumbs, and toes, or phalanges. Say the word *phalanges* and have the class repeat it. Calculate how many phalanges students have: 2 in each thumb, 3 in each finger, 2 in each big toe, 3 in each other toe. This equals 14 phalanges in one hand or foot, or 56 total! Have students wiggle their phalanges. To reinforce the bones taught, lead students in moving their skull, ribs, backbone, femur, and phalanges one at a time to a familiar song as you call out the different bones.

6 Conduct a role-play with six student volunteers. Give each volunteer a cutout from **BLM 10.4B Bone Role-Play**. Direct them to pretend they are the bone on their card and to describe that bone's location or function in the body. Allow the rest of the class to guess which bone each volunteer is pretending to be. (**Possible answers:** *skull*: I am found in the head. I protect the brain; *backbone*: I protect the spine. I am made of many small bones; *stapes*: I help with hearing. I am the smallest bone; *femur*: I am in the longest bone in the leg. I help a person stand; *phalanges*: I am found in fingers and toes and help them move; *ribs*: I protect the lungs.)

➕ Extension

Materials
• BLM 10.4B Bone Role-Play, scissors
• BLM 10.4C Recipe: Phalanges Cookie, TM-10.4 Hand Bones

Print **BLM 10.4B Bone Role-Play** for each student. Direct students to cut out and to lay the bone cards on their desk. Have students lift their cards high to respond to these questions: Which cards show head bones? (**skull, stapes**) Which card shows a leg bone? (**femur**) Which card shows bones in the chest? (**ribs**) Which card shows the bones that connect the head to the hips? (**backbone**) Which card shows finger bones? (**phalanges**)

Share the cookies made by parent volunteers (according to **BLM 10.4C Recipe: Phalanges Cookie** and **TM-10.4A Hand Bones**). Check student records for allergies.

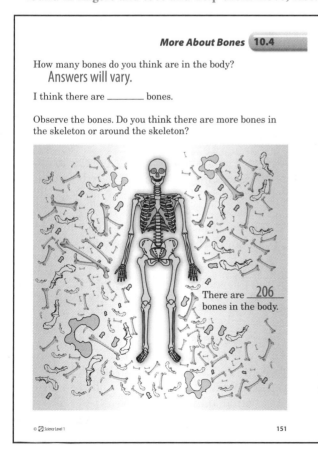

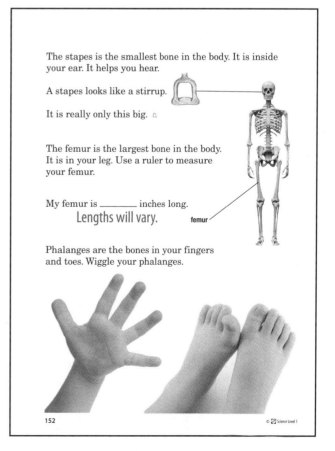

More About Bones 10.4

How many bones do you think are in the body?
   Answers will vary.

I think there are _____ bones.

Observe the bones. Do you think there are more bones in the skeleton or around the skeleton?

There are _206_ bones in the body.

The stapes is the smallest bone in the body. It is inside your ear. It helps you hear.

A stapes looks like a stirrup.

It is really only this big. ⌂

The femur is the largest bone in the body. It is in your leg. Use a ruler to measure your femur.

My femur is _____ inches long.
   Lengths will vary.   femur

Phalanges are the bones in your fingers and toes. Wiggle your phalanges.

© Science Level 1   151

152   © Science Level 1

Objective

Students will give examples of ways to keep bones and muscles healthy.

Materials

Introduction
- Rulers or BLM 10.4A Inch Ruler, BLM 10.5A Chart

Directed Instruction
- BLM 10.5B Food Groups, crayons
- Clay

Preparation

Have a RULER or premade ruler from **BLM 10.4A Inch Ruler** for each student (from Lesson 10.4) available. Print **BLM 10.5A Chart** for each student. (*Introduction*)

Print **BLM 10.5B Food Groups** and obtain CRAYONS for each student. (*Directed Instruction*)

Make a broken bone from CLAY for display. Have clay available for each student to make a bone. (*Directed Instruction*)

Content

Caring for and being a good steward of the gifts God has given is very important. First Corinthians 6:20 reminds Christians to honor God with their body. Eating well and exercising regularly are ways to care for the body. Acquiring the needed nutrients (including calcium) and exercising are important for the development of healthy bones and muscles. Caring for bones also includes wearing protective gear while participating in certain activities. Helmets, knee and elbow pads, shin guards, and elbow and wrist pads can prevent many bone injuries.

God's purposeful design is demonstrated in the way bones heal when they are broken. When a bone breaks, a blood clot is formed to close the space between the broken ends. Bone cells grow on both sides of the break to gradually fill the gap. An X-ray of the affected area shows the extent of the injury. A doctor may need to set the bone to be sure it is in the correct position and then protect it with a cast.

Introduction

Share with the class that some people grow quickly and some people grow slowly. Instruct students to use a RULER to measure their hand, arm, lower leg, and foot. If rulers are not available, use **BLM 10.4A Inch Ruler**.

Instruct students to measure each of the following by using these guidelines:
- Hand—from the wrist to the tip of their longest finger
- Arm—from their elbow to their wrist
- Lower leg—from their knee to their ankle
- Foot—from the back of their heel to the tip of their longest toe

Distribute **BLM 10.5A Chart** to each student. Read the directions as students follow along. Allow time for students to measure their own body or to work with a partner. As they work, have them write down the lengths in the corresponding boxes on BLM 10.5A. Alert students that if the measurement is between two whole numbers, they should write the higher number. Provide assistance as needed.

Directed Instruction

1 Inform students that God designed children's bones and muscles to grow as they get older. Share that bones and muscles grow as the whole body grows and that it is important to take good care of them.

Direct students' attention to the first student page. Have a volunteer read the sentences about foods. Point out the five food groups and some examples:
- Proteins—beef, chicken, meat, fish, eggs
- Dairy—milk, yogurt, cheese
- Vegetables—corn, asparagus, peas, lettuce
- Grains—bread, pasta, rice
- Fruits—oranges, apples, grapes, bananas

Reiterate that exercise helps bones and muscles grow strong and also stay strong. Read the information about exercise. Allow students time to respond to the question at the bottom of the page.

Emphasize that dairy foods like milk, yogurt, and cheese have calcium and other nutrients and are necessary for healthy bones and teeth. Proteins are necessary for muscle health. Distribute **BLM 10.5B Food Groups** and CRAYONS. Read the directions and assist students in classifying and sorting the foods on the page.

2 Have students turn to the second page, and take the class through the process shown in pictures and words. Discuss the bone's healing process that God provided. When a bone is broken, tiny parts of bone grow at the break until the two ends join to become one bone again. Share that it is important that a person go to a doctor if he or she suspects that a bone is broken. Convey that a doctor may request that an X-ray be taken in order to determine if a bone is broken. Give students time to complete the exercises at the bottom of the page.

3 Share with students that they will mend a clay bone that is broken. To demonstrate this process, display the premade broken bone of CLAY. Be sure the position of the bone is straight and use a tiny amount of clay to repair the break. Distribute a piece of scrap paper and a portion of clay to each student. Instruct students to make a bone, break it, and mend it by smoothing the clay of the broken bone together again. Read **Isaiah 64:8** and ask students what it means. (**that God made people**)

Notes:

Extension

Materials
- Chicken bone, jar with lid, vinegar
- White chocolate, small paper cups, microwave, mini marshmallows, pretzels

Place a cooked chicken bone in a jar of vinegar and cover it. Ask students to predict what will happen to this hard bone. After 24 hrs, rinse the bone. Flex it carefully to show that it is rubbery. Explain that vinegar, an acid, took the calcium out of the bone. Remind students that calcium is important to keep bones healthy.

Melt white chocolate in a microwave; pour it into cups for each student. Direct the class to stick a mini marshmallow onto each end of a pretzel stick and to dip the pretzels in white chocolate; the food will look like bones. Check student records for possible allergies before beginning.

Healthy Bones and Muscles **10.5**

Some foods help bones and muscles grow strong. You should eat these groups of foods every day.

Dairy Proteins

Vegetables Grains Fruit

Foods from the dairy group have calcium in them. Calcium helps bones grow strong. Proteins help make muscles healthy.

Exercise helps bones and muscles grow strong. When you move your body, you are exercising.

How are these children exercising? They are running.

How do you exercise? Answers will vary.

© Science Level 1   153

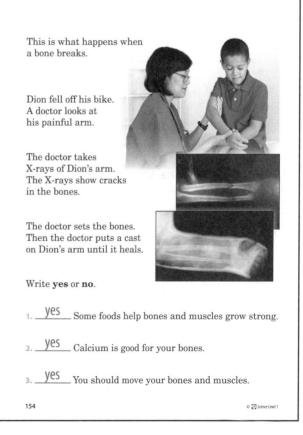

This is what happens when a bone breaks.

Dion fell off his bike. A doctor looks at his painful arm.

The doctor takes X-rays of Dion's arm. The X-rays show cracks in the bones.

The doctor sets the bones. Then the doctor puts a cast on Dion's arm until it heals.

Write **yes** or **no**.

1. __yes__ Some foods help bones and muscles grow strong.

2. __yes__ Calcium is good for your bones.

3. __yes__ You should move your bones and muscles.

154   © Science Level 1

10.6 Chapter 10 Review

Directed Instruction
• BLM 10.6A Bone and Muscle Facts
• Skeleton or TM-10.1A Skeleton
• BLM 10.6B Chapter 10 Test, crayons
• BLM 10.6C Gear Cutouts, scissors, glue

✋ Preparation

Print **BLM 10.6A Bone and Muscle Facts** for each student. (*Directed Instruction*)

Have the SKELETON from the ACSI Science Equipment Kit available or select **TM-10.1A Skeleton** for display. (*Directed Instruction*)

Draw the following Creation web on the board. (*Directed Instruction*)

Print **BLM 10.6B Chapter 10 Test** for each student, and obtain CRAYONS for them. (*Directed Instruction*)

Print **BLM 10.6C Gear Cutouts** for each student. Obtain SCISSORS and GLUE for each student as well. (*Directed Instruction*)

Introduction

Play a game of Funny Bone Says. Direct students to only follow commands preceded by the phrase "Funny Bone says touch your ..." Use this game as a review of terms discussed in the chapter—skull, backbone, ribs, femur, stapes, phalanges, elbow joint, knee joint, shoulder joint, hip joint. To make the game more challenging, try using definitions or descriptions as well, such as "Funny Bone says touch the longest bone in your body." If students make mistakes or move out of turn in the game, allow them to continue participating. This activity may assist you in assessment of student understanding.

Directed Instruction ✋

1 Review the definitions of *bone*, *muscle*, and *joint*. (***bone**: a hard part of the body that gives the body shape and helps it move; **muscle**: a part of the body that helps the body move; **joint**: a part of the body where bones meet*) Distribute **BLM 10.6A Bone and Muscle Facts**. Read the facts and say "blank" for the missing word. Allow time for students to fill in the words from the Word Bank. When students have completed the page, have volunteers read each fact with the answer.

Use the SKELETON or **TM-10.1A Skeleton** to review the names and functions of bones. Ask students why it is important that people have a skull. (**to protect the brain**) What shields the heart and lungs? (**ribs**) What bones give fingers and toes a shape? (**phalanges**) For which of the five senses is the stapes bone used? (**hearing**) What protects the spinal cord? (**backbone**) Which is the largest and strongest bone of the body? (**femur**)

2 Have students imagine what life would be like if they did not have bones and joints. (**I could not move in the same way.**) Mention that it would be impossible to sit, stand up, or walk without any joints.

Ask students to stand up and to demonstrate what it would be like if their backbone was one solid bone instead of separate bones. (Students will have to bend and move side to side without bending their back.) Reiterate that God purposefully gave people joints so that they could make many different movements with their body. Ask what body parts God designed to help people move. (**bones, muscles, joints**)

3 Explain that students will now observe what the bones, muscles, and joints of the face help people do. Cover your nose and mouth and allow students to guess the emotion made by your expression. Read a verse to go with each.
• Happy—Psalm 68:3 or Proverbs 15:13
• Sad—Genesis 40:7 or Nehemiah 2:2
• Shame—Psalm 44:15
• Radiant—Exodus 34:35

Encourage students to cover their nose and mouth and to make a facial expression for a partner. Allow the partner to guess the emotion.

4 Direct students' attention to the Creation web on the board. Remind students that God purposefully designed people with a body and a soul and spirit. Select a volunteer to read the parts of the body shown on the web. (**teeth, bones and muscles**) Ask students to name other parts of the body. (**Answers will vary.**)

5 Use student pages as a review or pretest. Complete these pages with your class. You may use **BLM 10.6B Chapter 10 Test** for individual assessment. Read through this test with your class. Provide CRAYONS and as much reading support as necessary. You may choose to use BLM 10.6B as an oral assessment or not to do it at all.

6 Distribute **BLM 10.6C Gear Cutouts**, SCISSORS, and GLUE. Give students time to cut out the protective gear and to glue the pieces correctly onto the page.

7 Chapter 10 Bones and Muscles has been completed. It can be stapled and sent home as a booklet to be shared with a family member.

Notes:

⊕ **Extension**

Materials
• Plastic food items, plastic money, plastic bags

Set up an area with plastic food and have students sort food items by food group. Or, create grocery lists for students by food group (such as 3 grains, 2 vegetables, 3 fruits, 1 dairy, 1 protein). Price each food item displayed. Distribute plastic money and plastic bags to students. Have them purchase items from the food groups on their grocery list. Assign a cashier to collect the money and to make sure students are paying the correct amount.

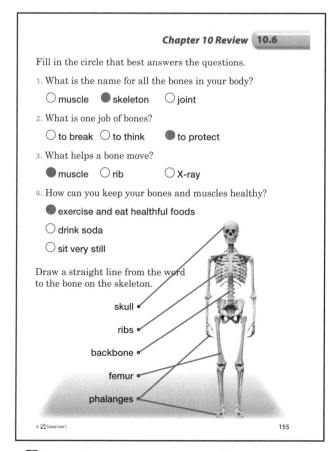

Heart and Blood

Chapter 11

Key Ideas

- The heart is a body part that pumps blood through blood vessels to the rest of the body.
- The body has its own way of healing cuts, including forming a scab over the cut to protect it and help it heal.
- Exercising and eating healthful food helps keep the heart strong.
- Technology provides ways to diagnose heart problems.

11.0 Chapter Preparation

heart

Looking Ahead

- Collect a paper-towel tube for each student to use in **Lesson 11.1**.
- For an *Extension* activity in **Lesson 11.3**, invite the school nurse to talk about first aid and cuts.
- For an *Extension* activity in **Lesson 12.3**, invite a musician or the music teacher to come speak to the class. Encourage him or her to demonstrate how to play woodwind instruments, such as a clarinet, a flute, or an oboe, and some brass instruments, such as a trumpet or a trombone. Encourage the guest to discuss with students the way in which the instruments work through the use of breath.

Introduction

A study of the heart reveals God's design to circulate blood throughout the body. By bringing attention to a familiar sensation—the heartbeat—students can relate to the function of the heart as a pump. They will identify that blood flows throughout the body through blood vessels. Electrocardiogram readouts and diagnostic procedures provide a technology connection that can save a person's life. Students are encouraged to make positive choices in the areas of food and exercise as a means of maintaining a healthy heart.

About This Chapter

Lesson 11.1 – What the Heart Is

Materials
- Ball
- Toothpaste
- Cups
- Paper-towel tubes
- Tape

Lesson Content
The heart is a part of the body that pumps blood. A heartbeat or pulse indicates that the heart is pumping. A doctor uses a stethoscope to listen to a patient's heartbeat.

Lesson 11.2 – Blood Vessels and Blood Flow

Materials
- Straws
- Tape
- Eyedroppers
- Cups
- Water
- Food coloring

Lesson Content
Blood travels in the body through blood vessels. When the heart squeezes, or pumps, it pushes blood into blood vessels, which then carry blood with necessary nutrients to sustain each body part.

Lesson 11.3 – Cuts Heal

Materials
- Flashlight
- Crayons
- Scissors
- Colored paper
- Glue
- Bulletin board paper
- Tape

Lesson Content
God designed the human body to heal itself when it is injured. When the skin is cut, the cut bleeds, and a scab forms. After new skin grows sufficiently, the scab falls off. The scab protects the cut as it heals and also prevents excess bleeding from the cut.

Lesson 11.4 – A Healthy Heart

Materials
- Index cards
- Timer
- Music (optional)
- Water
- Colored paper
- Potato chips
- Crayons
- Snack materials (optional)

Lesson Content
Exercising and eating healthfully are two ways to keep a healthy heart. Exercising strengthens the heart muscle. Eating healthful food keeps blood vessels clean. Eating from the five food groups and ingesting less fat keep the heart healthy and strong.

Lesson 11.5 – Tech Connect

Materials

• No additional materials are needed.

Lesson Content

Doctors and scientists have discovered many ways to help the heart stay healthy. An electrocardiogram test can show how the heart is working. An unhealthy heart shows a different reading from that of a healthy one.

Lesson 11.6 – Chapter 11 Review

Materials

• No additional materials are needed.

Teacher Resources

The Circulatory System by Susan Whittemore. Chelsea House, 2009.

First Aid for Babies and Children Fast. DK, 2006.

A Pocket Guide to the Human Body: Intricate Design That Glorifies the Creator by Dr. David Menton. Answers in Genesis, 2011.

Student Resources

3-D Close Up: The Human Body by Caroline Harris. Silver Dolphin, 2009.

The Heart: Our Circulatory System by Seymour Simon. HarperCollins, 2006.

Supplemental Materials

Blackline Masters

11.3A Cuts Heal

11.5A Raising Heart-Healthy Children

11.6A Heart and Blood Facts

11.6B Who I Am

11.6C Chapter 11 Test

Transparency Master

11.2A Heart

Computer Presentation

11.6 The Amazing Heart

11.1 What the Heart Is

Objective

Students will define and identify functions of the heart.

Materials

Introduction
• Small rubber ball

Directed Instruction
• Tube of toothpaste
• Small paper cups, paper-towel tubes, tape

Preparation

Obtain a SMALL RUBBER BALL for a demonstration. (*Introduction*)

Write the definition of *heart* on the board. (*Directed Instruction*)

Obtain a TUBE OF TOOTHPASTE for a demonstration. (*Directed Instruction*)

For each student, collect a SMALL PAPER CUP, a PAPER-TOWEL TUBE, and TAPE. Cut the bottoms out of the cups before distributing them to students. (*Directed Instruction*)

Alternatives

If paper-towel tubes are not available, roll construction paper to use as stethoscopes.

Content

The heart, an organ made up mostly of cardiac muscle, beats continually and involuntarily. A person's heart is approximately the size of his or her fist. Similar in shape to a strawberry, it is located in the chest between the lungs. A baby's heart begins to flutter and beat approximately three weeks after conception. An adult's heart beats an average of 70 times per minute. The pulse—a throbbing of the arteries caused by the heart's pumping of the blood into the arteries—can be felt in the neck and at the wrist.

The top chambers of the heart are called *atria*; the bottom chambers are known as *ventricles*. The heart's ventricles are separated by a partition, or septum. Each ventricle can be considered a pump. Blood delivers oxygen to the cells and picks up carbon dioxide, a waste product. The deoxygenated blood (blood with less oxygen) enters the right atrium and goes to the right ventricle through a valve. Heart valves prevent blood from flowing in the wrong direction. The right ventricle sends blood to the lungs, where carbon dioxide exits, and oxygen enters the blood.

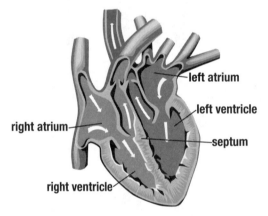

After the exchange of gases in the lungs, the oxygenated blood flows back to the heart. It enters the left atrium and then the left ventricle. The left ventricle pumps, sending blood to the body (including the heart itself), thereby delivering the newly acquired oxygen and needed chemicals to body cells.

Introduction

Hold a SMALL RUBBER BALL in your hand. Squeeze and relax your grip on the ball several times, and inform the class that the human heart squeezes and relaxes many times each minute. This process is called *a heartbeat*. Allow students to mimic a heartbeat by making a fist and squeezing and relaxing it several times. Have them place their fist over the location of their heart and squeeze and relax again. Convey that this action is similar to what happens in their chest. Their heart is approximately the size of their fist.

Directed Instruction

1 State that students will be studying the human heart. Read **1 Corinthians 12:18**. Reiterate that God designed all the parts of the human body. Read the definition of **heart**: *a part of the body that pumps blood.*

2 Ask students how the heart beats. (**It squeezes and relaxes.**) Close your hand gently around a TUBE OF TOOTHPASTE. Carefully squeeze your hand and allow the class to see the toothpaste coming out of the tube. Explain that your hand is the pump that pushed the toothpaste out of the tube. Ask what is pumped out when the heart squeezes or beats. (**blood**) Share that the main job of the heart is to pump blood to all parts of the body.

3 Direct the class to turn to the first student page. Read the definition of *heart*, and instruct students to place their hand over their heart to see if they feel their heart beating. (**Answers will vary.**) Help students try the ways shown on the page to check their heart rate, or the number of heartbeats per minute. Mention that they are feeling their pulse when they feel their neck and wrist. Point out that an adult's heart beats about 70 times per minute. A child's heart beats about 100 times per minute. Have students put a finger on the heart at the bottom of the page. Read the sentences about the heart being a strong pump, like a gasoline pump.

4 Share that doctors check for a healthy heart by using a stethoscope. Write the syllables *steth·o·scope* on the board. Pronounce the word *stethoscope* and have students repeat it. Direct students' attention to the second page. Ask if students have ever had a doctor use a stethoscope to listen to their heart. (**Answers will vary.**) How does a doctor use a stethoscope? (**The doctor puts one end on a person's chest, puts the other parts in his or her ears, and listens.**)

5 Share that students will use a SMALL PAPER CUP and a PAPER-TOWEL TUBE to make a stethoscope to listen to a heartbeat. Show the model stethoscope and demonstrate how the paper towel tube fits into the cup. Distribute materials and have students use TAPE to attach the cup to the tube. Upon completion, have students work in pairs. Instruct students to place the paper cup end on their own chest while their partner listens. Complete the rest of the page together. Have students take their stethoscope home to share.

⊕ Extension

Conclude the lesson by singing the following heart song to the tune of "Twinkle, Twinkle, Little Star."

My Heart's Pumping
My heart's pumping every day,
Pumping blood in special ways.
I can feel it beat and beat,
Sending blood to head and feet.
God made me so wonderfully,
A special heart for you and me.

What the Heart Is 11.1

The **heart** is a part of the body that pumps blood.

Feel your heart beating.

Place your hand over your heart.

Feel the side of your neck. Check your heart rate.

Feel your arm.

The heart is like a strong pump. It pushes blood through your whole body.

heart   gas pump

© *Science* Level 1   159

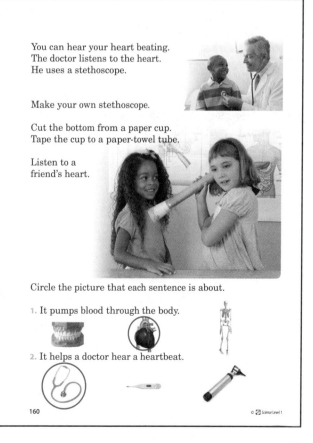

You can hear your heart beating.
The doctor listens to the heart.
He uses a stethoscope.

Make your own stethoscope.

Cut the bottom from a paper cup.
Tape the cup to a paper-towel tube.

Listen to a friend's heart.

Circle the picture that each sentence is about.

1. It pumps blood through the body.

2. It helps a doctor hear a heartbeat.

160   © *Science* Level 1

11.2 Blood Vessels and Blood Flow

Heart and Blood

Objective

Students will trace the path of blood from the heart to the toes and demonstrate blood flow through the body.

Materials

Directed Instruction
- TM-11.2A Heart
- Straws, tape, eyedroppers, cups, water, red food coloring

Preparation

Select **TM-11.2A Heart** for display. (*Directed Instruction*)

Have available 3 STRAWS, TAPE, an EYEDROPPER, 2 CUPS, WATER, and RED FOOD COLORING for pairs of students. Make two ¼-in. slits on opposite sides of one end of 1 straw for each pair of students. Assemble and tape the straws before class, or be prepared to allow enough time for students to assemble them. Eyedroppers can be found in the ACSI Science Equipment Kit. Use the red food coloring to make a cup of red water for each pair of students. (*Directed Instruction*)

Safety

Caution students that the red water will stain their clothes.

Content

The heart beats—contracting and relaxing—causing blood to be pushed out and away from the heart. Blood travels through a network of tubelike blood vessels to provide each cell in the body with the nutrients it needs to function. The blood also carries away the wastes made by the cells.

There are three main types of blood vessels: arteries, veins, and capillaries. Arteries carry blood away from the heart, while veins carry blood toward the heart. The size of blood vessels varies dramatically. The diameter of an adult's aorta—the largest artery in the body—is almost as big as a garden hose. Capillaries are very small in diameter, even thinner than sewing thread. Their function is to exchange oxygen and other nutrients for cell waste, such as carbon dioxide. Veins are about two-thirds the diameter of arteries. They contain valves to prevent the backflow of blood.

Blood cells possess the same basic needs as a human body—oxygen, food, water, and waste disposal. Oxygen is acquired through the lungs in exchange for carbon dioxide. It then travels to body cells via red blood cells. The red blood cells also gain nutrients from the food broken down during digestion and absorbed through structures in the small intestine. These nutrients then travel to each body cell via the blood.

Introduction

Instruct students to recount words that have to do with the heart, the body part they learned about in Lesson 9.1. Write their words on the board. (**Possible answers: pumps, beats, squeezes, relaxes, is strong**) Why is the heart so important? (**It pumps blood.**)

Directed Instruction

1 Direct students to make a fist and place it over their heart. Instruct them to tighten and relax their fist as though their heart is pumping. Ask how their heart is like a muscle in their body. (**It tightens and relaxes.**) Explain that the heart is a very special body part. The heart keeps pumping without a person thinking about it—even during sleep! Use **TM-11.2A Heart** to show the location of the heart and some of the blood vessels. Direct students' attention to the first student page. Read the sentences in the first caption box.

2 Invite a student to draw a square on the board to represent the classroom. Next, ask another student to draw a square to represent the school cafeteria or another separate room. Then request a third student to draw a line to connect the squares to represent the path students take to get from the classroom to the other room. Convey that the line represents a path students use to get from one place to another.

Direct students' attention back to the page and have them circle the heart and a toe on the large illustration. Have them place a finger on the heart and another finger on a toe. Ask how the blood gets from the heart to the toe. (**Answers will vary.**) Share with the class that blood travels in special tubes to get to the toe and all other parts of the body. These tubes are called *blood vessels*. Use TM-11.2A to trace the path blood takes through blood vessels from the heart to the other body parts. Read the bottom caption on the student page about blood vessels.

3 Direct students' attention to the second page. Read the directions and steps aloud, and refer to the photo. Explain that the following experiment will demonstrate how blood vessels work. Show how to slip 2 STRAWS into the slit end of a third straw and how to use TAPE to secure the straws. (See the photo below.) Display an EYEDROPPER and squeeze the end several times. Demonstrate how to fill the eyedropper from the CUP of RED WATER. Squeeze the eyedropper over the top straw and let students observe the flow of water down the straws and into the second cup placed below the straws. Share that when the heart squeezes, or pumps, the blood flows out of the heart and into blood vessels. Ask how the straws are like blood vessels. (**Liquid can flow through them.**)

Group students into pairs and provide the materials for their experiment. Have pairs work together to connect the straws and to secure them with tape if the straws were not previously assembled. Assist students as needed. Allow pairs to take turns squeezing the water into the straws.

4 Ask what makes the blood in the body flow. (**pumping of the heart**) Share that the straw activity represents the design and function of the blood vessels. God designed the heart to pump and push blood through many blood vessels to all parts of the body. Give students time to finish the page.

⊕ Extension

Materials
• Hose, thread
• Quart containers

Explain that God designed the body with different kinds of blood vessels. Display a piece of garden hose and a piece of thread. Share that the biggest artery, one that is connected to the heart, is as wide across in an adult as the hose. The smallest blood vessels, capillaries, are thinner than the thread.

Show students 5 empty qt containers. Convey that the adult human body has about 5 qts of blood. The heart pumps so much that the same blood makes many trips around the body—one trip every minute!

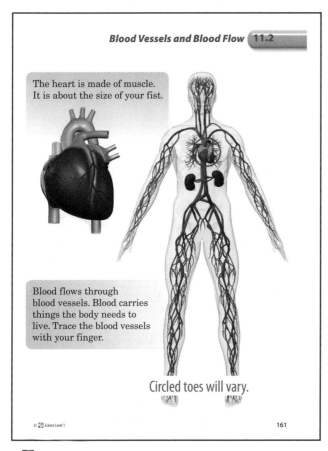

Blood Vessels and Blood Flow 11.2

The heart is made of muscle. It is about the size of your fist.

Blood flows through blood vessels. Blood carries things the body needs to live. Trace the blood vessels with your finger.

Circled toes will vary.

© Science Level 1   161

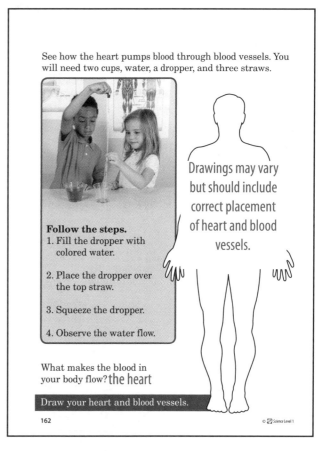

See how the heart pumps blood through blood vessels. You will need two cups, water, a dropper, and three straws.

Follow the steps.
1. Fill the dropper with colored water.
2. Place the dropper over the top straw.
3. Squeeze the dropper.
4. Observe the water flow.

What makes the blood in your body flow? the heart

Draw your heart and blood vessels.

Drawings may vary but should include correct placement of heart and blood vessels.

162   © Science Level 1

Objective

Students will simulate and sequence how cuts heal.

Materials

Introduction
• Flashlight

Directed Instruction
• BLM 11.3A Cuts Heal, brown crayons, scissors, red paper
• Crayons, scissors, glue
• Brown or tan bulletin board paper, brown paper, red paper, tape or glue

Preparation

Have available a FLASHLIGHT for a demonstration. (*Introduction*)

Print **BLM 11.3A Cuts Heal** for each student. Gather a BROWN CRAYON, SCISSORS, and a sheet of RED PAPER for each student. (*Directed Instruction*)

Have available CRAYONS, SCISSORS, and GLUE for students. (*Directed Instruction*)

Obtain a sheet of BROWN OR TAN BULLETIN BOARD PAPER and make a cutout section in the center and RED PAPER behind it. Then cut out a BROWN-PAPER CIRCLE for each student, and have TAPE or GLUE ready for students to use. (*Directed Instruction*)

Content

The circulatory system transports chemicals that body cells need. Blood carries oxygen and nutrients from digested food to these body cells and carries wastes away from them. Blood consists of plasma (a liquid made mostly of water), red blood cells, white blood cells, and platelets.

The concave, disk-shaped red blood cells contain hemoglobin, the substance that carries oxygen. Hemoglobin-laden red blood cells transport oxygen from the lungs through the heart to body cells. The red blood cells live approximately four months. Then new cells replenish the body's supply.

White blood cells, however, are fewer in number but larger in size than red blood cells. When invaders, such as bacteria or viruses, enter the body, white blood cells assist in the body's defense. Pus is a collection of dead white blood cells that have fought against invaders.

Lastly, colorless, irregularly shaped bodies called *platelets* assist in blood clotting. The clotting process involves many steps. During the process, platelets become enmeshed in a network of fibers that the body produces. A clot pulls together the edges of skin at the site of the injury. The clot then hardens and forms a scab.

Introduction

Display a FLASHLIGHT and shine it through your hand. Comment that the light makes it easier to see blood vessels. Allow time for students to use the flashlight to view one of their hands.

Directed Instruction

1 Share that God designed the human body to heal after it is injured. Discuss the steps of a healing cut—the skin is cut, the cut bleeds, a scab is formed, and the scab falls off when new skin is sufficiently formed. Explain that the scab protects the cut as the cut heals by covering it until enough new skin has grown underneath. The scab also prevents excess bleeding from the cut.

Share that it is important for students to tell their teacher or parent if they have cut their skin. Sometimes cuts that are bigger will require more care. It is important to thoroughly wash a cut with soap and water to remove germs and prevent infection. Using a bandage will protect the scab and the underlying cut while the body heals.

2 Distribute **BLM 11.3A Cuts Heal**, BROWN CRAYONS, SCISSORS, and RED PAPER. Instruct students to fold the paper along fold 1 and to cut on the dotted lines to make a small cut. Then have them open the fold. Direct students to color and cut out the scab on the bottom of the page. Guide students to fold the paper along fold 2. Next, demonstrate sliding the red sheet of paper into the folded sheet so that the red shows through the cut. Convey that the red represents blood in the cut. Allow time for students to insert the red paper.

Ask what happens after washing the cut and protecting it with a bandage. (**A scab forms.**) Have students place the brown scab on top of the cut. Encourage them to pretend that a few days have passed and direct them to pull out the red paper. Lift the paper still folded and let the scab naturally fall off. They will see that new skin is forming underneath and the cut is healing—no more red underneath! State that scabs naturally fall off when the new skin underneath is ready. Advise students not to pick at their scabs because the scab may come off before the new skin is ready. Inform students that eventually a cut will heal completely and they will no longer notice it. However, a deeper cut may leave a mark, or scar, on the skin.

3 Direct students' attention to the first student page. Read and discuss the captions and illustrations about the child's injury. State that students can clean their own cuts with soap and water. Make note of how God designed the body to stop the blood flow and to make a scab to protect the cut. Distribute CRAYONS, SCISSORS, and GLUE. Instruct students to design, color, and carefully cut out the bandage at the bottom of the page. It will cover the cut they will draw on the second page. Have students turn to the second page, and have them complete the exercise at the top. Then, direct students to draw and color, at the bottom of the page, an arm or a leg with a small cut and to cover it with their newly made bandage.

4 Convey that the class will now make a big scab. Display a piece of BULLETIN BOARD PAPER with a cut in the center and RED PAPER behind it. Distribute the BROWN CIRCLES precut from brown paper. Guide the class to work together to make a collage-style scab for this cut. Allow each student to put TAPE or GLUE on their brown circle and to place it on the cut to help form a scab. Have students tell a classmate what a scab does. (**A scab helps stop the bleeding and protects the cut while it heals.**)

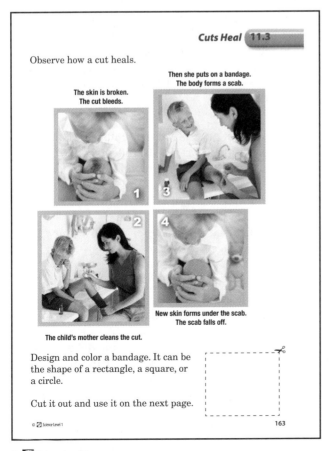

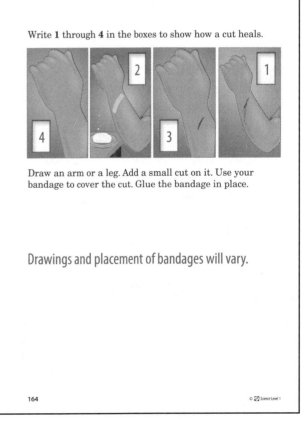

Drawings and placement of bandages will vary.

Extension

Materials
- School nurse as a guest speaker
- Chalk or tape, drum

Have the school nurse talk about first aid for cuts.

Escort students to a large open area. Use chalk or masking tape to make a large outline of a person with a heart in the center of the chest. Explain to students that they are the blood pumping from the heart to parts of the body. Designate a path for students to follow that leads from the heart to each part of the body. As students follow the path, beat a drum to represent the heartbeat.

Objective

Students will evaluate ways to keep the heart healthy, such as exercising and eating healthful foods.

Materials

Directed Instruction
- Index cards, timer, music (optional), water
- Colored paper, potato chips, crayons
- Optional: russet potatoes, knife, microwave-safe plate, nonstick spray, seasoning, microwave

Preparation

Choose a location for the class to take a short walk around campus. (*Introduction*)

Gather several INDEX CARDS, and write on each card an exercise that students can do in the classroom (stretching, moving to music, running in place, doing jumping jacks). Obtain a TIMER. Select upbeat MUSIC to play (optional). Have WATER available for students. (*Directed Instruction*)

Obtain a SHEET OF COLORED PAPER, POTATO CHIPS, and CRAYONS for small groups of students. Select a place in the room for groups to leave their experiment undisturbed for 1 hr. (*Directed Instruction*)

If desired, have ready a healthful snack: obtain RUSSET POTATOES, a SHARP KNIFE, a MICROWAVE-SAFE PLATE, NONSTICK SPRAY, SEASONING, and a MICROWAVE. One potato serves about six to eight students. (*Directed Instruction*)

Safety

Check student records for possible allergies.

Content

It is very important that children, even at very young ages, understand the factors necessary for a healthy heart. Since children can start to build plaque—deposits including fatty substances and cholesterol—in their arteries, they should develop and practice a healthful diet while young.

Exercise also plays a key factor in keeping the heart healthy. Doctors recommend 30 min of daily activity. Exercise improves mental health, by positively affecting depression, anxiety, stress, and anger. The physical benefits include decreasing the risk of heart disease and cancer by strengthening the immune system. Exercise also helps lower blood pressure and increase good cholesterol levels.

Exercise and eating healthfully also play a vital role in maintaining a healthy body weight. Obesity increases risks for heart disease and other health issues. For adults, smoking and stress can also lead to heart problems.

Introduction

Take students on a class walk around campus. Encourage them to quietly enjoy exercising their body as they move. If you have decided to walk outside, point out the beauty of nature, God's creation. Have students take several deep breaths of fresh air. Return to the classroom.

Directed Instruction

1 Convey that the walk students just enjoyed was one form of exercise. Exercise strengthens the heart muscle. Point out the prepared INDEX CARDS and the TIMER at the front of the room. Share that students will do plenty of exercising during class today. Set the timer for 7 min, and state that when the timer goes off, a student will pick a card for the class to complete an exercise in 30 sec. If desired, play upbeat MUSIC as students exercise. Throughout today's lesson, continue to reset the timer for 7 min, and join in the exercise with the class when it rings. Provide a break for WATER as needed or at the end of class.

2 Direct students' attention to the first page. Read the sentences at the top and the activities that are good for the heart. Have students identify and make a check mark by the exercises they do on a regular basis. State that since all students attended the class walk, they have all completed that exercise. Walking to class and at recess is also exercise.

Brainstorm with students their favorite way to exercise. Allow time for them to write their answer on the page.

3 Guide students' attention to the second page. State that eating healthful food keeps blood vessels clean. Read the sentences at the top of the page, and then read the potato chip experiment. Divide the class into small groups and assign a place for each group to set up its experiment. Remind the class that the potato chips are part of the experiment and are not to be eaten. Distribute a SHEET OF COLORED PAPER and several POTATO CHIPS to each group. Direct student groups to leave the experiment set up for 1 hr and then to observe the paper when they return. (They will notice grease spots on the paper.)

Discuss each of the pictures on the three paths. Check for understanding by asking why watching television for a long time does not help the heart stay healthy. (**It does not exercise the heart muscle.**) Distribute CRAYONS and give students time to color the correct path.

Discuss the last exercise on the page. Guide students to choose foods they enjoy that are also healthful. Remind them to select something from three different food groups. If students have already eaten lunch, discuss the foods they ate. Encourage them to evaluate how healthful their lunch was and what they could do to make it healthier. If students have not eaten lunch yet, encourage them to select healthful foods to eat.

4 After 1 hr, have students gather around their potato chip experiment. Encourage them to explain what they observe about the paper. (**It has grease spots on it.**) Reiterate that junk foods like potato chips have fat and grease that can clog up the blood vessels and keep the heart from working properly. Advise students to eat these foods sparingly.

If desired, provide students with this healthful snack—a healthier version of potato chips. Cut RUSSET POTATOES into paper-thin slices and arrange them in a single layer on a greased MICROWAVE-SAFE PLATE. Spray the potato slices lightly with NONSTICK SPRAY and add SEASONING. Place in a MICROWAVE for 2 to 4 min on high, or until golden brown.

To conclude the lesson, direct students to act out their favorite way to exercise. Have the class guess what exercise each student is demonstrating. Allow students the opportunity to drink water after exercising.

⊕ Extension

Materials
• Timer

Use the Internet to research an online physical challenge or competition for your class to participate in. Engage students in competing in a national challenge.

Before recess, have students each check their heart rate. Instruct students to find their pulse and to count the number of beats while you time them for 30 sec. Double the number to find beats per min. Direct students to record their time and to predict their heart rate after recess. After students play, have them record their heart rate again. Compare times. Create a class graph of the times and draw a conclusion.

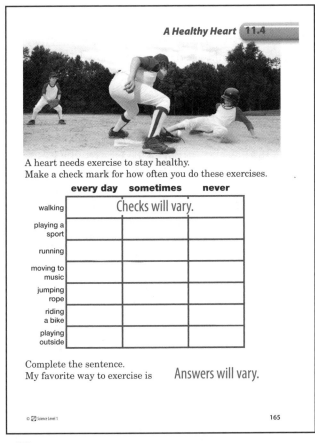

A Healthy Heart 11.4

A heart needs exercise to stay healthy.
Make a check mark for how often you do these exercises.

	every day	sometimes	never
walking	Checks will vary.		
playing a sport			
running			
moving to music			
jumping rope			
riding a bike			
playing outside			

Complete the sentence.
My favorite way to exercise is   Answers will vary.

© Science Level 1   165

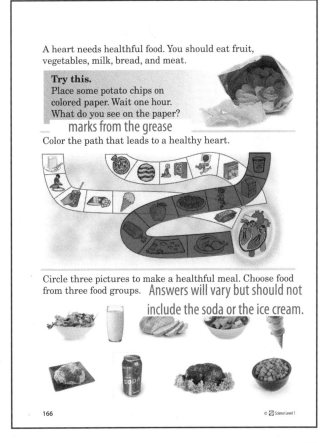

A heart needs healthful food. You should eat fruit, vegetables, milk, bread, and meat.

Try this.
Place some potato chips on colored paper. Wait one hour. What do you see on the paper?   marks from the grease

Color the path that leads to a healthy heart.

Circle three pictures to make a healthful meal. Choose food from three food groups.   Answers will vary but should not include the soda or the ice cream.

166   © Science Level 1

11.5 Tech Connect

Objective

Students will investigate the use of technology in keeping hearts healthy.

Preparation

Draw or obtain a picture of the following items and post them on the board: bicycle, teeth, shoes, eyeglasses, heart. (*Introduction*)

Content

Coronary disease has been one leading cause of death worldwide. Many factors are involved in the onset of heart disease. People can control some lifestyle factors such as diet, not smoking, and exercise; but others they cannot, such as family history. By focusing on the factors that can be controlled, people can reduce their overall risk of heart disease. Cigarette smoking, high blood pressure, and elevated levels of cholesterol and triglycerides may cause damage to the walls of arteries. Over time, deposits may build in the artery walls, causing reduced blood flow that can lead to a heart attack or stroke.

The electrocardiogram is a useful form of technology for diagnosing cardiac disease. The machine detects the rhythm of the heart and records the heart's electrical activity. This technology assists doctors in diagnosing and studying various heart maladies, such as heart attacks, heart failure, and arrhythmias.

Introduction

Indicate the pictures on the board. Ask students to name some ways to keep each of these things working well.
- Bicycle (**Possible answers: checking to see if there is enough air in the tires, oiling the gears, not leaving the bike out in the rain**)
- Teeth (**Possible answers: brushing, flossing, visiting a dentist, wearing a mouth guard while playing sports**)
- Shoes (**Possible answers: cleaning off dirt, trying to avoid puddles**)
- Eyeglasses (**Possible answers: cleaning lenses, trying not to drop or break them**)

State that today students will learn ways to keep the heart working well.

Directed Instruction ⊕

1 Explain that science and technology have helped people understand how God designed the heart. Scientists and doctors have found ways to help people keep their heart healthy.

2 Direct students' attention to the first page. Read the top part of the page. Convey that a special test called *an electrocardiogram* can show how the heart is working. Write *electrocardiogram* in syllables (*e·lec·tro·car·di·o·gram*) on the board. Pronounce the word and have students repeat it. Instruct students to count the syllables. (**seven**) Have students trace the healthy-heart line shown on the page. Direct students' attention to the second electrocardiogram reading—the unhealthy-heart line. Guide the class to notice the different patterns of the two tests. Allow students to compare and discuss the readings with a partner. Provide time and assistance with spelling as students write their comparisons.

Lead a discussion on how the second test shows a doctor that this person's heart needs special attention. Convey that if a doctor finds that a person's heart works in a way that is not healthy, the doctor will try to fix it. Often the doctor can give medicine to help, but sometimes the doctor may need to fix the heart with surgery. Read the bottom of the page and elaborate on the Bible truth that God is always with His people, no matter what is happening to them, their family, or their friends.

3 Explain that doctors do surgery on hearts every day. They are able to fix many heart problems. God has given these doctors a very special ability to help people. He gives everyone special gifts, talents, and abilities to serve Him by helping each other. Read **Galatians 6:10**. Discuss with students what they might do to help each other. Here are some ideas:

- A student who is very good at spelling might help a student who finds spelling very hard.
- A student who can walk might help a student who is using crutches or is in a wheelchair.
- A student with an extra pencil might lend it to a student who has lost his or her pencil.
- A student who is feeling happy might encourage and comfort a student who is feeling very sad.

Allow students to share in groups about times when others have helped them. Encourage them to think of ways that they might help each other.

4 Have students turn to the second page. Read the page together. Discuss how technology can help people exercise but can also prevent people from exercising. Guide students to evaluate their own video game, computer, and television habits. Encourage them to help keep their heart healthy by following the advice on the page. Brainstorm other ways students can keep active while participating in fun activities. To review, have students get a sheet of paper and write to the prompt, *Instead of watching television, I could ...* Direct students to illustrate their writing and to share it with a family member at home.

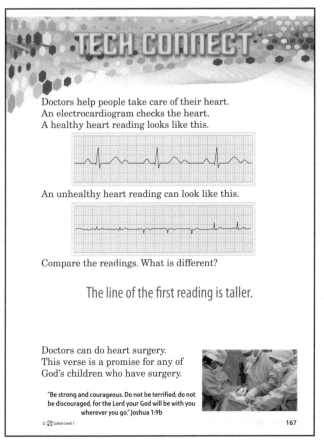

TECH CONNECT

Doctors help people take care of their heart.
An electrocardiogram checks the heart.
A healthy heart reading looks like this.

An unhealthy heart reading can look like this.

Compare the readings. What is different?

The line of the first reading is taller.

Doctors can do heart surgery.
This verse is a promise for any of God's children who have surgery.

"Be strong and courageous. Do not be terrified; do not be discouraged, for the Lord your God will be with you wherever you go." Joshua 1:9b

© *Science Level 1*   167

TECH CONNECT

Do you like video games?
Play games that make you move.

Some video games help you exercise while you play.

Do you like watching television?
Exercise during commercials.
Watch only one show.
Then go outside and play!

168   © *Science Level 1*

11.6 Chapter 11 Review

Heart and Blood

Materials

Directed Instruction
- BLM 11.6A Heart and Blood Facts
- BLM 11.6B Who I Am
- BLM 11.6C Chapter 11 Test

Preparation

Print **BLM 11.6A Heart and Blood Facts** for each student. (*Directed Instruction*)

Print 1 double-sided copy of **BLM 11.6B Who I Am** for a class game, or print enough copies for students to play the game in pairs. If desired, print on card stock and laminate for durability. Cut the cards apart. (*Directed Instruction*)

Draw the following Creation web on the board. (*Directed Instruction*)

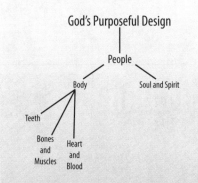

God's Purposeful Design

People

Body — Soul and Spirit

Teeth

Bones and Muscles — Heart and Blood

Print **BLM 11.6C Chapter 11 Test** for each student. (*Directed Instruction*)

Introduction

Direct students to either place a hand over their heart or to feel their pulse as they did in Lesson 11.1. Clap your hands quickly and ask if their heart is beating as quickly as your clapping rhythm. (**Answers will vary.**) Clap your hands slowly and ask if their heart is beating as slowly as your clapping rhythm. (**Answers will vary.**) Direct students to run or jump in place for 30 sec. Have them find their pulse again. Ask them to describe the difference in their heart rate now. (**The beat is faster and feels stronger.**) Emphasize that the heart beats faster and stronger when the body exercises.

Directed Instruction

1 Review the definition of *heart*. (**a part of the body that pumps blood**) Distribute **BLM 11.6A Heart and Blood Facts**. Review that the heart beats faster during exercise because the body needs more of what the blood is supplying. Read the words in the Word Bank and have students repeat them. Read the facts and say "blank" for the missing word. Allow time for students to fill in the blanks. When the class has completed their answer, ask a volunteer to read the fact with the answer inserted. Ask another volunteer to explain the fact in his or her own words.

2 Play a review game using the cards from **BLM 11.6B Who I Am**. Have volunteers read a clue on each card. Allow the class to guess the word. Or, have students quiz each other in pairs. They can self-assess by checking the answers on the back of the cards.

3 Direct students' attention to the Creation web on the board. Share that God purposefully designed people with a body and a soul and spirit. Select a volunteer to read the parts of the body shown on the web. (**teeth, bones and muscles, heart and blood**) What are some other parts of the body? (**Answers will vary.**)

4 Use student pages as a review or pretest. Complete these pages with the class, allowing time for the journal writing. You may use **BLM 11.6C Chapter 11 Test** for individual assessment. Read through this page with the class. Provide as much reading support as necessary. You may choose to use BLM 11.6C as an oral assessment or not to do it at all.

5 Read the following scenarios to the class. Have them give a thumbs-up when you read something healthful for the heart and a thumbs-down when you read something unhealthful for the heart.
- Manuel plays every day with his friends. He always eats fruits and vegetables with his meals. (**thumbs-up**)
- Noah plays video games every day and does not exercise. He eats lots of sweets and potato chips and loves drinking soda pop. (**thumbs-down**)
- Santiago and Ethan play basketball every day at school. They also eat lunch together and remind each other to eat good foods like apples, milk, and healthful sandwiches. (**thumbs-up**)
- Ava eats hamburgers from her favorite fast-food restaurant several times a week. She hates to exercise and instead sits on the couch and watches lots of television. (**thumbs-down**)
- Mina taught her little sister Amira how to jump rope. They jump every day in their backyard. When they are finished, they go to the kitchen for a glass of water. (**thumbs-up**)

Review the good and bad things that affect the heart. Have students work in small groups to decide upon one good thing they will do this week to keep their heart healthy. Allow the groups to share their plans with the class. Encourage students to share their plans with their family at home.

6 Conclude by reviewing **1 Corinthians 12:18**. Remind students that God made them wonderfully and designed them with and for a purpose. They need to care for their body to help it work well.

7 Chapter 11 Heart and Blood has been completed. It can be stapled and sent home as a booklet to be shared with a family member.

Notes:

⊕ Extension

Materials
• CP-11.6 The Amazing Heart

Present and discuss **CP-11.6 The Amazing Heart**.

In small groups have students complete a healthy heart scavenger hunt outside. Prepare a list of 10 activities the groups must complete. Have them return to you after each one to learn their next activity. Mark off each activity on your list as they complete it. If the class is all competing at once, start groups on different activities to avoid collisions. Ideas for hunt activities include touching two trees, sliding down a slide, doing three jumping jacks on a sidewalk, and finding and bringing back a leaf. The first group to complete all 10 activities wins.

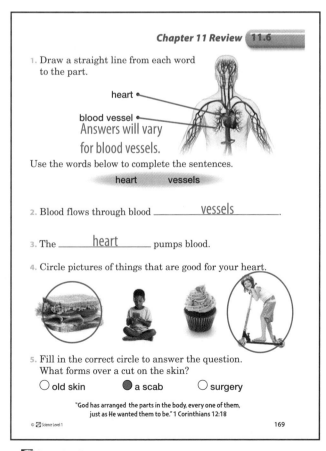

Lungs and Air
Chapter 12

Key Ideas

- When a person breathes, air travels into the nose and mouth, down the throat, through the windpipe, into the lungs, and back out.
- People need the oxygen in air to survive.
- Healthy lungs are maintained by avoiding germs and not smoking.
- Firefighters and others use air tanks to breathe. Practicing fire safety is important.

12.0 Chapter Preparation

Lungs and Air

Vocabulary

air
lung
inhale
exhale

Looking Ahead

• For an *Extension* activity in **Lesson 12.3**, invite a musician or a music teacher to visit. Encourage him or her to plan on demonstrating how to play woodwind instruments, such as a clarinet, a flute, or an oboe, and some brass instruments, such as a trumpet or a trombone.
• An activated charcoal capsule is needed for **Lesson 12.5**. Capsules can be purchased from a large discount retail store or a health food store.
• Arrange for a firefighter to speak to the class in **Lesson 12.6**.
• For an *Extension* activity in **Lesson 13.2**, invite a first-aid teacher to teach your class how to use abdominal thrusts (Heimlich maneuver) to help someone who is choking.

Introduction

Job 12:10 conveys the truth that the life of every creature and the breath of all humankind is in God's hand. God purposefully designed the human body to breathe the surrounding air. It is important for students to learn the anatomy and function of the lungs as well as to be informed about how to take care of their lungs. Students will become aware of some ways to prevent the spread of disease. They must recognize that there is a difference between contagious diseases such as colds, and noncontagious diseases such as asthma. This information can bring understanding in the care and needs of others. This chapter establishes the dangers of smoking as it presents the consequences of this unhealthful choice. Fire-safety principles are also presented. Understanding how the body works goes hand in hand with its care.

About This Chapter

Lesson 12.1 – Breathing
Materials
• Bag
Lesson Content
Air is a gas that has oxygen in it. People need oxygen to live. They breathe air into their lungs. A lung is a part of the body that takes in and lets out air.

Lesson 12.2 – How Breathing Works
Materials
• Straws   • Scissors
• Bags
• Tape
Lesson Content
People inhale and exhale air through their mouth and nose. The air travels down the throat, through the windpipe, into the lungs, and back out.

Lesson 12.3 – What Breath Affects
Materials
• Bags   • Cups   • Bubble wands
• Straws   • Water
• Balloon   • Bubble solution
Lesson Content
Not only does breathing keep people alive, it helps them do certain activities like singing, blowing out candles, playing a flute, and blowing bubbles.

Lesson 12.4 – Healthy Lungs
Materials
• Highlighters
Lesson Content
It is important to keep lungs healthy by following proper hygiene and care for the body. People should cover their mouth and nose when they cough or sneeze and remember to wash their hands regularly.

Lesson 12.5 – Troubled Breathing

Materials
- Sponges
- Lung model
- Charcoal capsule
- Needle
- Tape
- Poster board
- Markers
- Glue
- Magazines

Lesson Content

Smoking harms the lungs and can make breathing difficult. Asthma is a condition that also affects the lungs. People who have asthma may need to use an inhaler to help them breathe.

Lesson 12.6 – Air Tanks and Fire Safety

Materials
- Smoke detector

Lesson Content

Firefighters and others sometimes wear an oxygen tank. Firefighters also wear other equipment to protect themselves from the fire and to help rescue people. Planning ahead can help people be safe if there is a fire. Families should have a fire-escape plan, and children should know what to do in the event of a fire.

Lesson 12.7 – Chapter 12 Review

Materials
- Straws
- Tape
- Index cards
- Crayons

Teacher Resources

Body of Evidence: Respiratory System by Dr. David Menton. DVD. Answers in Genesis, 2011.

Made in His Image: Examining the Complexities of the Human Body by Randy J. Guliuzza. Institute for Creation Research, 2009.

Seeing God Through the Human Body: A Doctor's Meditation on the Human Miracle by Dr. Robert Peprah-Gyamfi. Anomalos, 2009.

Student Resources

Lungs: Your Respiratory System by Seymour Simon. HarperCollins, 2007.

Peter, the Knight with Asthma by Janna Matthies. Albert Whitman and Company, 2009.

The Respiratory System by Christine Taylor-Butler. Children's Press, 2008.

Supplemental Materials

Blackline Masters

12.2A–B Lungs, Parts 1–2
12.3A Ways Animals Breathe
12.4A Daniel's Cold
12.4B Lungs and Word Shapes
12.5A A Promise to My Lungs

12.6A Life-Saving Tips
12.7A Lungs and Air Facts
12.7B Chapter 12 Test

Transparency Master

12.2A Lungs

12.1 Breathing

Lungs and Air

Objective

Students will express that lungs play a vital role in breathing air and that people need oxygen from the air in order to live.

Materials

Introduction
• Ziplock bag

Directed Instruction
• Ziplock bag

Preparation

Have a ZIPLOCK BAG available. (*Introduction, Directed Instruction*)

Write the definitions of *air* and *lung* on the board. (*Directed Instruction*)

Content

God designed the human body with structures to acquire what it needs to maintain life. The lungs are structures used to breathe oxygen. Oxygen, which makes up about 21% of air, enters the body through the mouth or nose. It then travels down the throat to reach the lungs. The diaphragm lowers and the intercostal, or rib, muscles contract, increasing the capacity of the chest cavity. This chest expansion allows air to enter the lungs and inflate them. Oxygen goes into the blood at the tiny alveoli of the lungs. From there it is carried in red blood cells to the left side of the heart and then pumped by the heart to other body cells.

The human respiratory system comprises all the structures that move air to and from the lungs. Though most breathing occurs through the nose, God's purposeful design allows people to eat, drink, and breathe from the mouth without food entering the lungs. Each structure of the respiratory system works in concert with the other structures to effectively provide cells with the vital oxygen they need to survive.

Introduction

Inform students that you are about to collect something very important. Remind them to use their senses to observe what you are collecting. Display a ZIPLOCK BAG as you walk around the room. Report that you are collecting the important thing at this very moment. Trap air in the bag by sealing the bag tightly.

Directed Instruction

1 Ask students what they see in the bag. (**nothing**) Do you hear anything in the bag? (**No.**) Do you think what is inside the bag smells? (**No.**) What would you feel if you put your finger inside the bag? (**nothing**)

Ask students what they think is in the bag. (**Answers will vary.**) What makes the bag puffed out? (**air**) Slightly unseal the bag and then allow a volunteer to gently press the bag with his or her hands to push the air out. Ask students how they know there is almost nothing in the bag now. (**The bag is flat.**)

Review with students that when they observed the bag, they could not see, hear, feel, or smell anything even though the bag was filled with air. Explain that air is all around each student. It has no color, no shape, and no taste. Read from the board the definition of **air**: *a gas that has oxygen in it*. Convey that the air people breathe is made of different gases. One of the gases is called *oxygen*. People need oxygen to live. They breathe air through their lungs. Read the definition of **lung**: *a part of the body that takes in and lets out air*.

2 Direct students' attention to the first page and ask a volunteer to read the sentences beside the boy at the top of the page. Relate the information about air to the introductory activity. Share that there was a lot of air in the bag when it was filled or puffed out. There was almost no air in the bag when it was flat. Emphasize that people breathe air continually because the body needs oxygen all the time.

Have students sit quietly while they count the number of breaths they take in 1 min (approximately 17–19). Direct them to record the number of breaths on the chart in the middle of the page. Now instruct students to run in place for 1 min. Ask them to sit quietly and count their breaths again (approximately 30–68). Give students time to write that number on the chart. Explain that people breathe more during and after exercising because their muscles need more oxygen when they are working hard. Remind students that all people need oxygen to stay alive. Direct them to circle the correct picture at the bottom of the page.

3 Have students turn to their second page, and display the ZIPLOCK BAG again. Emphasize that although people cannot see, hear, smell, feel, or taste the air they breathe, they can observe what it does, such as fill up the bag. Read and discuss the sentences. Allow time for students to circle the correct answers.

Explain that sometimes there are scents in the air that can be smelled, such as gasoline or perfume. Ask students how the air smells after a skunk sprays. (**bad, stinky**) Share that sometimes what is in the air can be seen also. Ask how the air looks and smells above a burning campfire. (**smoky**)

4 Read **Genesis 2:7**. Mention that when God created Adam, the first man, God breathed into him and gave him life. Since that time, all human beings have been designed by God to breathe. God is the one who gives all people life.

⊕ Extension

Materials
• Stethoscope, cotton balls, rubbing alcohol

Borrow a stethoscope from the school nurse or a medical clinic. Allow students to use it to listen to the air in their nose and throat. Between volunteers, be sure to clean the stethoscope with cotton balls dipped in rubbing alcohol.

Have students complete different activities for 20 sec (sitting, reading, jumping rope, stretching, running). After each activity, have them record how many breaths they take in 1 min. Make sure to allow enough resting time between activities so student breathing returns to a normal rate. Guide students to graph and explain their results.

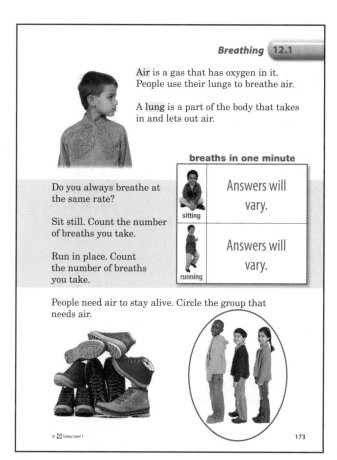

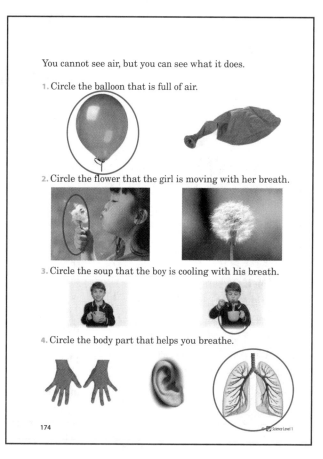

12.2 How Breathing Works

Objective

Students will describe how the human body breathes.

Materials

Directed Instruction
- TM-12.2A Lungs
- Wide straws, ziplock bags, tape
- BLMs 12.2A–B Lungs, Parts 1–2; scissors; tape

Preparation

Write the definitions of *inhale* and *exhale* on the board. (*Directed Instruction*)

Make a lung model using **3 WIDE STRAWS** (at least ¼ in. wide), **2 ZIPLOCK BAGS**, and **TAPE**. Cut 2 straws to be 5 in. long, and 1 straw 3 in. long. Cut slits into the 2 longer straws and insert them into one end of the third straw. Secure with tape. Place the 2 long straws into ziplock bags and seal the bags around the straws. Keep this lung model for reuse in Lesson 12.5. (*Directed Instruction*)

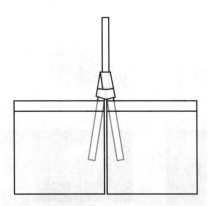

Select **TM-12.2A Lungs** for display. (*Directed Instruction*)

Print **BLMs 12.2A–B Lungs, Parts 1–2** for each student. Have **SCISSORS** and **TAPE** available. (*Directed Instruction*)

Content

Involuntary breathing occurs as the brain stem directs. In order for oxygen to reach the cells of the body, air must go through the nose or mouth and then through the throat—the pharynx or upper part of the throat and the larynx or lower part of the throat. The air continues through the trachea (windpipe), bronchi, bronchioles, and alveoli. At the alveoli, capillaries transport red blood cells that pick up oxygen from the inhaled air. Carbon dioxide is released. The muscular diaphragm contracts and flattens while the intercostal muscles (between the ribs) contract and pull the rib cage out and up. The result is that the chest cavity becomes larger and air enters the lungs—inhalation. As the muscles relax, air exits the lungs—exhalation.

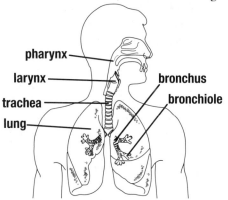

Introduction

Review with the class that ribs protect the heart and lungs and make up the rib cage. Direct students to place the palms of their hands on the sides of their rib cage, a few inches below their armpits. Instruct them to take a slow, deep breath in and observe what their rib cage does. (**It goes up and out.**) Next, have them breathe out slowly and observe what happens to their rib cage. (**The rib cage goes down and in.**) .

Directed Instruction

1 Inform the class that when people breathe, air travels on a specific path in order to reach the lungs. From there, the heart delivers the oxygen from the air to the rest of the body. Read the definitions of *inhale* and *exhale* from the board—**inhale**: *to take air into the lungs;* **exhale**: *to let air out of the lungs.* Practice inhaling and exhaling with the class. Point out the prefix *in* within the word *inhale* and reiterate that air is going into the lungs. Note the prefix *ex* in *exhale* and make the connection to the word *exit.* State that when students exhale, air is exiting the lungs.

2 Display **TM-12.2A Lungs**. Share that when a person inhales, the air goes through the nose or mouth to the throat. The air enters the windpipe next. Point to the tubes that go into the lungs. Share that the tubes are lined with very tiny hairs as well as mucus that both function as dust removers. The small hairs, which are smaller than the ones in the nose, wave and push the mucus and dust out of the lungs so the lungs stay clean.

Direct students' attention to the first student page. Read the top of the page. Reiterate that when a person inhales air through the nose, the air goes past tiny hairs and mucus that line the nose. Then the air goes through the windpipe and into the lungs. Have students place a finger on each part of the diagram on their student page as you share the information. Review the definitions at the bottom of the page.

Demonstrate the process of air entering the lungs by displaying the lung model made from STRAWS, ZIPLOCK BAGS, and TAPE. Explain that the top straw is like the windpipe that air flows through to get to the lungs. Point out how the straw splits into two straws, like the windpipe that splits into two tubes. Slowly blow air into and suck air from the straw to show how a person inhales and exhales. Note how the bags expand and contract with each breath. Retain the lung model for Lesson 12.5.

3 Direct students' attention to the second page. Read and review the information at the top of this page. Reiterate that the windpipe is lined with very small hairs and ask a volunteer to describe the job of the tiny hairs and mucus in the windpipe. (**Mucus catches the dust in the air. The tiny hairs move the mucus and dust out of the windpipe.**) Allow students time to draw tiny hairs in the windpipe and the other tubes leading into the lungs. Use this as an opportunity to assess student understanding of anatomy by observing where students draw the hairs. Guide students to answer the questions independently. Check for accuracy.

4 Distribute **BLMs 12.2A–B Lungs, Parts 1–2**; SCISSORS; and TAPE. Allow time for students to cut out the lungs and to attach them to their clothing over their lungs. If you choose, allow them to wear their paper lungs for the rest of the day. Have students explain to a partner the job of the lungs and the tiny hairs lining the tubes. Share with students that by God's design the lungs stay healthy and clean.

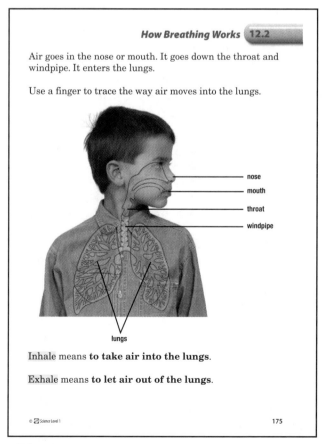

How Breathing Works 12.2

Air goes in the nose or mouth. It goes down the throat and windpipe. It enters the lungs.

Use a finger to trace the way air moves into the lungs.

- nose
- mouth
- throat
- windpipe

lungs

Inhale means **to take air into the lungs**.

Exhale means **to let air out of the lungs**.

© Science Level 1   175

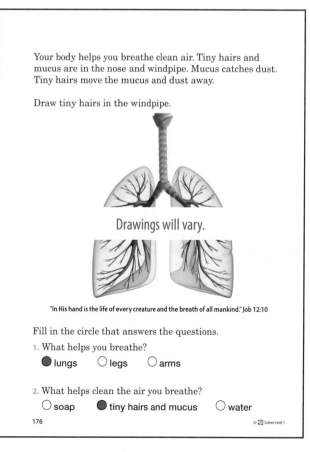

Your body helps you breathe clean air. Tiny hairs and mucus are in the nose and windpipe. Mucus catches dust. Tiny hairs move the mucus and dust away.

Draw tiny hairs in the windpipe.

Drawings will vary.

"In His hand is the life of every creature and the breath of all mankind." Job 12:10

Fill in the circle that answers the questions.

1. What helps you breathe?
   ● lungs   ○ legs   ○ arms

2. What helps clean the air you breathe?
   ○ soap   ● tiny hairs and mucus   ○ water

176   © Science Level 1

12.3 What Breath Affects

Objective

Students will indicate the effects breath has on objects.

Materials

Introduction
- Ziplock bags, straws

Directed Instruction
- Balloon
- Water, small cups, straws
- Bubble solution, bubble wands

Preparation

Gather a ZIPLOCK BAG and a STRAW for each student and for yourself. (*Introduction*)

Obtain a BALLOON for a demonstration. (*Directed Instruction*)

Have a SMALL CUP and WATER available for each student. Plan to reuse the STRAWS from the *Introduction*. (*Directed Instruction*)

Supply BUBBLE SOLUTION and a BUBBLE WAND for each student. Plan for students to blow bubbles in an outdoor space. (*Directed Instruction*)

Safety

Alert students that they are not to put the plastic bag directly over their mouth.

Alternatives

If an outdoor space is not available for students to blow bubbles in, cover the classroom floor with newspaper before beginning the activity to prevent students from slipping on the solution.

Content

Exhaled air contains a greater percent of carbon dioxide than inhaled air. As air comes from the lungs and out of the mouth or nose, it can be used for many things such as talking, singing, whistling, blowing bubbles, and playing a musical instrument.

Introduction

Display a ZIPLOCK BAG and a STRAW. State that students are going to trap and keep air in the bag. Demonstrate placing the straw in the bag, sealing the bag around the straw, and blowing into the straw. Once the bag is filled, remove the straw and quickly finish sealing the bag. Distribute a bag and a straw to each student. Direct students to do as you have done with the bag and straw. Assist any students who might need help filling their bag with air. Have students retain their straws for use in the *Directed Instruction*.

Remind students that although they cannot see, hear, smell, feel, or taste air, it is all around. People breathe air to acquire oxygen, and they can use the air they breathe out to accomplish various activities.

Directed Instruction

1 Hold up a BALLOON and inflate it for the class. Ask students what they think will happen when you pull the sides of the neck opening and let some of the air out. (**Answers will vary.**) Hold each side of the neck of the balloon with your fingers and stretch the balloon (outward) to let the air out a little at a time. Discuss with students that as air moves out of the balloon, the neck of the balloon vibrates. This vibration produces the sound they hear.

2 Have students gently place their fingers on the front center of their neck. Direct them to say their name out loud. Inform students that moving air vibrates the vocal cords. Encourage them to feel the vibrations made by the air passing through the larynx. Explain that the tension of the muscles in the larynx determines the pitch of the sound. Share that the teeth, tongue, throat, and lips help make sounds into words.

3 Direct students' attention to the first page. Read the text and point out the picture of the girl singing. Explain that people cannot see the air they breathe, but they can see the effects of their breath on objects. Discuss with students what happened to the balloons and bubbles shown on the page when the children breathed air into them.

Have students turn to the second page. Discuss that in order to play some types of musical instruments, a musician must blow air into them. Sounds are made as air travels into the instrument. Solicit the names of any musical instruments that require the use of a person's breath. (**Possible answers: flute, clarinet, oboe, trumpet, trombone, harmonica**)

Read and discuss the other uses for air coming out of a person's mouth and nose. Add that whistling is another fun thing that people can do with the air that comes out of the mouth.

4 Ask students what happens when they breathe air out through a straw that is in a cup of water. (**Air goes into the water and makes bubbles.**)

Give each student a SMALL CUP of WATER. Have students place one end of their STRAW in the cup of water, and have them blow air through the straw and into the water. Collect the materials after students have completed the activity.

5 Read and discuss **Job 33:4**. Ask how God is involved in each student's life according to the verse. (He made me; He gives me life.) Read the directions for the writing section at the bottom of the student page and brainstorm ideas. Allow time for students to write and to share their answer with a partner.

6 Escort students to an outdoor space, and distribute BUBBLE SOLUTION and BUBBLE WANDS. Allow students to blow bubbles. Reinforce that they are using the air from their lungs to form the bubbles and that the bubbles are filled with air.

Notes:

⊕ Extension

Materials
• Guest musician or music teacher
• BLM 12.3A Ways Animals Breathe

Have the pre-invited musician or music teacher speak to the class. Suggest that the guest demonstrate how to play woodwind instruments, such as a clarinet, a flute, or an oboe, and some brass instruments, such as a trumpet or a trombone. Encourage the guest to discuss with students the way in which the instruments work through the use of breath.

Distribute and discuss **BLM 12.3A Ways Animals Breathe**. Have students classify animals by the way they breathe. Reiterate that God made each creature according to His purposeful design.

What Breath Affects 12.3

Your breath helps you talk and sing.

Lungs give your breath power. Vocal cords in the throat vibrate. The throat, nose, and mouth form words to help you talk or sing.

Your breath can help you do other things.

Your breath can fill a balloon.

Your breath can help form bubbles.

© Science Level 1   177

Your breath can blow out birthday candles.
Your breath can help you play a flute.
Your breath can warm your hands.
Your breath can cool hot chocolate.

Write about something your breath can help you do.

Answers will vary.

178   © Science Level 1

12.4 Healthy Lungs

Objective

Students will evaluate ways to keep lungs healthy.

Materials

Introduction
• Blue and orange highlighters

Directed Instruction
• BLM 12.4A Daniel's Cold
• BLM 12.4B Lungs and Word Shapes

Preparation

Prepare slips of paper for each student by using a BLUE HIGHLIGHTER to make a mark on three-fourths of the papers and an ORANGE HIGHLIGHTER to mark the remaining papers. Tightly fold each paper in half. (*Introduction*)

Print 1 copy of **BLM 12.4A Daniel's Cold**. (*Directed Instruction*)

Print **BLM 12.4B Lungs and Word Shapes** for each student. (*Directed Instruction*)

Content

Cold viruses spread in many different ways. It is important that students learn to cover their mouth and nose with a tissue when they cough or sneeze and to wash their hands afterward. Students should know that some diseases, such as colds, are contagious.

Fortunately, the body has ways of ridding itself of diseases and sickness. Tiny hairs, called *cilia*, as well as mucus in the nose catch dust and other foreign particles in the air. Breathing through the nose allows air to be cleaned, warmed, and humidified. Tiny blood vessels in the nose warm the air. As the air travels down the pharynx, trachea, bronchi, and bronchioles, it goes through more filtering in the form of mucus that catches dust. The cilia that line the trachea, bronchi, and the bronchioles wave or beat continuously. They push mucus and foreign particles trapped by the mucus up toward the pharynx; the particle-ladened mucus is usually swallowed.

Introduction

Distribute a PRE-HIGHLIGHTED, FOLDED SLIP OF PAPER to each student. Engage students to imagine Henry, a make-believe student in the class. (You may want to change the name if you have a student named *Henry* in your class.) Explain that Henry has a cold and some students in the class caught Henry's cold.

Instruct students to open their slip of paper and to stand if they have a blue mark. State that these students did not catch Henry's cold. Read one reason from the list below to indicate why each standing student did not get a cold from Henry. (Answers may be used more than one time.)
• Washed hands before eating
• Washed hands before touching his or her eyes
• Did not drink out of Henry's cup
• Used Henry's ruler and washed hands afterward
• Said, "No, thank you," when Henry offered some of his ice-cream cone
• Washed hands after using the computer in the classroom

Then have students with an orange mark stand. State that each student who received a paper with an orange mark got a cold from Henry. Read one reason from the list below to indicate why each student got a cold.
• Threw away Henry's tissues and did not wash hands
• Used Henry's pencil and did not wash hands afterward
• Did not wash hands after reading the book Henry sneezed on
• Was standing near Henry when he sneezed without a tissue
• Had a bite of Henry's sandwich after Henry took a bite
• Sat at Henry's desk and did not wash hands afterward

Collect the papers and play again as time allows. If students play a second round, have them state a reason why they did or did not catch Henry's cold. (**Answers will vary but should include a reason from the lists above.**)

Directed Instruction

1 Share that God designed hairs and mucus inside the nose and windpipe to help people breathe clean air to stay healthy. Convey that sometimes germs do get into the body and people get sick. Direct students' attention to the first page. Read the top part of this page and discuss with the class the picture of the girl. Ask students why it is important to cover their mouth and nose with a tissue when they cough or sneeze. (**to prevent germs from spreading**) Inform students that a germ is a tiny speck that can cause a disease if enough germs of the same kind are present.

2 Have students turn to the second page. Convey to students that germs are in the air they inhale and on the things they touch. When they get a cold, germs have gotten into their body. The body then fights the germs. Explain that a cold can affect the lungs because a cold creates extra mucus, which makes breathing difficult. Reinforce that washing hands is an important way to prevent the spread of germs. Share that there are some diseases, like colds, that are contagious—one person can pass the germs on to another person, which can cause the second person to get sick. Assist students in completing the questions at the bottom of their page.

3 Read aloud **BLM 12.4A Daniel's Cold**. Ask volunteers to name good things that the children in the story did to help prevent the spread of cold germs. (**used a tissue when sneezing and coughing, didn't touch eyes, washed their hands**)

4 Distribute a copy of **BLM 12.4B Lungs and Word Shapes** to each student. Write the word *air* on the board. Draw a box around each letter as is shown on BLM 12.4B. Erase the letters and let the boxes remain. Point out that the boxes show the shape of the word *air*. Rewrite the letters in the boxes. This activity provides visual cues to the placement of each letter in a word so students will visualize the whole word. Have students complete the activity.

⊕ Extension

Materials
• Glitter, lotion, soap, tub, water, paper towels

Before class, mix superfine glitter into a small amount of lotion. At the start of class, discretely rub the lotion on your hands. Greet students with a handshake and instruct them to shake one another's hands as well. Students will start to notice the glitter traveling around the room. Display the lotion container and discuss how the glitter traveled as germs do from person to person. With soap and a tub of water, demonstrate proper hand-washing technique. Allow students to properly wash and dry their hands after the demonstration.

Brainstorm with students ways they can prevent the spread of germs in the classroom.

Healthy Lungs 12.4

Help keep your lungs healthy.

Germs are so small you cannot see them. But they are in the air you breathe. Germs can make you sick.

Cover your mouth and nose with a tissue when you cough or sneeze. This keeps germs from spreading.

Here is what some germs look like.

© Science Level 1   179

A cold makes it hard to breathe. Wash your hands often if you have a cold or if you are around someone with a cold.

Circle the word that answers each question.
1. What is in your nose that helps keep dirt away from your lungs?

bones   (tiny hairs)   blood

2. What part of your body is protected when you wash your hands?

feet   teeth   (lungs)

180   © Science Level 1

Objective

Students will identify smoking and asthma as inhibitors to breathing well.

Materials

Directed Instruction
- Sponges
- Lung model from Lesson 12.2, activated charcoal capsule, needle or tack, tape
- Poster board, markers, glue, magazine pictures

🖐 Preparation

Obtain a MOIST SPONGE and a DRY SPONGE for a demonstration. (*Directed Instruction*)

Have available the LUNG MODEL from Lesson 12.2. Obtain an ACTIVATED CHARCOAL CAPSULE from a large discount retail or health food store. Carefully pierce both ends of the capsule with a NEEDLE or TACK. Cut the top straw crosswise in half and insert the pierced capsule. Use TAPE to secure the straw back together around the capsule. Allow some air to be trapped inside the bags, but make sure the ziplock bags are tightly sealed around the straws. (*Directed Instruction*)

Obtain POSTER BOARD, MARKERS, and GLUE for small groups of students. Cut out several MAGAZINE PICTURES of people exercising and maintaining healthy lungs. For a challenge, also cut out pictures of people not keeping their lungs healthy, such as those of people smoking or ones of people living in a smog-filled city. (*Directed Instruction*)

Content

Smoking is a major cause of death. Smoking damages the lungs and affects other parts and functions of the body. Smoking causes cancer, emphysema, heart disease, stroke, and other ailments. Cigarette smoke paralyzes the cilia, preventing the dust from being trapped and expelled as God designed. Smoking can cause the alveoli to lose elasticity and sometimes break, resulting in emphysema. There are more than 4,000 chemical compounds in tobacco and smoke, including many carcinogens, or cancer-causing chemicals. Even second-hand smoke is harmful—especially to children.

Asthma is a disease of the lungs; it is identified by wheezing, troubled breathing, chest tightness, and coughing. An asthmatic person's airways may be easily irritated by smoke and fumes, animal dander, pollen, or dust. These irritants cause the bronchioles to constrict and spasm. Asthma is not curable, but it is treatable through the use of inhalers that control inflammation and even stop spasms.

Introduction

Read the scenarios below and ask students to decide which child is making a healthful choice:
- Michael brushes and flosses his teeth every day. Aarav brushes his teeth every other day and never uses floss. (**Michael**)
- Misaki comes home from school and plays outside on her bike with her friends. Emily comes home from school every day and watches television until dinner. After dinner, she sits and plays computer games. (**Misaki**)
- Alexander eats fruits and vegetables for snacks. Jayla eats only candy for snacks. (**Alexander**)

Reinforce that in each of these scenarios, the children made a choice. The children who made healthful choices will have good consequences. Michael will help his teeth stay healthy. Misaki will help her heart and muscles stay strong. Alexander will get more vitamins to help his body stay healthy.

Directed Instruction

1 State that some people make a choice not to keep their lungs healthy by choosing to smoke cigarettes. Smoking is an unhealthful choice. Display the MOIST SPONGE and convey that it is similar to a lung because it is soft and elastic. Share with the class that people who choose not to smoke are choosing to keep their lungs healthy. Display the DRY SPONGE. Pass it around for all students to feel while sharing that this sponge is similar to unhealthy lungs—hard and stiff. Explain that people who choose to smoke hurt their lungs. Ask students how they think smokers with unhealthy lungs feel. (**sick, unhealthy, sad that they chose to smoke**)

Read the top of the first page. Point out that healthy lungs are spongy and pinkish. Ask what people with healthy lungs can do. (**Possible answers: breathe easily, play**) Compare the healthy lung to the smoker's lung.

Display the LUNG MODEL with the inserted ACTIVATED CHARCOAL CAPSULE, and remind students of the lung demonstration from Lesson 12.2. State that when people inhale cigarette smoke, it goes down into the lungs. Pinch the bags tightly next to the straws to ensure the charcoal does not filter out of them. Then blow gently into the straw; charcoal will enter the bags. Do not inhale from the straw. Explain that people can get diseases such as lung cancer or emphysema from smoking. Smoking also affects the teeth, mouth, nose, and throat, and it can hurt the heart and make colds more severe. Have students read the rest of the page.

2 State that some people might have a condition or disease that makes it hard for them to breathe even though they make healthful choices in life. Write the word *asthma* on the board and cross out the silent *th*. Say the word and allow students to repeat it several times. Share that asthma is not contagious like a cold; it is not a result of a poor choice like smoking. Some people are born with asthma, and some acquire it as they get older. When a person has asthma, the tubes that carry air in and out of the person's lungs can suddenly get smaller, which makes it harder to breathe. Share that if students see a friend having trouble breathing, it may be because of asthma. They can help their friend by telling a teacher or a parent.

Direct students' attention to the second page. Read the information about asthma. Ask a volunteer to describe how having trouble breathing might feel. (**scary, sad**) Point out that many people have asthma and that doctors sometimes give people inhalers that contain special medicine to help them breathe. Complete the exercises as a class.

3 Distribute POSTER BOARD, MARKERS, GLUE, and precut MAGAZINE PICTURES to small groups of students. Direct each group to make a poster about healthy lungs. Encourage students to display people exercising. If you have cut out pictures of people not keeping their lungs healthy, inform students that they must evaluate which pictures are appropriate for their poster. Upon completion, allow each group to share its poster with the class. Display the posters in the classroom if desired.

⊕ Extension

Materials
• BLM 12.5A A Promise to My Lungs

Distribute **BLM 12.5A A Promise to My Lungs** to each student and allow time to complete it.

Troubled Breathing 12.5

Make good choices to keep your lungs healthy. Smoking is not a healthful choice. Smoking can hurt your mouth, teeth, nose, and throat.

This is what a healthy lung looks like.

This is what an unhealthy lung looks like.

Keep your body healthy. Do not smoke!

Offer your bodies as living sacrifices, holy and pleasing to God …
Romans 12:1b

© Science Level 1   181

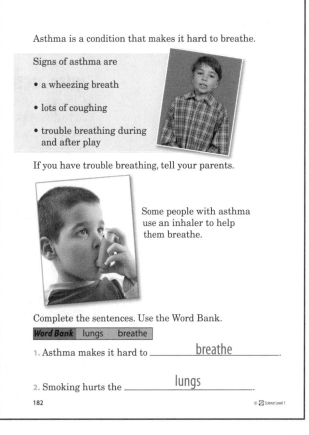

Asthma is a condition that makes it hard to breathe.

Signs of asthma are

• a wheezing breath

• lots of coughing

• trouble breathing during and after play

If you have trouble breathing, tell your parents.

Some people with asthma use an inhaler to help them breathe.

Complete the sentences. Use the Word Bank.

Word Bank lungs   breathe

1. Asthma makes it hard to _____breathe_____.

2. Smoking hurts the _____lungs_____.

182   © Science Level 1

12.6 Air Tanks and Fire Safety

Objective

Students will identify and demonstrate fire-safety skills.

Materials

Directed Instruction
• Smoke detector
• BLM 12.6A Life-Saving Tips

🖐 Preparation

Bring in a SMOKE DETECTOR for a demonstration. (*Directed Instruction*)

Verify that the invited firefighter is ready to speak to the class about fire safety. (*Directed Instruction*)

Print **BLM 12.6A Life-Saving Tips** for each student. (*Directed Instruction*)

⚠ Safety

Alert administration and other classroom teachers in your area of the school that you will be testing a smoke alarm.

Content

Since the leading cause of deaths in a fire is not burns but smoke inhalation, it is important for students to have fire-safety knowledge to protect their lungs as well as the rest of their body. Students should be able to identify the sound of the family's smoke detector. They should know to get out of the house if there is a fire and to call 911 only after escaping the fire. Students and their families should have several fire-escape plans from their home, including a meeting place away from the house. Once out, they should not go back inside. If the doors in the house are blocked and they cannot get out, they should get on their hands and knees to stay below smoke and fumes. Also, they should yell or wave something in front of a window to let others know where they are. If their clothes are on fire, they need to stop, drop, and roll. Toxic fumes (gases) in and just under the smoke are also very dangerous. Getting on the floor keeps a person not only below the smoke but also below the toxic fumes. Firefighters wear special safety equipment that might take students by surprise, but students should not be afraid of them—it is a firefighter's job to help them. Also, it is important that people use the staircase and avoid elevators in burning buildings. Students should know not to play with matches or lighters. Fire is a tool, not a toy.

Another breathing fatality is carbon monoxide. Carbon monoxide (CO) is an odorless and colorless gas that is dangerous and even fatal at certain concentration levels. Surprisingly, these dangerously high levels can be attained in an average home. Even if levels are high, there is no warning unless a special meter is in place that sounds an alarm. Carbon monoxide is dangerous because it attaches to the hemoglobin of red blood cells in place of oxygen causing the body to be deprived of the oxygen necessary to sustain life. Running a car or using a grill in an attached garage can cause carbon monoxide to seep into the house, even if the garage door is left open. Following safety precautions and being aware of breathing hazards can save many lives from the dangers of fire, smoke, toxic fumes, and carbon monoxide.

Introduction

Convey to students that sometimes people use special tools to help them breathe. Ask if they have ever seen firefighters or scuba divers wearing tanks on their backs. (**Answers will vary.**) Why do scuba divers take an air tank when they go underwater? (**to be able to breathe underwater**) State that similarly, firefighters must wear an air tank when fighting fires so they can get the oxygen they need and not inhale smoke or gases from the fire.

Directed Instruction 🖐 ⊕ ⚠

1 Direct students' attention to the first page. Read the sentence at the top and lead a discussion about the firefighter at the top of the page. Remind students that although the firefighter might look frightening in all of his or her equipment, they must remember that the firefighter is at work to help people trapped by fire and to help put out the fire. Read the captions and discuss the pictures of the astronaut and the scuba diver. Mention that the baby needs help breathing because his lungs have not yet grown enough.

2 Display the SMOKE DETECTOR to your class. Warn students that the alarm it emits is very loud. Press the test button. Ask what this sound tells people. (**There is too much smoke in the house.**)

3 Ask students why it is important to have fire drills in school. (**to practice safely getting outside in case of a fire**) Point out that it is important to practice an escape route at home also. Direct students' attention to the second page. Read each life-saving tip and allow time for students to check the box. Allow a few students at a time to practice stop, drop, and roll.

4 Have the pre-invited firefighter discuss fire safety with the class. Allow time for questions. Have students take home **BLM 12.6A Life-Saving Tips** to share with their family.

Notes:

⊕ Extension

Materials
• Fire-safety book
• Play phone, props
• Rewards

Read aloud a children's book about fire safety, such as *Fire Safety* by Dana Meachen Rau, (Marshall Cavendish, 2009).

Have small groups role-play a fire in a house. Direct students in the house to escape to safety, and designate a student to call 911 on a play phone. Assign a few firefighters to come put out the fire. If desired, use other props like firefighter hats and hoses.

Encourage students to make an escape plan with their family. Motivate students with a reward, such as a sticker or pencil, to bring their family's plan to class.

Air Tanks and Fire Safety 12.6

A firefighter uses an air tank to breathe during a fire.

Other people need help breathing too.

| An astronaut in space uses an oxygen tank to breathe. | A scuba diver uses an air tank to breathe underwater. | This baby was born early. He needs extra oxygen to live. |

© *Science* Level 1   183

As your teacher reads each sentence about fire safety, make a check mark in its box.

☑ Never play with matches or lighters!

☑ Know the sound of a smoke detector.

☑ Make an escape plan.

☑ Get out of the house! Do not go back inside. Go to a meeting place.

☑ Protect your lungs. Crawl on your hands and knees to stay below the smoke.

☑ Yell, or wave something in a window.

☑ Stop, drop, and roll if your clothes are on fire.

☑ Look for a firefighter. He or she will help you.

☑ Keep yourself safe during a fire.

184   © *Science* Level 1

Materials

Introduction
• Straws, masking tape

Directed Instruction
• BLM 12.7A Lungs and Air Facts
• Index cards, masking tape
• Crayons, BLM 12.7B Chapter 12 Test

Preparation

Obtain a STRAW and crumpled paper for each student. Have MASKING TAPE available. (*Introduction*)

Print **BLM 12.7A Lung and Air Facts** for each student. (*Directed Instruction*)

Collect **10** INDEX CARDS; write one word on each card: *lung, exhale, breath, fire, oxygen, hairs, asthma, nose, contagious, hurts.* Use MASKING TAPE to attach the cards in random order to the board. (*Directed Instruction*)

Draw the following Creation web on the board. (*Directed Instruction*)

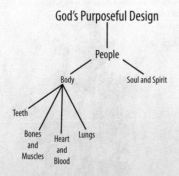

Have CRAYONS available. Print **BLM 12.7B Chapter 12 Test** for each student. (*Directed Instruction*)

Safety

Prior to conducting this activity, consult parents or the school nurse about students who have breathing problems.

Introduction

Play the game The Paper Race. Inform students that they will move crumpled pieces of paper by blowing through STRAWS. Use MASKING TAPE on the floor to indicate a starting line and a finish line. Assign students to groups of four. Instruct each student to move the paper by blowing air through the straw. The first student to move the piece of paper across the finish line wins the round. Continue until all first-round winners have been established. Allow the first-round winners to play again until a final winner is determined.

Directed Instruction

1 Review the definitions of *air, lung, exhale,* and *inhale.*(**air**: a gas that has oxygen in it; **lung**: a part of the body that takes in and lets out air; **exhale**: to let air out of the lungs; **inhale**: to take air into the lungs) Distribute **BLM 12.7A Lungs and Air Facts** to each student. Complete as a class.

2 Indicate the TAPED INDEX CARDS on the board. Inform students that you will give them a clue to identify each word on the board. Read the clues below and allow one student to remove a word card from the board as the word on it is identified.
  1. You have tiny hairs in here that help keep your lungs clean. (**nose**)
  2. When you blow air out of your body, you do this. (**exhale**)
  3. Sebastian uses this to blow out candles on his birthday cake. (**breath**)
  4. Malik and his family have several ways to get out of the house in case this happens. (**fire**)
  5. When you take a deep breath, your lungs are getting this from the air. (**oxygen**)
  6. These are very tiny, and they help mucus keep dust from going into your lungs. (**hairs**)
  7. Chloe uses an inhaler to help with this condition. (**asthma**)
  8. This is a part of your body that breathes air. (**lung**)
  9. Diya has a cold now because Mia's cold was this. (**contagious**)
  10. Anthony knows that smoking would do this to his lungs. (**hurt**)

Mix up the word cards. Hold each card up, one at a time, to the class. Allow a volunteer to say the word on the card and to use the word in a sentence about lungs, air, or breathing.

3 Direct students' attention to the Creation web on the board. Share that God purposefully designed people with a body and a soul and spirit. Select a volunteer to read the parts of the body shown on the web. (**teeth, bones and muscles, heart and blood, lungs**) Ask students to name other parts of the body. (**Answers will vary.**)

4 Use student pages as a review or pretest. Provide CRAYONS and have students complete these pages. Allow time for them to write their journal entry. You may use **BLM 12.7B Chapter 12 Test** for individual assessment. Read through this page with your class. Provide as much reading support as necessary. You may choose to use BLM 12.7B as an oral assessment or not to do it at all.

5 Conclude by reading **1 Corinthians 12:18**. Remind the class that God designed each person in a wonderful way and for a special purpose. Students need to care for their body to help it work well.

6 Chapter 12 Lungs and Air has been completed. Its pages can be stapled and sent home as a booklet to be shared with a family member.

Notes:

➕ Extension

Materials
• Tape, soccer ball

Line 2 desks up against a blank wall and tape a sign labeled *Heart* to 1 desk and one labeled *Lungs* to the other. Direct students to form a line about 3 ft in front of the desks. Hand a soccer ball to the first student. Inform students that you will say a phrase about either the heart or the lungs, and they must gently kick the ball under the appropriate desk. Phrases about the heart include *pumps blood, attaches to blood vessels, creates a pulse, is heard by a stethoscope, can be read by an electrocardiogram*. Phrases about the lungs include *takes air in and out, inhales and exhales, connects to the windpipe, helps you blow bubbles*.

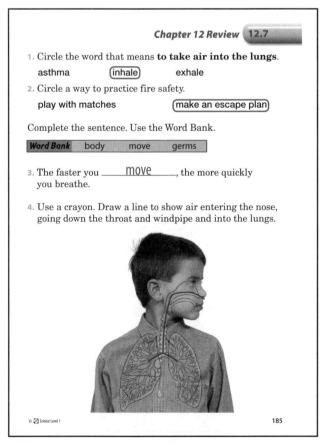

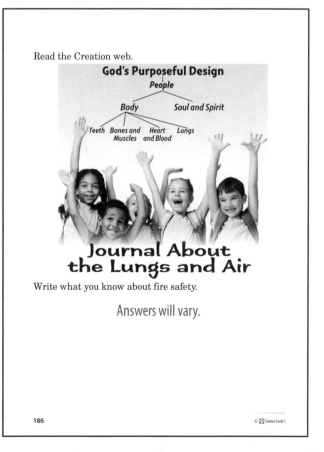

Stomach and Food
Chapter 13

Key Ideas

- Food comes from many sources and gives people the energy they need to move and grow.
- The mouth, throat, esophagus, stomach, and intestines all help in the digestion of food.
- It is important to eat a variety of healthful food from each of the food groups.

13.0 Chapter Preparation

Vocabulary

stomach

Looking Ahead

- For an *Extension* activity in **Lesson 13.2**, invite a first-aid teacher to teach your class how to help someone who is choking by using abdominal thrusts (the Heimlich Maneuver).
- Collect several grocery ads for **Lesson 13.3**.
- Plan to cut and refrigerate fruit for **Lesson 13.5**.

Introduction

Food is a subject familiar to students, and they will develop and apply the concept of healthful eating and portion control while studying this topic. Food must reach the cells in order to fuel the body. Students will explore the human digestive system by studying the parts of the body through which food passes. They will understand that as food travels through the body, it is processed in ways that are unique to each body part—the small intestine absorbs nutrients and the large intestine expels waste.

About This Chapter

Lesson 13.1 – Kinds of Food

Materials
- No additional materials are needed.

Lesson Content
Food comes from many different sources. Some food comes from plants, from which the edible parts for people grow either in the soil or above ground. Other food comes from animals, whether they live in water or on land, or fly in the sky. God's design provides the nutrients for the plants and animals that people rely on to survive.

Lesson 13.2 – Food as Fuel

Materials
- Electrical device
- Battery-powered device

Lesson Content
People need food for energy. They use this energy to work and grow. The five senses help people enjoy the food they ingest.

Lesson 13.3 – Food-Guide Plate

Materials
- Plate
- Food items
- Scissors
- Grocery ads
- Glue
- Markers
- Construction paper

Lesson Content
MyPlate helps people know what kinds of food they should eat to be healthy. People should match their portion sizes to the sizes on the plate graphic. Fats, oils, and sugar should be eaten in moderation.

Lesson 13.4 – Where Food Goes

Materials
- Bowl
- Walnuts
- Bags
- Hammer
- Sugar cubes
- Cups
- Water
- Paper-towel tube
- Bread
- Spoons

Lesson Content
Teeth and saliva help break down food in the mouth. The chewed food then goes down the esophagus and enters the stomach, which mashes and mixes the food. The small intestine provides a pathway for food to follow. This part of the body absorbs the nutrients from the food as fuel. The large intestine then passes waste out of the body.

Lesson 13.5 – Food Experiment

Materials
- Candies
- Jars
- Apples
- Crayons
- Hammer
- Blindfolds
- Pears
- Water
- Plates
- Containers

Lesson Content

An experiment with an apple and a pear demonstrates how the senses of sight, smell, and taste work together to make eating an enjoyable experience. The process of eating and digesting food requires many parts of the body to work together as God designed.

Lesson 13.6 – Chapter 13 Review

Materials
- Yarn
- Crayons

Teacher Resources

Digestive Wellness: Strengthen the Immune System and Prevent Disease Through Healthy Digestion by Elizabeth Lipski, PhD. McGraw-Hill, 2012.

Gut Feelings: Your Digestive System (You: The Owner's Manual) by Michael F. Roizen, MD and Mehmet Oz, MD. With Lisa Oz and Ted Spiker. HarperCollins, 2008.

Incredible Human Machine. DVD. National Geographic Society, 2007.

Student Resources

The Digestive System by Christine Taylor-Butler. Scholastic, 2008.

The Digestive System: What Makes Me Burp? by Sue Barraclough. Heinemann, 2009.

The Quest to Digest by Mary Corcoran. Charlesbridge, 2006.

Supplemental Materials

Blackline Masters

13.1A Recipe: Banana Bread
13.3A Food-Guide Place Mat
13.6A Food-Group Cards, Part 1
13.6B Food-Group Cards, Part 2
13.6C Stomach and Food Facts
13.6D Chapter 13 Test

Transparency Masters

13.3A Food-Guide Plate
13.4A Stomach

Computer Presentation

13.3 The Food Groups

13.1 Kinds of Food

Objective

Students will examine the origin of some foods.

Preparation

Write the following words in columns on the board:

Food	Plant or Animal
apple	pig
milk	tree
eggs	cow
ham	chicken
(Introduction)	

Content

People need a variety of foods in order to provide the chemicals necessary for proper functioning of their body. Eating a variety of foods ensures that the different kinds of proteins, fats, carbohydrates, minerals, and vitamins are available as needed by the body. God designed the digestive system to break down food into the tiny parts that body cells need. The body can then reorganize these ingredients into a form it can use. For example, a person may eat a piece of meat containing protein. The meat's protein is broken down into amino acids—the building blocks of protein. The body then reconstructs these building blocks into a form that can be used in processes such as repairing cells and making new ones.

Introduction

Point to and say each word on the *Food* list written on the board. Explain that food comes from a source prior to arriving at a grocery store. Each of these foods comes from a plant or an animal. Point to and say each of the words on the *Plant or Animal* list. Return to the *Food* list and ask where each food came from. (*apple*: tree; *milk*: cow; *eggs*: chicken; *ham*: pig) Draw a line from each food to its source.

Directed Instruction

1 Ask students where their family buys apples. (**Possible answers: grocery store, farmer's market**) Explain that before arriving at the store, apples are picked from apple trees in an orchard. Ask students if they like french fries. (**Answers will vary.**) Explain that french fries are made from potatoes, which grow on underground stems of potato plants. Reiterate that the food people eat comes from plants and animals.

2 Direct students' attention to the first page. Read the sentences about carrots and strawberries, and discuss that each of these foods comes from a plant. Ask the class to name some other foods people eat that come from plants. (**Possible answers: lettuce, oranges, peppers**)

Convey that most plants need sun, air, soil, and water in order to be healthy. Discuss how God created the sky (Genesis 1:6–8) and dry ground, or land (Genesis 1:9–10). After these things were in place, God created plants (Genesis 1:11). Then He made the sun to provide light during the day (Genesis 1:14–18). All the things that plants need God provided. Inform students that God then created people and provided for their needs.

Read from the board the examples of food that comes from animals. Then read through the second portion of the student page. Ask students what animal provides the milk most people drink. (**cow**) What else comes from cow's milk? (**Possible answers: yogurt, cheese, ice cream, butter**) What is a plant that a cow eats? (**grass**) Remind students that grass needs sun, air, soil, and water in order to live. The cow eats the grass to live. Then, people drink milk from a cow. Share other examples, such as how the chicken eats grain and insects and lays eggs.

3 Instruct students to turn to the second page. Read the sentences at the top, and then lead a class discussion about the origin of each ingredient in banana muffins—flour, bananas, sugar, eggs, butter. Complete the exercise at the bottom of the page as a class.

4 Engage students in a discussion of God's provision for plants and animals. Reiterate that plants receive the sunlight, air, water, and soil that they need in order to grow. Each animal lives in an environment that provides the necessary food—rabbits feed on plants and lions feed on other animals.

5 Since Earth has air, water, sunlight, soil, plants, and animals, people are provided with food. Read and discuss **Philippians 4:19**.

Notes:

 Extension

Materials
• BLM 13.1A Recipe: Banana Bread

Follow **BLM 13.1A Recipe: Banana Bread** in class, or send the recipe home with students. Check student records for possible allergies.

Share that the Bible has many records of God's provision of food. In Exodus 16:13–16, God provided the Israelites, who were in the desert, quail for meat and a breadlike substance called *manna*. Exodus 16:31 explains that the manna was white and tasted like wafers (or crackers) made of honey. God wanted His people to know that they could trust Him to meet their needs. God provided food for the Israelites for 40 years, until they entered the Promised Land.

Kinds of Food 13.1

People need food.
Some food comes from plants.

Some grows in the soil.   Some grows out of the soil.

Some food comes from animals.

Tuna and fish sticks come from fish.   Fried chicken and eggs come from chickens.   Hamburgers and steaks come from cows.

Milk comes from animals that eat plants.

189

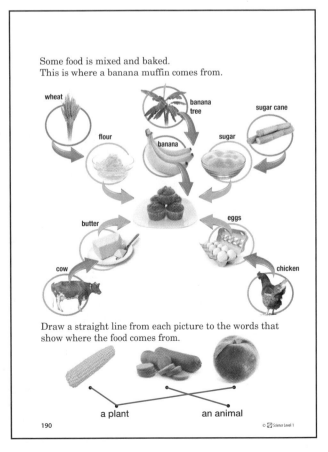

Some food is mixed and baked.
This is where a banana muffin comes from.

wheat   banana tree   sugar cane
flour   banana   sugar
butter   eggs
cow   chicken

Draw a straight line from each picture to the words that show where the food comes from.

a plant   an animal

190

13.2 Food as Fuel

Objective

Students will discuss that food provides the body energy to move and grow.

Materials

Directed Instruction
- Electrical device, battery-powered device

Preparation

Obtain an ELECTRICAL DEVICE, such as a lamp or a radio, and also a BATTERY-POWERED DEVICE, like a clock or a cell phone, for a demonstration. (*Directed Instruction*)

Content

A variety of food provides people with the essential raw materials the body needs. Once digested by the organs of the digestive system, these raw materials are available for life's processes throughout the body. There are six nutrients: proteins, fats, carbohydrates, minerals, vitamins, and water; each is vital to specific functions.

- Proteins: These break down in the digestive system into amino acids. Amino acids are like building blocks. They help maintain cellular function by building and repairing cells. Hemoglobin, a protein in red blood cells, carries oxygen. Similarly, collagen is a protein found in bones, tendons, ligaments, and other tissues. Some proteins affect specific organs, stimulating them to control certain activities.
- Fats: Some fats break down into glycerol and fatty acids. Certain vitamins can be absorbed only in the presence of fat. In addition, fat stored in the body acts as an energy reserve.
- Carbohydrates: Starches and other carbohydrates are broken down into simple sugars. Carbohydrates are the main energy source in the body. The liver converts some simple sugars into glucose, which is used in the process of cellular respiration to produce energy for the body.
- Minerals: The body uses minerals in a variety of ways. Examples include iron in hemoglobin, iodine for hormones produced by the thyroid gland, and calcium for bones.
- Vitamins: These serve many functions, such as aiding in blood clotting. Vitamin A helps people see.
- Water: This is an essential nutrient and a major component of the body.

Introduction

Have students stand along the walls of the classroom. Direct students to march in a circle around the classroom and then to return to their seat. Point out that students had to use their body's energy to march around. Remind them that they learned in Chapter 6 that energy is the ability to do work. Explain that the energy students have comes from food. Ask volunteers to name other activities that require energy. (**Possible answers: writing, playing, running, walking**)

Directed Instruction

1 Ask students what food a pet cat eats. (**cat food**) What gives a pet dog energy? (**dog food**) Display an ELECTRICAL DEVICE. Ask students what gives this device energy to work. (**electricity**) Plug in the device to show it working. Display a BATTERY-POWERED DEVICE and point out the battery. Ask what gives this device the energy needed for it to work. (**the battery**) Show the device working.

2 Direct students' attention to the first page. Read the examples. State that gasoline is the fuel that gives a vehicle energy; some toy trucks get energy from a battery; and a person needs food for energy. People use energy so the body can work and grow. Discuss that people designed the truck and toy. The truck and toy designers made the parts to work together and designed them to work by using something to fuel them. Compare the cars to the parts of the human body that God designed to work together. Convey that He also provided the food needed in order to get energy to make the body work and grow. Ask students what kinds of food are giving them energy today. (**Answers will vary.**) Check for understanding by asking why people need food (**for energy**) and why people need energy.

(for their body to work and grow) Direct students' attention to the second page. Allow time for students to draw a picture of what they ate for breakfast. Reinforce that the food they eat gives them energy for their body to work and grow. Assist students as they make their list of activities they have done today, and ensure that the exercise has been completed.

3 Divide the class into small groups. Allow them to discuss their favorite food and why it is important that they eat food. (**for their body to work and grow**)

4 Review the five senses related to the study of the human body. Restate that God designed people with body parts for sensing—eyes, ears, nose, skin, and tongue. The brain understands the messages from the senses and allows people to know what is going on around them. Have students refer to the front of their book for information about the five senses. Convey that the five senses help people enjoy food so it is fun to take in body fuel. Food tastes good; it looks nice; it smells good; and some foods feel fuzzy, like a peach, or smooth, like an apple. Some foods make crunchy sounds. Have students verbally answer the questions below.
- Which word has to do with the sense of touch, *soft* or *quiet*? (**soft**)
- Which word has to do with the sense of sight, *pretty* or *salty*? (**pretty**)
- Which word has to do with the sense of hearing, *spicy* or *loud*? (**loud**)
- Which word has to do with the sense of smell, *stinky* or *flat*? (**stinky**)
- Which word has to do with the sense of taste, *salty* or *tiny*? (**salty**)

Mate
• Fi

Ha
tea
thrus
help son
movements
movements can be used on another
person or on oneself.

Food as Fuel 13.2

This truck needs gasoline so it can move.

This toy truck needs
a battery so it can move.

People need food so they can move. Food gives the body
energy so it can work and grow.

© Science Level 1   191

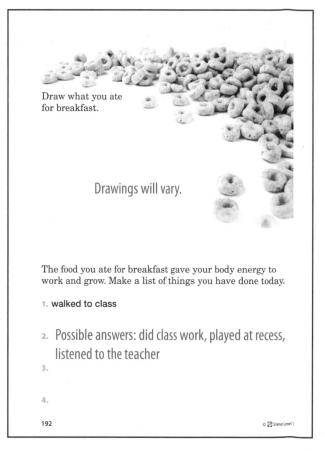

Draw what you ate
for breakfast.

Drawings will vary.

The food you ate for breakfast gave your body energy to
work and grow. Make a list of things you have done today.

1. **walked to class**

2. Possible answers: did class work, played at recess,
listened to the teacher

3.

4.

192   © Science Level 1

Content

Taking care of the body includes maintaining a healthful diet. The United
States Department of Agriculture (USDA) has designed a food-guide plate,
MyPlate, to provide guidelines for healthful eating. The USDA recommends
that a daily diet include specific portions of five food groups. MyPlate is
designed to look like a plate to provide a visual example of portion sizes
and food groups to select. Fats and sweets are not included on MyPlate and
should be eaten in moderation. Servings differ with age and activity level.
Serving size can also be seen on packaging information. The MyPlate plan
fulfills the dietary needs of the general public—not necessarily those with
dietary restrictions or other health issues.

Introduction

Remind students that food provides fuel for the body. Display the PAPER
PLATE and PACKAGED FOOD or PLAY-FOOD ITEMS. Explain to the class that you
are going to fill your plate with a fuel source to help you move through the
rest of your day. Dramatically begin filling your plate with unhealthful foods
and bypass all the fruits and vegetables. Overfill the plate so that it becomes
obvious to students that you are not making healthful food choices. Ask
students if they think your meal will give you energy to get you through the
day. (**Answers will vary.**) State that you will not be eating this meal today,
but that it was a demonstration to show the importance of making good
food choices every day. State that eating only junk food hurts a person's body
and keeps the person from growing strong and healthy. Reiterate that poor
food choices like the ones you piled on the plate today will not provide you
with the energy you need for the rest of the day. State that in today's lesson,
students will learn which foods they should put on their plate, as well as how
much food should go on their plate.

Directed Instruction

1 Display **TM-13.3A Food-Guide Plate**. Share that this food-guide plate,
  MyPlate, helps people know what kinds of food they should eat to be
  healthy. People should use the same portion sizes on their own plate as is
  shown on MyPlate.

  Instruct students to turn to their first page. Read the sentence at the top.
  Discuss each food group and explain that protein includes foods like meat
  and some beans. Point out the examples of foods from the other groups
  at the bottom of the page. Encourage students to think of other examples.
  Read the following tips for selecting food from each group:
  • Fruits—Eat whole fruits and drink juices that are 100% juice.
  • Dairy—Switch to low-fat milk.
  • Grains—Make at least half of your grains whole grains, such as brown
    rice, whole-grain bread and pasta, and whole-grain cereal.
  • Vegetables—Vegetables and fruits should fill half of the plate. Eat more
    vegetables than fruits. Eat a variety of vegetables.
  • Protein—Trim off the fat from the meat. Eat grilled meat instead of
    fried meat.
  Point out that junk food like candy, ice cream, cookies, and soda pop are
  not on MyPlate. They do not help a person grow strong and healthy. They
  should only be eaten occasionally and only after a person has eaten food
  from all the food groups first.

2 Direct students' attention to the second page. Read the directions at the top and give time for students to draw the foods. Allow students to refer to TM-13.3A as needed. Then read the directions for the exercise at the bottom of the student page. Guide students to observe, to decide which meal is more healthful, and to explain their choice. (**Answers will vary but should include that the more healthful meal has food from all the food groups, and it does not include junk food like the unhealthful meal.**)

3 Distribute **BLM 13.3A Food-Guide Place Mat**, SCISSORS, GROCERY ADS, GLUE, MARKERS, and CONSTRUCTION PAPER. Allow students to cut out the plate shape and to glue it to their sheet of construction paper. Then have students cut out pictures from the ads to place around each section of the plate. Remind them that junk food should not be on their place mat. The place mat is for healthful food that will help students become strong. Allow students to decorate their place mat, then collect the place mats to laminate before sending them home. Encourage students to use their place mat at home to remember how to select healthful foods and portions.

4 Refer to TM-13.3A to check for understanding. Ask students which they should eat more of—protein or grains. (**grains**) What two groups should take up half the plate? (**fruits and vegetables, or protein and grains**) What kind of bread should you eat instead of white bread? (**whole-wheat bread**) Remind the class that God designed the human body to get what it needs from healthful food. Eating a healthful diet is one way students can take care of their body. Have students share with a classmate the kinds of healthful food they should eat.

➕ Extension

Materials
• CP-13.3 The Food Groups
• Internet

Present and discuss **CP-13.3 The Food Groups** to review healthful eating habits involving each of the food groups.

Check the USDA website for resources to use with MyPlate.

Have students create a Venn diagram from two food groups.

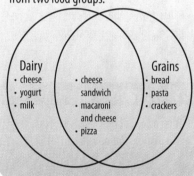

Dairy		Grains
• cheese	• cheese sandwich	• bread
• yogurt	• macaroni and cheese	• pasta
• milk	• pizza	• crackers

Food-Guide Plate 13.3

Use MyPlate to choose healthful food.

You should choose food from these groups.

Use the food-guide plate to grow strong.

Label the food groups. Draw a food for each group.

Drawings will vary.

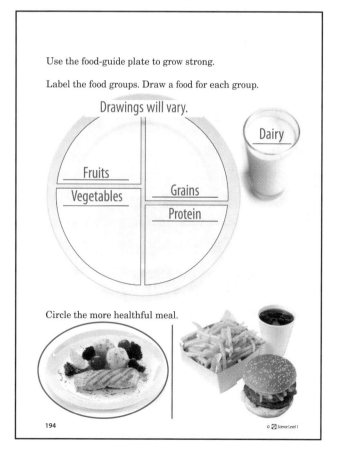

Circle the more healthful meal.

13.4 Where Food Goes

Students will identify some organs of the digestive system and the function of each.

Materials

Introduction
• Bowl, walnuts, ziplock bag, hammer

Directed Instruction
• TM-13.4A Stomach
• Sugar cubes, ziplock bag, clear cup, water
• Paper-towel tube, clear cup, water
• Bread, ziplock bags, clear cups, water, spoons

Preparation

Gather a BOWL of WALNUTS, a ZIPLOCK BAG, and a HAMMER. (*Introduction*)

Write the definition of *stomach* on the board. (*Directed Instruction*)

Select **TM-13.4A Stomach** for display. (*Directed Instruction*)

Obtain 2 SUGAR CUBES, 1 ZIPLOCK BAG, and 1 CLEAR CUP of WATER. (*Directed Instruction*)

Have available 1 PAPER-TOWEL TUBE, 2 CLEAR CUPS, and WATER. (*Directed Instruction*)

Obtain for each student a ¼ SLICE OF BREAD, a ZIPLOCK BAG, a CLEAR CUP of WATER, and a SPOON. (*Directed Instruction*)

Safety

Check student records for possible allergies.

Content

The purpose of the digestive system is to ingest food, break it down into usable parts, and transfer those parts to the cells of the body. Digestion occurs in a tube called *the alimentary canal,* made up of the following parts:
• Mouth: Food is broken down mechanically by the process of chewing and chemically by saliva.
• Esophagus: Swallowed food travels through the esophagus until it reaches the stomach. A flap called *the epiglottis* covers the opening to the trachea during swallowing so the food does not move into the windpipe and lungs.
• Stomach: This baglike organ can comfortably store, in an adult, about four cups of food in preparation for passing the food along to the small intestine. The stomach also breaks down food chemically by the action of the enzyme known as *pepsin.* Hydrochloric acid helps dissolve food as well as kill harmful bacteria. Mucus coats and protects the stomach lining from this powerful acid.
• Small intestine: Further digestion occurs in the first part of the small intestine. Nutrients are small enough at this point to pass into tiny structures called *villi* in the walls of the entire small intestine, into capillaries, and on to every cell in the body. There can be 20,000 villi per square inch of small intestine. The total surface area of this organ in an adult is approximately 250 square meters—the size of a tennis court!
• Large intestine: Water is absorbed to make the waste solid. Waste exits the body through the rectum and anus.

Introduction

Show the class a BOWL of WALNUTS. Explain that often walnuts must be broken down into smaller pieces before they are used in cookies or breads. People can break walnuts into smaller pieces in a number of ways, such as chopping them in a food processor or blender. This can even be accomplished in a very simple way like putting the walnuts in a ZIPLOCK BAG and tapping them gently with a HAMMER. Demonstrate this in front of the class. When the walnuts are in small pieces, reinforce the idea that they are now in a form that can be used in cookies or bread.

Directed Instruction

1 Relate the *Introduction* activity to the human body by explaining that God designed the body to break down food so that it can be used as energy. State that the stomach helps in this process. Read the definition of **stomach**: *a part of the body that breaks down food.*

Direct students' attention to the first page. Allow a volunteer to read the sentence at the top. Display **TM-13.4A Stomach**. Follow the path of food on the transparency, and guide students to do the same on their page. Name and point to the parts shown. Read the sentences at the bottom of the student page and point to the body parts mentioned. Emphasize that as food goes through these parts, it is made small enough for the body to use. What the body cannot use is waste.

2 Place a SUGAR CUBE in a ZIPLOCK BAG and seal the bag. Tap it with a book and hold up the broken sugar cube. Direct students to turn to the second page. Have a volunteer read the first sentence. Remind students that teeth crunch and cut food. Mention that the mouth also begins to break down food in another way. Have a volunteer read the next sentence. Hold up another sugar cube. Place it in a CLEAR CUP filled with WATER. Ask students

what is happening to the sugar cube in the water. (**It is getting smaller.**)
Explain that saliva is the liquid in the mouth. It helps break down and mix
food. Emphasize that chewing food well makes it smaller so the stomach
can work better. Have a student read the next two sentences.

Read the sentences about the esophagus. Indicate the esophagus on
TM-13.4 and engage students in wondering how it works. Display a
PAPER-TOWEL TUBE with its bottom end in a CLEAR CUP. Pour WATER through
the tube. Relate that when food is swallowed, the tubelike esophagus
transports food to the stomach. Ask where the food goes. (**to the stomach**)
Direct students to place a hand on their stomach. Point to the stomach on
TM-13.4. Share that God designed a person's body to use food for energy
so the body can work and grow.

3 Share that each student will make a model of a stomach. Distribute a
¼ SLICE OF BREAD, a ZIPLOCK BAG, a CLEAR CUP of WATER, and a SPOON to
each student. Demonstrate placing the bread inside the bag to represent
the stomach. Add 3 spoonfuls of water and close the bag tightly.
Allow time for students to prepare their bag. When all bags are sealed,
instruct students to squeeze the bag gently to mix the bread. As they are
squeezing, share that the stomach uses muscles to squeeze the food. The
food then goes to the intestines where it finishes being broken down and
is sent throughout the body to be used for energy so it can work and grow.
Read the sentences about the stomach and the intestines. Share that solid
wastes exit the body through the end of the large intestine. Have students
review where food goes after it enters the mouth. Then have them
complete the exercise at the bottom of the page.

➕ Extension

Materials
• Water, paper towels, panty hose,
  aluminum pan

To demonstrate the job of the small
intestine, have students push a wet
paper-towel ball through a 1-ft-long
strip of panty hose. They should hold the
panty hose over an aluminum pan and
notice the water dripping through the
hose. Relate the panty hose to the small
intestine, and the wet ball to food passing
through. State that the intestine must use
muscles to push the food along. Compare
the water dripping out to nutrients that
the body absorbs from the food.

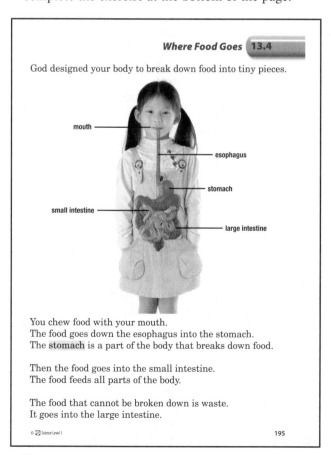

Where Food Goes 13.4

God designed your body to break down food into tiny pieces.

mouth
esophagus
stomach
small intestine
large intestine

You chew food with your mouth.
The food goes down the esophagus into the stomach.
The **stomach** is a part of the body that breaks down food.

Then the food goes into the small intestine.
The food feeds all parts of the body.

The food that cannot be broken down is waste.
It goes into the large intestine.

© Science Level 1
195

Teeth crush food into pieces.
Saliva breaks down food.

The sugar cube breaks down in water.
This is how the mouth works.

The esophagus is a tube
that food goes down.

Water travels down the tube.
This is how the esophagus works.

Your hands mash bread in a bag.
In the same way, the stomach
mixes and mashes food.

The intestines use the food to
give the body energy.

Number the parts in the order that food follows.

stomach __3__   mouth __1__

196   intestines __4__   esophagus __2__   © Science Level 1

13.5 Food Experiment

Content

The senses play a powerful role in eating. Before tasting a food, the body uses the sense of sight to recognize it. Certain foods have a powerful smell that can be identified even if a person cannot see or taste them. Popcorn, coffee, and fresh-baked cookies all have a distinguishable aroma. Even while a person is tasting, the sense of smell is at work. In fact, about 80% of the flavor a person tastes in food is actually from smell. Flavor is the combination of taste, smell, texture, temperature, and other physical features of that particular food. Taste buds alone are only able to recognize food as sweet, salty, sour, bitter, or savory. However, God provided the amazing connection of senses and body features to allow the intake of food to be a uniquely enjoyable experience.

Scientists conclude that children have a higher taste sensitivity than adults. Children may tend to prefer sweet-tasting foods and beverages. Some may even be overly sensitive to bitter tastes, depriving them of much-needed nutrients found in vegetables and other healthy foods. For example, raw vegetables may be better accepted by children than cooked ones. Studies show that this sensitivity lessens with age, but in the meantime, exposing children to varieties of foods early on can help develop their sense of taste. Experts recommend not forcing children to eat foods they do not like but encouraging them to keep trying those foods and new ones—children may need multiple exposures to the same food before they will like it.

Introduction

Display 4 HARD CANDIES and 2 JARS of WATER. Explain that the class will conduct an experiment to see which candy breaks down first: a whole candy in saliva, a smashed candy in saliva, a whole candy in water, or a smashed candy in water. Allow students to make a prediction based on what they have learned in this chapter. (**Predictions will vary.**) Smash 2 candies with a HAMMER: 1 to give to a student and 1 to place in a jar. Select a volunteer to dissolve a whole candy in his or her mouth and also one volunteer to dissolve a smashed candy. Instruct the volunteers to place the candy in their mouth but not to bite or chew the candy. Select two more volunteers to drop the remaining whole candy and smashed candy into the jars at the same time that the other volunteers place their candy in their mouth. Discuss the results. Students will observe that the broken candy in saliva breaks down first. Explain that the mouth helps with digestion by chewing food and providing saliva to mix with and break down the food.

Directed Instruction

1 Inform students that they will conduct a new experiment to better understand how their senses work during the act of eating. Refer to the Scientific Inquiry section at the beginning of this book for the method of conducting an experiment. Direct students' attention to the first student page. Remind students that an experiment means a way to test, or try out, a science question to learn or confirm something. Proceed through each step:
   1. Ask a question: Read the question that students will try to answer through the experiment.
   2. Make a hypothesis: Ask students if they think sight and smell will affect taste. Have them circle their guess. (**Answers will vary.**)
   3. Plan and do a test: Explain that students will plan and do an experiment to test their hypothesis. Direct students to put on a BLINDFOLD. Assist as needed. Distribute PAPER PLATES with CUBES OF PEELED APPLE to half

of the class and CUBES OF PEELED PEAR to the other half. Keep track of which students received each fruit. Direct students to pinch their nose shut with one hand and pick up the food to eat with their other hand. Direct students not to discuss the food as they eat.

4. Record and analyze your results: After all students have finished eating, instruct them to remove their blindfold and to discreetly write down what food they think they ate. Then share with students what food they actually did eat. Allow time for students to record their answer.

5. Make a conclusion: Have students turn to the second page and compare the results with their hypothesis. Reassure students that scientific inquiry is not about being right or wrong; it is about discovering something they did not know or confirming something they do know. Ask if students correctly identified their fruit. (**Answers will vary.**)

6. Share your results: Tally results on the board. Then have the class use CRAYONS to color the bar graph to indicate how many students correctly tasted their fruit. Consider graphing each fruit in a different color.

Ask students questions after the experiment: Did you lose your sense of taste when you pinched your nose shut? (**Answers will vary.**) Did you get nervous about what you would put in your mouth when you could not see or smell? (**Answers will vary.**) Did pinching your nose make anything taste better or worse? (**Answers will vary.**) Did your tongue taste the sweetness of the fruit better with your nose closed? (**Answers will vary.**)

Remind students that sight, taste, and smell are different senses that work together to help a person experience the flavor of foods. Praise God for giving people senses that make getting food into the body enjoyable.

➕ Extension

Materials
- Scissors, large paper bags, glue, pasta, crayons, tape, straws, ziplock bags, paper-towel tubes, yarn

Create with students a wearable human-body-part project. Cut out arm and head holes from a large paper bag. On the back of the bag, have students glue on pasta pieces to represent the spine and the ribs. On the front, guide students to draw a heart and tape on straws and ziplock bags for the lungs. Have students tape a paper-towel tube for the esophagus and attach a ziplock bag for the stomach. Then have them glue yarn below the stomach for the intestines. If desired, have students blow into the straws to inflate the lungs or have them drop a piece of food into the esophagus to watch it fall into the stomach.

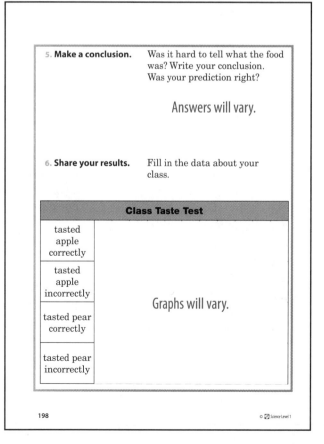

Introduction
- BLMs 13.6A–B Food-Group Cards, Parts 1–2

Directed Instruction
- TM-13.4A Stomach
- Yarn
- BLM 13.6C Stomach and Food Facts
- Crayons, BLM 13.6D Chapter 13 Test

✋ Preparation

Make enough food group cards from **BLMs 13.6A–B Food-Group Cards, Parts 1–2** to provide 1 card per student. (*Introduction*)

Select **TM-13.4A Stomach** for display. (*Directed Instruction*)

Cut PIECES OF YARN the following lengths: 4 in., 9 in., 5 ft, 23 ft. (*Directed Instruction*)

Draw the following Creation web on the board. (*Directed Instruction*)

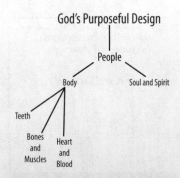

God's Purposeful Design

People

Body — Soul and Spirit

Teeth

Bones and Muscles — Heart and Blood

Print **BLM 13.6C Stomach and Food Facts** for each student. (*Directed Instruction*)

Have CRAYONS available. Print **BLM 13.6D Chapter 13 Test** for each student. (*Directed Instruction*)

Introduction

Distribute food-group cards from **BLMs 13.6A–B Food-Group Cards, Parts 1–2**. Instruct students whose cards are from the same food group to stand together. When all of the groups are formed, call out the name of a food group. Have members from that group name the foods belonging to that food group. (*grains*: pancakes, pretzel, bread, bagel; *vegetables*: corn, carrot, peas, salad; *fruits*: banana, apple, strawberry; *dairy*: milk, yogurt, cheese; *protein*: egg, fish, steak, chicken) Repeat this procedure for each food group. Shuffle the cards and play again as time allows.

Directed Instruction

1 Ask students what kind of food a pepperoni pizza is. (**Answers will vary.**) Share that some foods, such as pizza, contain more than one food group. Discuss the foods in a slice of pepperoni pizza and the food group in which each food belongs: *crust*: grains; *tomato sauce*: vegetables; *cheese*: dairy; *pepperoni*: protein.

2 Ask students what happens to food when it is eaten. (**It is broken down into tiny parts.**) Display **TM-13.4A Stomach**. Ask for volunteers to point out and describe what the following body parts do: mouth, esophagus, stomach, small intestine, and large intestine. (*mouth*: **begins to break down food by chewing, mixes food with saliva;** *esophagus*: **transports swallowed food;** *stomach*: **breaks down food into even smaller parts;** *small intestine*: **finishes breaking down food and sends it to body cells to give the body energy;** *large intestine*: **collects waste and then passes it out of the body**) Review the definition of *stomach*. (**a part of the body that breaks down food**)

Use PIECES OF YARN to show the approximate length of an adult esophagus, stomach, small intestine, and large intestine as you review each body part: esophagus—9 in.; stomach—3 to 6 in.; small intestine—23 ft; large intestine—5 ft. Discuss how God's design of the intestines allows them to be coiled up in order to fit in the body. Ask students to calculate how tall adults would be if each adult's intestines were not curled. (**Answers will vary but should include over 28 ft tall.**)

3 Direct students' attention to the Creation web on the board. Share that God purposefully designed people with a body and a soul and spirit. Have a volunteer read the parts of the body that are shown. (**teeth, bones and muscles, heart and blood, lungs, stomach**) Ask students to name other parts of the body. (**Answers will vary.**) Distribute **BLM 13.6C Stomach and Food Facts** to each student. Read the facts and allow time for students to write in the answers.

4 Use student pages as a review or pretest. Distribute CRAYONS and complete these pages with your class. Allow time for the journal writing. You may use **BLM 13.6D Chapter 13 Test** for individual assessment. Read through this page with your class. Provide as much reading support as necessary. You may choose to use BLM 13.6D as an oral assessment or not to do it at all.

5 To review all of the body parts learned in Unit 4, have students create a chart with three columns. Direct them to label the columns shown in the following example and then to fill in the first column with the body parts. Encourage students to work with a partner to come up with answers for the remaining columns. Review the chart with students as they finish.

body part	where	what
teeth	mouth	help people eat, talk, and smile
bones	all over	give the body shape and help it move
muscles	all over	help the body move
heart	chest	pumps blood
lungs	chest	take in and let out air
stomach	chest	breaks down food

6 Chapter 13 Stomach and Food has been completed. Its pages can be stapled and sent home as a booklet to be shared with a family member.

Notes:

Extension

Materials
• Snacks, crayons
• Chalk, beanbags

Plan a Healthful Restaurant Day. Ask parents to provide a healthful snack. Allow students to design colorful menus with healthful foods. Check student records for possible allergies.

On a concrete floor, draw a large outline in chalk of a human body. Hand a student volunteer several beanbags. State a part of the body that students have learned about in Unit 4 (teeth, skull, femur, knee joint, lungs, heart, stomach, esophagus). Have the student try to toss a beanbag onto the body where that part would be located.

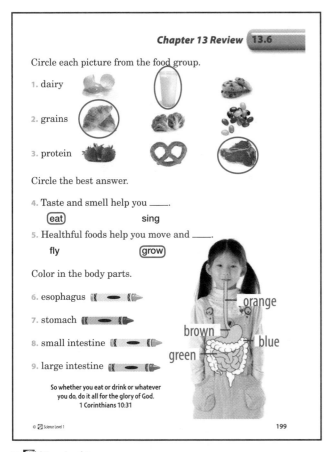

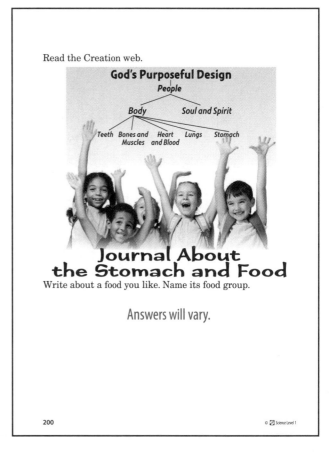

Glossary

The first number refers to the lesson number. The information in parentheses refers to the page number in the student book.

A

air a gas that has oxygen in it 12.1 (page 173)

animal a living thing that needs air, food, water, and a place to live 1.2 (page 5)

B

bird an animal that lays eggs and has feathers and wings 3.1 (page 36)

bone a hard part of the body that gives the body shape and helps it move 10.1 (page 145)

E

energy the ability to do work 6.1 (page 81)

exhale let air out of the lungs 12.2 (page 175)

F

fish an animal that lives in water 2.1 (page 19)

force a push or a pull 6.1 (page 81)

G

graph a chart that shows and compares information 4.4 (page 60)

H

habitat the place where an animal lives 1.2 (page 5)

heart a part of the body that pumps blood 11.1 (page 159)

I

inhale take air into the lungs 12.2 (page 175)

insect an animal that has three main body parts and six legs 4.1 (page 53)

J

joint a part of the body where bones meet 10.2 (page 147)

L

living thing a thing that needs air, food, and water to stay alive. It grows and changes 1.1 (page 3)

lung a part of the body that takes in and lets out air 12.1 (page 173)

M

mammal an animal that has hair and can make milk to feed its young 1.3 (page 7)

matter what things are made of 12.4 (page 103)

metamorphosis the change of shape of an insect as it goes through stages of growth 4.4 (page 59)

migration a move from one place to another 3.6 (page 46)

movement a change of position or place 5.1 (page 67)

muscle a part of the body that helps the body move 10.2 (page 147)

N

nonliving thing a thing that is not alive and does not grow 1.1 (page 3)

O

orbit the path a planet takes around the sun 8.1 (page 115)

P

permanent teeth the second set of teeth 9.2 (page 133)

primary teeth the first set of teeth 9.2 (page 133)

S

school of fish a large number of one kind of fish swimming together 2.1 (page 20)

season a time of year 12.1 (page 97)

space the area outside Earth's atmosphere 8.2 (page 117)

Index

The index refers to the lesson number. The boldfaced numbers signify vocabulary word definitions.